ENCYCLOPAEDIA OF RESEARCH METHODOLOGY IN APPLIED SCIENCES

ENCYCLOPAEDIA OF
RESEARCH METHODOLOGY IN APPLIED SCIENCES

Volume 1

Harmeet Kour

ANMOL PUBLICATIONS PVT. LTD.
NEW DELHI - 110 002 (INDIA)

ANMOL PUBLICATIONS PVT. LTD.
H.O.: 4374/4B, Ansari Road, Daryaganj,
New Delhi-110 002 (India)
Ph.: 23278000, 23261597
B.O.: No. 1015, Ist Main Road, BSK IIIrd Stage
IIIrd Phase, IIIrd Block,
Bangalore - 560 085 (India)
Visit us at: www.anmolpublications.com

Encyclopaedia of Research Methodology in Applied Sciences

First Edition, 2009

ISBN 978-81-261-3814-2 (Set)

PRINTED IN INDIA

Printed at Mehra Offset Press, Delhi.

Contents

Preface

Applied Science is the application of knowledge from one or more natural scientific fields to solve practical problems. Fields of engineering are applied sciences. Applied science is important for technology development. Its use in industrial settings is usually referred to as research and development (R&D). No doubt, science is important to humans. It is a subject that teaches critical thinking and problem solving in a much applied way. Applied Science is all sciences "rolled" into some product or principle that we use every day. Applied science can be found in all sciences. Science and math is a reminder that two fields work together to solve problems. Physics explains the natural world into physical relationships with one another. Technology highlights examples of how science is used in society. Build Environment reflects technology's affect on the living planet. Major fields of applied sciences include: Artificial intelligence; Ceramic engineering; Computing technology; Electronics; Energy; Energy storage; Engineering physics; Environmental technology; Fisheries science; Materials science and engineering; Microtechnology; Nanotechnology; Nuclear technology; Optics; Zoography. In other words, Applied Science & Technology covers a wide range of specialties, such as: Acoustics; Aeronautics; Applied Mathematics; Artificial Intelligence; Atmospheric Sciences; Automatic Control; Automotive Engineering; Chemical Engineering; Chemistry; Civil Engineering; Communication & Information Technology; Computer Databases & Software; Construction; Electrical & Electronic Engineering; Engineering & Biomedical Materials; Energy Resources & Research; Environmental Engineering; Fire & Fire Prevention; Food & Food Industry; Geology; Industrial Engineering; Machine Learning; Machinery; Marine Technology; Mechanical Engineering; Metallurgy; Mineralogy; Mining Engineering; Neural Networks; Nuclear Engineering; Oceanography; Optical & Neural Computing; Petroleum & Gas; Physics; Plastics; Robotics; Solid State Technology; Space Science; Textile Industry & Fabrics; Transportation; Waste Management; Other Industrial & Mechanical Arts. Applied Sciences also have following major subcategories:

- Administration
- Agriculture
- Applied mathematics
- Aquariology

- Audiology
- Cybernetics
- Earth sciences
- Education
- Engineering
- Ergonomics
- Forestry science
- Health sciences
- Industrial design
- Management
- Military science
- Pyrotechnics
- Simulation
- Tactics

Majors and Programs in Applied Science Research Guides include:

- Architecture and Construction Management
- Business and Commerce
- Chemical Technology
- Culinary Arts and Science
- Electrical and Computer Engineering
- Fire Science
- Horticulture
- Information Technology
- Mathematics and Physics
- Mechanical Engineering
- Professional Practice
- Sport Administration

Methodology is defined as the analysis of the principles of methods, rules, and postulates employed by a discipline or the systematic study of methods that are, can be, or have been applied within a discipline or a particular procedure or set of procedures. The primary aim for research is discovering, interpreting, and the development of methods and systems for the advancement of human knowledge on a wide variety of scientific matters of our world and the universe. Research can use the scientific method, but need not do so. A hypothesis can never be proven, but rather only supported by surviving rounds of scientific testing and, eventually, becoming widely thought of as true, but this is not the same as it has been proven. A useful hypothesis allows prediction and within the accuracy of observation of the time, the prediction will be verified. The goal of the research process is to produce new knowledge. Research methodology applies exploratory approach. All of the techniques, methods and procedures adopted in terminology work to carry out terminology research. M*ethodology* includes the concepts as they relate to a particular discipline or field of inquiry, such as; a collection of theories, concepts or ideas; comparative study of different approaches; and critique of the individual methods. Methodology refers to more than a simple set of methods; rather it refers to the rationale and the philosophical assumptions that underlie a particular study. This is why scholarly literature often includes a section on the methodology of the researchers.

This publication titled "Encyclopaedia of Research Methodology in Applied Sciences" provides readers with an introduction to research methodology in applied sciences. It also focuses on the research methodology in engineering physics and optical science. The research methodology in materials science is also covered. Similarly, the research methodology in energy science and electronic science are dealt in detail. The research methodology in nuclear science has received considerable coverage. The research methodology in artificial intelligence science, computer science nanoscience and micro sciences have been discussed in detail. The research methodology applied in ceramic science has been also highlighted. Glossary of terms, acronyms/ abbreviations, bibliography and links have been provided to make this publication more users' friendly.

—Editors

Glossary

Absorber: Any material that stops ionizing radiation. Lead, concrete, and steel attenuate gamma rays. A thin sheet of paper or metal will stop or absorb alpha particles and most beta particles.

Alpha particle (alpha radiation, alpha ray): A positively charged particle (a Helium-4 nucleus) made up of two neutrons and two protons. It is the least penetrating of the three common forms of radiation, being stopped by a sheet of paper. It is not dangerous to living things unless the alpha-emitting substance is inhaled or ingested or comes into contact with the lens of the eye.

Applied Sciences: Educational programmes that fall in between engineering programmes and classical sciences. Generally, applied science programmes are more focused on using science to solve practical problems than in preparing students to advance the state of knowledge in the field. In the context of the Summit applied sciences are those that focus on the creation and deployment of technology. Examples include computer science and material science.

ATM: Asynchronous Transfer Mode. A wide-area network technology; a transfer mode for switching and transmission that efficiently and flexibly organises information into cells. It is asynchronous in the sense that the recurrence of cells depends on the required or instantaneous bit rate. Thus, empty cells do not go unutilised when data is waiting. ATM's powerful flexibility lies in its ability to provide a high-capacity, low-latency switching fabric— for all types of information, including data, video, image and voice — that is protocol , speed and distance independent. Of the plethora of benefits ATM will accrue to its users, probably the most significant is that it represents an enduring, architectural approach due to its inherent scalability. It scales well from small to large systems, from very low to very high transmission speeds (more than 100 Mbps), and from local-area, through metropolitan-area, to wide-area networking environments. This promising technology is not anticipated to be widely used until 1998.

Atom: A particle of matter indivisible by chemical means. It is the fundamental building block of elements.

Atomic number: The number assigned to each element on the basis of the number of protons found in the element's nucleus.

Atomic weight (atomic mass): Approximately the sum of the number of protons and neutrons found in the nucleus of an atom.

Backbone network: A high-speed transmission facility, or an arrangement of such facilities, designed to interconnect lower-speed distribution channels or clusters of dispersed user devices.

Background radiation: The radiation of man's natural environment originating primarily from the naturally radioactive elements of the earth and from the cosmic rays. The term may also mean radiation extraneous to an experiment.

Bandwidth *(Bande Passante)*: 1) The range of frequencies that can be passed through a channel. A channel carrying digital information has a data rate proportional to its bandwidth. 2) The signal-to-noise ratio of a modulate signal is tested within a range of frequencies on either side of the carrier frequency. This range is also called a bandwidth.

Base memory: Refer to "Conventional Memory".

Basic rate interface: The Integrated Services Digital Network basic rate interface consists of two 64-Kbps data or voice channels, which are designated as B (bearer) channels. The interface also has a 16-Kbps signalling or packet-data channel designated as the D (delta) channel. The interface is, therefore, often referred to as 2B+D

Baud: Origin of the name: a mister BAUDOT invented many decades ago the telex system, and the associated data coding technique. It measures, for a signal, the speed of state changing. It can correspond to more than the number of bits transmitted per unit of time.

Baud rate: A measure of the speed at which computers send data from one device to another, typically 300, 1,200 or 2,400, with the higher numbers representing faster transmissions. One Baud may carry one or some bits of data per second.

Benchmark: A routine or programme used to evaluate computer performance.

Beta particle (beta radiation, beta ray): An electron of either positive charge (ß+) or negative charge (ß-), which has been emitted by an atomic nucleus or neutron in the process of a transformation. Beta particles are more penetrating than alpha particles but less than gamma rays or x-rays.

BIOS: Basic Input Output System. In as DOS system, software residing in ROM which provides the basic functionality of the computer.

B-ISDN: Broadband Integrated Services Digital Network. A high-speed (greater than ISDN primary rate), asynchronous, time division multiplexed transmission facility, or an arrangement of such facilities, designed to provide a wide range of audio, video and date application in the same network.

Bit: Abbreviation for binary digit, the minimum unit of binary information. A bit can have only two states, on or off, which are commonly called one and zero.

BitMap police: Character set generated using a method which handles each character as a pixel set. Contrarily, the vectorial polices handle the characters by representing their shape, thus being independent of the actual size.

Blob: Binary Large Object. A generic term used to describe the handing and storage of long strings of data by middleware. Typically associated with image and video. Refer to Binary Large Object Support.

CA90s: Computer Associates's integrated software architecture that attempts to bring order and form to existing CA technology. Its advantage include its lack of hardware bias and the fact that it is not standard-dependent. One of its main components is CA-UNICENTER, selected as System Administration software in France.

Cache memory *(Memoire Cache)*: Very fast memory (generally SRAM) used often as intermediate between the CPU and the central storage, thus accelerating the system throughput. For example, on a 100MHz CPU, one cycle is executed in 10 ns, that is much faster than the 70 ns RAM cycle.

CAD/CAM: Computer-Aided Design/Computer-Aided Manufacturing. Two highly specialised technical applications of a computer to improve the productivity of the engineer.

CASE: Computer-Aided Software Engineering. CASE is an umbrella term for a collection of tools and techniques which are said by their distributors to promise revolutionary gains in analyst and programmer productivity. The two prominent delivered technologies are application generators and PC-based workstations that provide graphics-oriented automation of the front end of the development process.

CCD: Charge Coupled Device. A semiconductor device capable of both photodetection and memory, which converts light to electronic impulses. One- and two-dimensional CCD arrays are used in scanners to perform the first stage in converting an image into digital data. They are particularly attractive because they can step the signals from each detector across the array in response to a clock signal, permitting each scan line to be read through a single electrical connection.

CCITT: Abbreviation of the French name for the International Telegraph and Telephone Consultative Committee.

Contamination: Radioactive material deposited or dispersed in materials or places where it is not wanted.

Curie (Ci): The basic unit used to describe the intensity of radioactivity in a sample of material. One curie equals thirty-seven billion disintegrations per second, or approximately the radioactivity of one gram of radium.

Data dictionary: A repository of information about data, such as its meaning, relationships to other data, origin, usage and format. The dictionary assists company management, database administrators, systems analysts and lication programmers in effectively planning, controlling and evaluating the collections, storage and use of data. A data dictionary manages data categories such as alias, data elements, data records, data structure, data store, data models, data flows, data relationships, processes, functions, dynamics, size, frequency, resource consumption and other user-defined attributes.

Data model: The logical data structure developed during the logical database design process is a data model or entity model . It is also a description of the structural properties that define all entities represented in a database and all the relationships that exist among them.

Data Set Ready (DSR): Signal emitted by a modem indicating that it is ready to exchange signals with the computer.

Data Terminal Ready (DTR): Signal emitted by a computer indicating that it is ready to exchange signals with the modem.

Daughter: A nucleus formed by the radioactive decay of a different (parent) nuclide.

DB/DC: Database/Data Communication.This acronym refers to IBM's collection of transaction managers and database managers, e.g., Customer Information Control System, Information Management System, Database-2 and SQL/DS.

DBA: Database Administrator. The person responsible for managing data at a logical level, namely data definitions, data policies and data security.

Decay (radioactive): The change of one radioactive nuclide into a different nuclide by the spontaneous emission of alpha, beta, or gamma rays, or by electron capture. The end product is a less energetic, more stable nucleus. Each decay process has a definite half-life.

Decontamination: The removal of radioactive contaminants by cleaning and washing with chemicals.

Degree pathways: Describing the relationship of educational programmes and integrated work experiences to careers. Effectively communicating this information to students to allow them to make informed and productive decisions. Pathways may provide multiple entry and exit points for students who cannot complete all their educational goals at one time and thus join the workforce after completing one or more levels with the possibility of returning to an educational programme later.

Density: That property of a substance which is expressed by the ratio of its mass to its volume.

Dose: A general term denoting the quantity of radiation or energy absorbed in a specific mass.

Electromagnetic radiation: Radiation consisting of electric and magnetic waves that travel at the speed of light. Examples: light, radio waves, gamma rays, x-rays.

Electron capture: A radioactive decay process in which an orbital electron is captured by and merges with the nucleus. The mass number is unchanged, but the atomic number is decreased by one.

Electron: An elementary particle with a unit electrical charge and a mass 1/1837 that of the proton. Electrons surround the atom's positively charged nucleus and determine the atom's chemical properties.

Eluant: Washing solution (The solution that is introduced into the cow).

Elute: To separate by washing (to milk).

Excited state: The state of an atom or nucleus when it possesses more than its normal energy. The excess energy is usually released eventually as a gamma ray.

FDDI: Fiber Distributed Data Interface. An American National Standards Institute standard for 100 Mbps fiber-optic local area networks. Incorporates token processing and supports circuit-switched voice and packetized data. Components include: PMD (Physical Layer Medium Dependent), which deals with physical connections including fiber links, cables and connectors.; PHY (Physical Layer Protocol) which includes the encoding/decoding of packets and data clocking; MAC (Media Access Control) which includes parameters for token passing, addressing, packed sizes and framing; and SMT (Station Management) which governs management of the physical network.

Fission products: Nuclei formed by the fission of heavy elements. They are of medium atomic weight and almost all are radioactive. Examples: strontium-90, cesium-137.

Fission: The splitting of a heavy nucleus into two roughly equal parts (which are nuclei of lighter elements), accompanied by the release of a relatively large amount of energy in the form of kinetic energy of the two parts and in the form of emission of neutrons and gamma rays.

Formal standards: Specifications or styles that are approved by vendor-independent standards bodies, such as the American National Standards Institute, the International Standards Organisation, the Institute of Electrical and Electronics Engineers, and the National Institute for Standards and Technology.

Fragmentation: File division in physically separated segments in a disk. Fragmentation is due to file increase in a highly used disk, thus leading to a lack of sufficient contiguous free space.

Frame relay: An International Telegraph and Telephone Consultative Committee (CCITT) recommendation (I.122) and American National Standards Institute standard (T1S1). Frame relay is an ISDN (Integrated Services Digital Network) packet-mode bearer service that defines a user-to-network interface. The two main benefits are bandwidth on demand and integrated access. The standard currently addresses data communications speeds up to 2 Mbps over permanent virtual circuits. By reducing the network functions performed, frame relay takes advantage of more robust physical facilities to improve throughput.

Gamma ray: A highly penetrating type of nuclear radiation, similar to x-radiation, except that it comes from within the nucleus of an atom, and, in general, has a shorter wavelength.

Gateway: A physical or logical network station that interconnects two otherwise incompatible networks, network nodes, subnetworks, or devices. Gateways perform protocol-conversion operations across a wide spectrum of communications functions or layers.

Geiger counter: A Geiger-Müller detector and measuring instrument. It contains a gas-filled tube which discharges electrically when ionizing radiation passes through it and a device that records the events.

Generator: A cow-a system containing a parent-daughter set of radioisotopes in which the parent decays through a daughter to a stable isotope. The daughter is a different element from that of the parent, and, hence, can be separated from the parent by elution (milking).

Giga: Prefix corresponding to a one billion quantity. One GB (Giga-Bytes) is equal to 1,000 MB or 1,000,000 KB or 1,000,000,000 Bytes. In 1995, disk storage have a capacity expressed in GB: generally between 0.2 and 4 GB.

Graphical accelerator ***(Acc‰ l‰ rateur graphique)*:** Specialised component in charge of processing graphical data display instead of the CPU. Mainly used for workstations large screens display.

Grey levels ***(Niveau de gris)*:** Scale of grey varieties between the black and the white. Graphical software generally propose 16 or 256 grey levels.

Groupware: "Groupware" was originally coined to describe a new class of applications designed to provide electronic support for groups of individuals working together toward a common goal. In the last several years, the term has been applied to applications ranging from unstructured electronic mail to rigorously structured work-flow systems. Groupware is more useful as a concept when it is broken down into three major stages: communication, coordination and cooperation. In this light, groupware applications can be viewed in terms of the degree of structure in the group interaction and in complexity of that structure, and the rigor with which the activity itself is monitored.

Half-life: The time in which half the atoms of a particular radioactive nuclide disintegrate. The half-life is a characteristic property of each radioactive isotope.

Hanford: Hanford was a mad scientist who had invented a radioisotope-marked virus which could be used in the process of force-growing cloned animals. He was building an army of radioactive dinosaurs to take over the world, and also had created a cadre of radioactive spiders that spit green fire. Hanford was arrested by Benjamin Prester before our story begins.

Health physics: That science devoted to recognition, evaluation, and control of all health hazards from ionizing radiation.

IDE: Integrated Device Electronics. Control electronic circuits embedded on a hard disk according to a specific interface.

IEEE: Institute of Electrical and Electronics Engineers. Organisation of engineers, scientists and students involved in electrical, electronics and related fields; also functions as a publishing house and standards-making body.

IEEE 802.3: The physical and medium access control standards developed by the Institute of Electrical and Electronics Engineers for CSMA/CD (Carrier sense Multiple Access with Collision Detection) local-area networks, such as Ethernet.

Induced radioactivity: Radioactivity that is created by bombarding a substance with neutrons in a reactor or with charged particles produced by particle accelerators.

Integrated circuit: Electronic circuit engraved on a semi-conductor material, most generally crystalline silicon.

Interface: Transfer channel allowing communication between different elements inside a computer, between different computers, between a computer and an external equipment, or between different programmes.

Internet: World largest network, on which tens of thousands of servers and tens of millions of workstations are connected. It is not centrally governed: anyone can create data accessible to the whole users community.

Interruption: Signal sent to a processor to invite it to interrupt the operation in progress, to allow to proceed to another operation.

Ion: An atomic particle that is electrically charged, either negative or positive.

Ionizing radiation: Radiation that is capable of producing ions either directly or indirectly.

IPX: Internetwork- Packet eXchange. A local-area network transport protocol often found in Novell's family of Net Ware network operating systems.

IRQ: Interruption ReQuest. Same as "Interrupt" for PC systems.

Irradiate: To expose to some form of radiation.

ISA: Industry Standard Architecture. It is a PC architecture based upon three key elements: an 8088 Intel microprocessor, MS-DOS operating system, and an 8 bit I/O bus.Historically, this "standard" has been defined by IBM in its famous PC (in 1981); IBM always denied to publish the specifications, and the competitors had to discover them (it was not tricky enough to resist to skill, patience and oscilloscopes) in order to be able to manufacture compatible PCBs, and lastly compatible PCs.

Isomer: One of several nuclides with the same number of neutrons and protons capable of existing for a measurable time in different nuclear energy states.

Isometric transition: A mode of radioactive decay where a nucleus goes from a higher to a lower energy state. The mass number and the atomic number are unchanged.

Isotope: Isotopes of a given element have the same atomic number (same number of protons in their nuclei) but different atomic weights (different number of neutrons in their nuclei). Uranium-238 and uranium-235 are isotopes of uranium.

K-capture: The capture by an atom's nucleus of an orbital electron from the first K-shell surrounding the nucleus.

keV: One thousand electron volts.

MeV: One million electron volts.

MIB: Management Information Base. In the Simple Network Management Protocol, a collection of objects that are logical representations of network devices and their internal components.

Microcode: The microinstructions, especially of a microprocessor, that govern the details of operations. For example, the hardware of 3081 fetches and executes 108-bit microinstructions wholly different from the instruction set of System/370. Yet IBM supplies a microprogramme that causes the 3081 to act like a System/370. The instructions in such a programme are referred to as microcode. The execution of each System/370 instructions puts the hardware into a subroutine of microinstructions that execute the function defined for that instruction. Microcoded functions can improve performance but add a layer of complexity. For example, microcode errors appear to software as being hardware failures.

Microcurie (μCi): One millionth of a curie (3.7 x 104 disintegrations per second).

Microprocessor: Central processor in micro-computers, composed of only one integrated circuit.

Microprogram: Software routine stored in ROM, thus remaining unaltered in case of power off.

Microsoft: Software world leader. The main products are Windows and MS-Office which is composed of WORD, EXCEL, PowerPoint and MAIL.

Middleware: The set of software facilities that an application programme may use to receive services from the platform. IBM's systems Application Architecture and Digital Equipment Corp.'s Network Applications Support are examples of middleware-based architectures. Middleware includes database management systems, library and search services, mail systems and compound document services. Middleware typically has application programming interface available to applications.

Minigenerator: A trademark of Union Carbide Corporation that is used to identify radioisotope generator systems for educational use.

Minolta: Japanese electronic manufacturer.

MIPS: Million Instructions Per second. An approximate figure to denote a computer's raw processing power. It is often misleading, since it does not necessarily provide a good throughput figure of merit.

Mirror disk: Technology allowing to replicate data on two different hard disks, thus allowing continuous operation in case of failure on one disk.

Modem: A conversion device installed in pairs, at each end of an analog communications line. The word is a contraction of modulate and demodulate. The transmitting-end modem modulates digital signals received locally from a computer or terminal (sending analog signals over the line). The receiving-end modem demodulates the incoming signal, converting it back to its original (i.e., digital) format and passes it to the destination business machine.

Monitor *(Moniteur)*: Computer hardware used for displaying digital output.

Moon: The natural satellite of the Earth. The Moon has a number of cities on its surface, most of which are engaged in mining, heavy industry, or vacuum-intensive industries such as chemical processing. Because they are in a hostile, airless environment, Lunar cities require a number of specialized technologies to survive: enclosed domes, atmospheric reclamation plants, and large bodies of water to serve as both drinking reservoirs and thermal dumps. The government of the Moon is neo-Stalinist; its people live in drab, towering apartment blocks or in converted storage facilities. Benjamin's friend Djaya lives in one such converted facility.

Motif: Graphical user interface specified by the Open Software Foundation and built on the Massachusetts Institute of Technology's X-Windows.

MPEG: Motion Pictures Experts Group. An emerging standard for compression of full motion images driven by the same committee as the Joint Photographic Experts Group (JPEG) standard.

Neutrino: An electrically neutral particle with negligible mass. It is produced in many nuclear reactions such as in beta decay.

Neutron: One of the basic particles which make up an atom. A neutron and a proton have about the same weight, but the neutron has no electrical charge.

Nuclear reactor: A device in which a fission chain reaction can be initiated, maintained, and controlled. Its essential components are fissionable fuel, moderator, shielding, control rods, and coolant.

Nucleon: A constituent of the nucleus; that is, a proton or a neutron.

Nucleonics: The science, technology, and application of nuclear energy.

Nucleus: The core of the atom, where most of its mass and all of its positive charge is concentrated. Except for hydrogen, it consists of protons and neutrons.

Nuclide: Any species of atom that exists for a measurable length of time. A nuclide can be distinguished by its atomic weight, atomic number, and energy state.

ODA: Open Document Architecture. An international standard that enables users to exchange text and graphics generated on different types of office products.

ODBC: Open Database Connectivity. An interface based on the Structured Query Language Access Group specifications. The application programming interfaces enable Windows applications to access data in various back-end relational database servers (and xBase files), without the applications having to understand the differences between the various back-end data sources. Microsoft has also stated its intent to port ODBC to the Macintosh.

OEM: Original Equipment Manufacturer. Usually refers not to the manufacturer of a device, but to the system integrator that resells the devices as part of a system. When used as a verb, as in "Company B is going to OEM Company A's drive," this means that Company A will manufacture the drive and Company B will integrate it into a system.

OLE: Object Linking and Embedding. Microsoft-defined mechanism for program-to-programme communication. OLE enables a user to create compound documents incorporating work from multiple applications.

Open Systems: A concept based on offering hardware and software and capabilities defined by standards - produced by standards committees as well as those supported or demanded by users (i.e., de facto standards, such as those developed by Unix International or the Open Software Foundation). Typically, an open system provides Unix as a basic operating system, although that is not a requirement; what is required is that the system provide standard interfaces. An open system is a compliant implementation of an evolving set of vendor-neutral specifications for interfaces, services, protocols and formats. It is designed to let users configure, operate and substitute an entire system, its applications and components with other equally compliant implementations, preferably available from different vendors.

Optical disk *(Disque optique)*: Disk whose reading and writing mechanisms use laser optics instead of magnetism. Their lifetime is probably long: more than 30 years for the support, but can we ensure to find decades later compatible reading mechanisms ? They can record relatively large quantities of data (500 MB in 1995), but their access time is slow.

OS: Operating System. A computer's operating system mediates between user application programmes and the processor and peripheral hardware environment. Under the control of the operating system, the computer recognises and obeys commands from the user and interprets application and network commands. The operating system also provides built-in routines that enable users to perform input/output operations without specifying the exact underlying hardware configuration of the computer.

OS/2: Micro computer operating system developed by IBM. Although rather advanced, this system was never accepted by the users community.

OSI: Open Systems Interconnection. A standard approach to network design developed by the International Standards Organisation that introduces modularity by dividing the complex set of functions into more manageable, self-contained, functional slices.

Outsourcing: A contractual relationship with an external provider characterised by the transfer of assets (both physical and human), to include facilities management, network management, network management, PC services, and/or application development/maintenance.

Parallel interface *(Port parall^le)*: Interface allowing to exchange data in parallel mode: in this mode several bits are exchanged simultaneously, one on each data line. On a micro computer, used for example to connect a printer. To be opposed to "serial interface".

Parameter *(Param^tre)*: Variable affected to a command or a programme. Characteristic of an element or a system , which can be adapted by the user.

PARC: Palo Alto Research Center. In this famous Xerox research center, most of the concepts used today in the micro computers were invented in the 70', such as graphical user interface, mouse, and Ethernet.

Parent: A radionuclide that decays to another nuclide which may be either radioactive or stable.

Passive matrix display *(Affichage matriciel passif)*: Display composed of a layer of LCD placed in a transparent network made of electrodes and red, green and blue filters. The current passes through the pixel rows and the display is back-lit in order to provide a better luminosity.

Password *(Mot de passe)*: Software security function preventing any access to the computer until this unique, predefined and secret password has been keyed in.

Pathway: Emulation software produced by the Wollongong company.

Photon: A quantity of electromagnetic energy. Photons have momentum but no mass or electrical charge.

Presentation Layer *(Couche Presentation)*: In the Open Systems Interconnection model, that layer of processing that provides services to the application layer, enabling it to interpret the data exchanged, as well as to structure data messages to be transmitted in a specific display and control format.

Proton: One of the basic particles which makes up an atom. The proton is found in the nucleus and has a positive electrical charge equivalent to the negative charge of an electron and a mass similar to that of a neutron: a hydrogen nucleus.

PTT: Postal Telegraph and Telephone. An agency in a European country, usually a government-run monopoly, that is responsible for all postal, telegraph and telephone services. It also has certain regulatory functions for telecommunications, such as providing specifications for modems and certifying that equipment may connect to the telephone network. In some countries, the PTT also provides its own line of equipment, such as modems. Now also called Telecommunications Administrations (TAs), these entities are undergoing varying amounts of structural change.

Rad: Radiation Absorbed Dose. The basic unit of an absorbed dose of ionizing radiation. One rad is equal to the absorption of 100 ergs of radiation energy per gram of matter.

Radioactive dating: A technique for estimating the age of an object by measuring the amounts of various radioisotopes in it.

Radioactive waste: Materials which are radioactive and for which there is no further use.

Radioactivity: The spontaneous decay of disintegration of an unstable atomic nucleus accompanied by the emission of radiation.

Radioisotope: A radioactive isotope. A common term for a radionuclide.

Radionuclide: A radioactive nuclide. An unstable isotope of an element that decays or disintegrates spontaneously, emitting radiation.

Rate meter: An electronic instrument that indicates, on a meter, the number of radiation induced pulses per minute from radiation detectors such as a Geiger-Muller tube.

Real mode: For Intel microprocessors, production mode used to address the first storage MB. In real mode, the memory address used by the application is equal to the physical address in storage.

Refresh: Regular rewrite allowing to maintain displayed data on a screen or data in RAM storage.

Removable hard disk: Hard disk that can be removed from a laptop computer. This type of unit generates a special risk in terms of security.

Removable storage units: Magnetic tape, disk or cartridge on which are recorded data. Removable units are most frequently used to create safety copies of hard disk data.

Resolution: It defines the thinness of restitution of information provided by an output device such as a screen or a printer. It is usually measured in number of points. On screens, in 1995, the most frequent resolutions are 640 points per row and 480 points per column (called VGA), 800x600 (called SVGA) and 1024x768. On printers, it is measured in number of points per inch. On laser printers, in 1995, it is most frequently 300 or 600 points per inch. We can observe that resolution is much higher on printers than on screens.

Response time *(Temps de r‰ponse)*: The time period between a terminal operator's completion of an inquiry and the receipt of a response. Response time includes the time taken to transmit the inquiry, process it by the computer, and transmit the response back to the terminal. Response time is frequently used as a measure of the performance of an interactive system.

RGB: Red Green Blue. Coloured components used for color display screens.

RISC: Reduced Instruction Set Computer. An architecture that shifts the analytical process of a computational task from the execution or run time to the preparation or compile time. By using less hardware or logic, the system can operate at higher speeds. A processor architecture that cuts down on the number and complexity of instructions, on the theory that each one can be accessed and executed faster, and that less semiconductor circuitry is required to process them. The result is that for any given semiconductor technology, a more powerful microprocessor can be produced with RISC than with CISC (complex instruction set computer) architectures. However, the compilers role becomes critical, and the effective throughput of the system will heavily depend on them.

RJ11: Standard jacket for telephone line interface.

RJ45: Standard interface type between computers and LANs, using UTP cables.

RNIS: French name for ISDN. The commercially available service proposed by the national operator.

ROM: Read-Only Memory. Storage unit which retains data even when the computer is powered off. This storage cannot be modified by the user.

Router *(Routeur)*: Performs a function similar to a local or remote bridge, but routing occurs at Layer 3 of the Open Systems Interconnection reference model.

Routine: Part of a programme responsible for a complete function. A programme composed of a number of distinct but linked routines is called "modular".

RPC: Remote Procedure Call. A mechanism that extends the notion of a local (i.e., contained in a single address space) procedure call to a distributed computing environment, enabling an application to be distributed among multiple systems in a way that is highly transparent to the application-level code. Examples of RPCs are Apollo's Network Computing System., Sun Microsystem's Open Network Computing, Sybase's Open Client/Open Server and the Open Software Foundation's Distributed Computing Environment RPC.

RS-232-C: A technical specification published by the Electronic Industries Association that establishes mechanical and electrical interface requirements between computers, terminals and communications lines.

Satellite DNA: Regions of highly repetitive DNA from a eucaryotic chromosome, usually identifiable by its unusual nucleotide composition. Satellite DNA is not transcribed and has no known function.

Saturated: An organic molecule is described as saturated if it is a closed shell species lacking double or triple bonds; forming a new bond to a saturated molecule requires the cleavage of an existing bond.

Scaler: An electronic instrument for counting radiation induced pulses from radiation detectors such as a Geiger-Muller tube.

Scanning Force Microscope : Scanning Force Microscope invented in 1986 by Binnig et al., scanning force microscopy has become a powerful tool for the investigation of surfaces. A great advantage of this method is the high resolution—down to the atomic scale—which can be achieved even in air and even on insulating surfaces. However, the greatest advantage is the possibility to investigate surfaces *in situ* in a liquid phase.

Scanning Near Field Optical Microscopy: A method for observing local optical properties of a surface that can be smaller than the wavelength of the light used. A type of scanning probe microscopy that maps the near-field optical properties of an interface.

Scintillation counter: An instrument that detects and measures gamma radiation by counting the light flashes (scintillations) induced by the radiation.

SCSI chain: Up to seven SCSI peripherals can be serially connected to the same computer SCSI port.

SCSI: Small Computer System Interface. A peripheral interface for up to seven devices. SCSI provides a high-speed, parallel data transfer of up to 4 Mbytes per second and has the advantage of connecting multiple peripherals while taking up only one slot in the computer.

Sealed Assembler Lab: A general-purpose assembler system in a container permitting only energy and information to be exchanged with the environment.

Sealed Assembler Laboratory: A work space, containing assemblers, encapsulated in a way that allows information to flow in and out but does not allow the escape of assemblers or their products.

Second Messenger: Small molecule that is formed in or released into the cytosol in response to an extracellular signal and helps to relay the signal to the interior of the cell. Examples include cAMP, IP3 and Ca2+.

Secondary Structure: Regular local folding pattern of a polymeric molecule; in proteins, a helices and b-pleated sheets.

Secretory Vesicle: Membrane-bounded organelle in which molecules destined for secretion are stored prior to release. Sometimes called secretory granule because darkly staining contents make the organelle visible as a small solid object.

Sector *(Secteur)*: Recording zone on a disk. Of a fixed size, the sectors are the smallest addressable units on a disk. A sector generally contains 512 data bytes.

Secular equilibrium: A state of parent-daughter equilibrium which is achieved when the half-life of the parent is much longer than the half-life of the daughter. In this case, if the two are not separated, the daughter will eventually be decaying at the same rate at which it is being produced. At this point, both parent and daughter will decay at the same rate until the parent is essentially exhausted.

Selectivity: The ability of a sensor to measure only one metric or, in the case of a chemical sensor, to measure only a single chemical species.

Self-Assembler: A specific type of assembler that makes use of self-assembly such that the assembly process would theoretically not require external energy or information input.

Self-assembling Biomolecular Materials: Examples of self- assembly include protein folding, the formation of liposomes, and the alignment of liquid crystals. While this type of equilibrium self- assembly is the central focus of this report, it is important to emphasize that much biological assembly is also driven by energy sources such as adenosine triphosphate (ATP), which power biomotors.

Self-replication: More accurately labeled "exponential replication," self-replication refers to the process of growth or replication involving doubling within a given period. Example: create one assembler. Program it to create another, and program that one likewise, etcetera, until you have a speficied amount. Self replication is an effective route to truly low cost manufacturing. Our intuitions about self replicating systems, learned from the biological systems that surround us, are likely to seriously mislead us about the properties and characteristics of artificial self replicating systems designed for manufacturing purposes. Artificial systems able to make a wide range of non- biological products (like diamond) under programmatic control are likely to be more brittle and less adaptable in their response to changes in their environment than biological systems. At the same time, they should be simpler and easier to design. The complexity of such systems need not be excessive by present engineering standards. The act of objects making copies of themselves—similar to biological reproduction except that self-replicating objects should make exact copies of themselves.

Sensitivity: The amount of change in a sensor's output in response to a change at a sensor's input over the sensor's entire range. Provides an indication of a sensor's ability to detect changes. For some sensors, the sensitivity is defined as the input parameter change required to produce a standardized output change.

Sensor Web: An independent network of wireless, intra- communicating sensor pods, deployed to monitor and explore a limitless range of environments. This adaptable instrument can be tailored to whatever conditions it is sent to observe.

Sensors: An equipment which detects, and may indicate, and/or record objects and activities by means of energy or particles emitted, reflected, or modified by objects.

Sentience Quotient: In the article "Xenopsychology" by Robert Freitas in Analog of April 1984 there is an interesting index called "Sentience quotient". It is based on: The sentience of an intelligence is roughly directly related to the amount of data it can process per unit time and inversely to the overall mass needed to do that processing. This would be something like baud/kilograms. And since that would rapidly turn into a real big number, base 10 logs are used. The "least sentient" would be one bit over the lifetime of the universe massing the entire known universe, or about -70. The "most sentient" is claimed to be +50. Homo sapiens are around +13, a Cray I is +9, a venus flytrap is a peak of +1 with plants generally -2.

Separator: Special character in charge of delimiting words or values. This separator is not part of the character string it delimitates.

Serial interface *(Port s‰ rie)*: Interface allowing to exchange data in serial mode: in this mode one bit is exchanged at a time. On a micro computer, used for example for modem interface. To be opposed to "parallel interface".

Server: A system or a programme that receives requests from one or more client systems or programmes to perform activities that allow the client to accomplish certain tasks. A processor that provides a specific service to systems on a network. Routing servers connect subnetworks of like architecture, gateway servers connect networks of different architecture by performing protocol conversions and terminal, printer and file servers provide interfaces between peripheral devices and systems on the network.

Shape Memory Alloys: (SMA's) are a unique class of alloys which are able to "remember" their shape and are able to return to that shape even after being bent. The ability is known as the shape memory effect. ... This property has lead to many uses of SMA from orthodontics and coffee makers to methods of controlling aircraft and protecting buildings from earthquake damage. ... The first SMA to be discovered and the most commonly used is called Nitinol.

Shielding: A protective barrier, usually a dense material, which reduces the passage of radiation from radioactive materials to the surroundings.

SI Units: International System of units based on the metric system and units derived from the metric system.

Sigma bond: A covalent bond in which overlap between two atomic orbitals (e.g., of *sp, sp2,* or *sp3* hybridization) produces a single bonding orbital in which the distribution of shared electrons has a roughly cylindrical symmetry about the axis linking the two atoms; see pi bond, single bond, double bond, triple bond. By themselves, sigma bonds present little barrier to rotation of one substructure with respect to another, although steric effects and cyclic structures may hinder or block rotation.

Signal to noise: Ratio which can interfere with detection. Can also refer to data analysis. Biological data is often very "noisy". This is particularly seen when trying to look at low abundance biomolecules.

Signal-to-noise-ratio: The ratio of the output signal with an input signal to the output signal with no input signal.

Single cell repair unit: A cell repair unit using cilia for propulsion and equipped with a nanocomputer having 10 megabytes of fast RAM and 1 gigabyte of slower-access memory. The unit is extending 1000 individually-controlled molecular manipulators.

Single crystal: A crystalline solid for which the periodic and repeated atomic pattern extends throughout its entirety without interruption.

Single electron devices : Nanoscale devices that control the movement of individual electrons, may one day make it possible for integrated circuits to have as many as 10 billion electronic devices in a square centimeter, a density 1000 times greater than that believed feasible for conventional integrated circuits. In development since the mid- 1980s, these devices consist of two electrodes (typically 30 nm wide) separated by a 1 nm- deep insulating layer through which single electrons can tunnel. These devices have many potential applications, from building more sensitive measurement devices to understanding fundamental problems in physics. In the last several years, researchers have built two- junction devices that share a middle electrode. These devices are called *"single- electron transistors,"* because, like conventional transistors, their current can be controlled by modifying the surface charge on the middle electrode, making it an ideal element for an integrated circuit. A circuit made of single- electron devices, however, would have to be operated at a temperature of 4 K or below to reduce thermal effects which disturb the movements of single electrons in the solid.

Single-pair FRET spFRET: Designed to overcome the averaging effects of ensemble studies because measurements are made on single molecules freely diffusing in solution. This method limits the observation period to the diffusion time of each molecule through the focal spot of a laser on the order of a few hundred milliseconds, but it permits the rapid gathering of data at single-molecule resolution on a large number of molecules in a short time period. SpFRET can be used to study intramolecular conformational changes by placing the donor and acceptor fluorescent tags on two different sites of the same macromolecule, or alternatively, intermolecular interactions can be studied by attaching the donor and acceptor tags to two different macromolecules.

Singularity: Defined by Vernor Vinge as the "postulated point or short period in our future when our self-guided evolutionary development accelerates enormously (powered by nanotechnology, neuroscience, AI, and perhaps uploading) so that nothing beyond that time can reliably be conceived. ...a future time when societal, scientific and economic change is so fast we cannot even imagine what will happen from our present perspective, and when humanity will become posthumanity."

Sky hook: A long, very strong, cable in orbit around a planet which rotates around its center of mass in such a way that when one end is closest to the ground, its relative velocity is almost zero. It would function as a kind of space elevator; shuttle craft would anchor to the end and then be lifted into orbit where they would be released. It is closely related to the idea of a beanstalk.

Slip casting: A forming technique used to shape ceramic materials. A slip or suspension of solid particles in water is poured into a porous mold. A solid layer forms on the inside wall as water is absorbed by the mold, leaving a shell (or a solid piece) in the shape of the mold.

Small molecule therapeutics: Low molecular-weight drug. Compared to larger molecular weight pharmaceuticals such as proteins, peptides, and carbohydrates, small molecules can more easily penetrate cell membranes and the blood brain barrier. Can be delivered orally or intravenously. These molecules tend to incur lower process development and manufacturing costs.

Small molecules: Preferred for drugs as they are orally available (unlike proteins which must be administered by injection or topically). Size of small molecules is generally under 1000 Daltons, but many estimates seem to range between 300 to 700 Daltons.

Smart materials and products: Here, materials and products capable of relatively complex behavior due to the incorporation of nanocomputers and nanomachines. Also used for products having some ability to respond to the environment.

Smart sensor: A sensor in which the electronics that process the output from the sensor, and forms the modifier, are partially or fully integrated on a single chip.

Source: A radioactive material that produces radiation for experimental or industrial use.

Spectrograph: An instrument that spreads out the light gathered by a telescope so that it can be analyzed to determine many different properties of celestial objects. These properties include the chemical composition and abundance of different elements, temperature, radial velocity, rotational velocity, and magnetic fields.

Spectroscopic dyes: These dyes—in particular, nanoparticles — are emerging as alternatives to fluorescent dyes. Because the emission spectra of nanoparticles vary according to these particles' specific size and shape, these nanostructures can be used in multicolor detection formats, potentially offering much greater multiplexing than is currently achievable. The fact that chemists have been able to create a great variety of structures (and properties) in nanoparticles suggests that these particles might be more "finely tunable" than organic dyes, allowing better results from biological assays.

Spill: The accidental release of radioactive materials.

Spinning: Fiber forming process: a multitude of fibers are spun as molten material is forced through many small orifices.

Spin-stabilized: Attitude control is done by having the entire satellite spin. It becomes very stable because the satellite as a whole is acting as a gyroscope.

Spintronics: The technology utilizing the electron spin to manipulate (calculate) or store information. The 'classical' electronics, with respect to spintronics should possibly be called 'chargetronics' since it uses electron charge, i.e. charge currents to manipulate the information (fire the transistors and similar). The spin is the quantum number of an electron which can take two values (states)—'up' and 'down'. In spintronics, the *spin* currents are of relevance to the function of electronic devices. Note that the spin currents are also the charge currents, since the carrier of spin (electron) is also a carrier of charge. The materials that would support the spintronical applications would have to be sensitive to the sign (up or down) of the spin currents, i.e. their response should be dependent on the sign of the spin current. Materials containing several layers of different magnetic and nonmagnetic metals that have thicknesses in the range of several nanometers are the candidates for such applications. This, of course, requires material nanostructuring.

Squeeze-film damping: Effect of ambient fluid and spacing on the vertical movement of a structural member with respect to a substrate.

Stability: The ability of a sensor to retain specified characteristics after being subjected to designated environmental or electrical test conditions.

Stable: Strictly speaking, a system is termed stable if no rearrangement of its parts can form a system of lower free energy. In practice, the term is used with an implicit proviso regarding the transformations to be considered. Hydrogen is not considered unstable merely because it is subject to nuclear fusion at extreme temperatures. A system is usually regarded as stable if its rate of transformation to a state of lower free energy is negligible (by some standard) under the ambient conditions. In nanomechanical systems, a structure can commonly be regarded as stable if it has an extremely low rate of transformations when subjected to its intended operating conditions.

Staining and labeling: The marking of biological material with a dye or other reagent for the purpose of identifying and quantitating components of tissues, cells or their extracts.

Steady-state diffusion: The diffusion condition for which there is no net accumulation or depletion of diffusing species. The diffusion flux is independent of time.

STEM antennas: An acronym for Storable Tubular Extendible Member. STEM antennas are stored in the body of a satellite to save space at launch and unrolled when the satellite reaches orbit. Canada's first satellite, Alouette, used four STEM antennas.

Step coverage: If a layer of material is to be deposited on top of a thin strip of material, it is the ratio of film thickness along the walls of the step to the film thickness at the bottom of the step. LPCVD and PECVD offer excellent step coverage.

Step response: The response of a system to an instantaneous jump in the input signal.

Steric hindrance: Slowing of the rate of a chemical reaction owing to the presence of structures on the reagents that mechanically interfere with the motions associated with the reaction, typically by obstructing the reaction site.

Steric: Pertaining to the spatial relationships of atoms in a molecular structure, and in particular, to the space-filling properties of a molecule. If molecules were rigid and had hard surfaces, steric properties would merely be an opaque way of saying "shape"; a flexible side-chain, however, has definite steric properties but no fixed shape. Nanomechanical systems make extensive use of the steric properties of relatively rigid molecules, for which the term "shape" has essentially its conventional meaning so long as one remembers that the surface interactions are soft on small length-scales.

Stiffness: The stiffness of a system with respect to a deformation (e.g., the stiffness of a spring with respect to stretching) is the second derivative of the energy with respect to the corresponding displacement; this measures the curvature of the potential energy surface along a particular direction. Positive stiffness is associated with stability, and a large stiffness can result in a small positional uncertainty in the presence of thermal excitation. Negative stiffnesses correspond to unstable locations on the potential energy surface. Alternative terms for stiffness include force gradient and rigidity.

Stoichiometry: For ionic compounds, the state of having exactly the ratio of cations to anions specified by the chemical formula. Stoichiometric quantities refers to quantities of reactants mixed in exactly the correct amounts so that all are used up at the same time.

Store-and-forward: A delivery method for data within a network in which information moves from one node to another toward its target. If any node in the paths is unavailable, the last active node in the chain holds the information until that node becomes available, at which time the transfer continues. The originator need not maintain the information as each node receiving the object accepts responsibility for its delivery. Although store-and-forward is most often associated with electronic mail, it can be used for file transfer, software updates and other functions that do not require a "quick" or synchronised response.

Strain gauge: An element (wire or foil) that measures a strain based on electrical resistance changes of the gauge that result from a change in length or dimension strain of the wire or foil.

Strain: In mechanical engineering, strain is a measure of the deformation resulting from stress (that is, force per unit area); the displacement of one point with respect to another, divided by their equilibrium separation in the absence of stress. In chemistry, a molecular fragment generally has some equilibrium geometry (bond lengths, interbond angles, etc.) when the rest of the molecular structure does not impose special constraints (e.g., bending bonds to form a small ring). Deviations from this equilibrium geometry are described as strain, and increase the energy of the molecule. Strain in the mechanical engineering sense causes strain in the chemical sense.

Stress corrosion (cracking) : A form of failure resulting from the combined action of a tensile stress and a corrosion environment, occurring at lower stress levels than required when the corrosion environment is absent.

Stress: Force per unit area applied by one part of an object to another. Pressure is an isotropic compressive stress. Suspending a mass from a fiber places it in tensile stress. Gluing a layer of rubber between two plates and then sliding one over the other (while holding their separation constant) places the rubber in shear stress.

Structural volume: The interior of a diamondoid structure typically consists of a dense network of covalent bonds; a larger excluded volume, however, is determined by nonbonded repulsions at the surface. The structural volume corresponds to a region smaller than the excluded volume, chosen to make properties such as the strength and modulus nearly size independent by correcting for surface effects.

Structure based design: A design strategy for new chemical entities based on the three- dimensional (3D) structure of the target obtained by X-ray or nuclear magnetic resonance (NMR) studies, or from protein homology models.

Switched connection: A connection that requires a manual or an automated sequence to establish a connection before it can be used by any software or hardware component. Often referred to as a "dialled" connection because of the need to complete a phone call to establish the connection, its characteristics are different from a dedicated line (always available for use) and it requires different support. Applications using switched lines cannot assume the connection is made or that communication has been initialised.

Synchronous *(Synchrome)*: Having a constant time interval between successive bits, characters or events. Synchronous transmission uses no redundant information to identify the beginning and the end of the characters, and thus is faster and more efficient than asynchronous transmission, which uses start and stop bits. The timing is achieved by transmitting sync characters prior to data; usually synchronisation can be achieved in two or three character times.

TPC-A: Transaction Processing Performance Council. A revised and superior version of the debit/credit on-line transaction processing (OLTP) benchmark. The major improvements in TPC-A were the requirements for full disclosure and the inclusion of the front-end network and terminals. TPC-A is intended to replace debit/credit as the only industrywide measure for OLTP performance and price/performance. It is good test since it measures end-to-end performance, but it still is only one test reflecting a single type of transaction.

Tracer: A small amount of radioactive isotope introduced into a system in order to follow the behavior of some component of that system.

Track *(Piste)*: Circular recording zone on a diskette or hard disk. Tracks generally are generally composed of sectors.

Transaction: A logical update that takes a database from one consistent state to another.

Transmutation: The transformation of one element into another by a nuclear reaction.

Transport Layer *(Couche Transport)*: In the Open Systems Interconnection (OSI) model, the network processing entity responsible, in conjunction with the underlying network, data link and physical layers, for the end-to-end control of transmitted data and the optimized use of network resources.

Two-Phase Commit: Method for co-ordinating a single transaction across two or more database management systems or other resource managers. Two-phase commit guarantees the logical integrity of data by ensuring that transaction updates are finalised ("committed") in all of the separate databases or are fully backed out of all participating databases, i.e., all or nothing based on transaction boundaries. Two-phase commit is a necessary component of distributed database and is implemented in "transaction management" software, which may be part of a database management system, on-line transaction processing monitor, or front-end application tool.

Unix: A family of operating systems known for its relative hardware independence and portable applications interface. This time-sharing operating systems is available on all AT&T computers, and is widely used in technical and scientific computing applications. It has recently made great strides in entering mainstream commercial computing. Unix System V is the version of Unix supported by AT&T and its user group, Unix International.

Valence: In covalent compounds, the valence of an atom is the number of bonds it forms to other atoms.

Van der Waals Bond: A secondary, permanent or induced, interatomic bond between adjacent molecular dipoles. Any of several intermolecular attractive forces not resulting from ionic charges; in this volume, only London dispersion forces are described by this name. Descriptions of the potential energy of nonbonded interactions follow the convention of expressing van der Waals attractive forces and overlap repulsion forces as a single *van der Waals potential*.

Van der Waals Forces: Any of the noncovalent attractive or repulsive forces acting upon neutral atoms or molecules.

Vasculocyte: In medical nanorobotics, a theorized (nanorobotic) device capable of performing repairs of an injured vascular luminal surface.

Vectored air shield: A Martian device which controls the vectors of air molecules around a person. This allows one to walk through vacuum without a space suit or to use enhanced air friction to stop bullets.

Venus: Venus is the second world out from the Sun. It has been terraformed, and harbors a human population of several million. When Venus was first being colonized, while the terraforming process was still ongoing, the seas were quite acidic as sulfuric acid was rinsed from the atmosphere. Thus, the cities on Venus tend to be on cliffs high above the water. The government of Venus is oppressive and authoritarian, a relic of the days when the authorities had to rule with an iron hand in order to maintain public safety in the face of rapidly changing weather and dangerous geological or hydrological changes during the terraforming process.

Very large scale integration (VLSI): Very-large-scale integration (VLSI) is the process of creating integrated circuits by combining thousands of transistor-based circuits into on a single chip. VLSI began in the 1970s when complex semiconductor and communication technologies were being developed. The first semiconductor chips held one transistor each. Subsequent advances added more and more transistors, and as a consequence more individual functions or systems were integrated over time. The microprocessor is a VLSI device.

Virtual Microscope: The Virtual Microscope project is an initiative supervised by Rutgers University to make micromorphology and behavior of some small organisms explorable online. The server is located in the northern USA and the images are from Antarctica and the Baltic Sea. The user can click into the details of interest and get images of higher magnification or resolution, increasing to Scanning Electron Microscopy images, Transmission Electron Microscopy images, and at the end, peer reviewed publications. On larger objects the arrow keys of the keyboard can be used as the crosstable on a real microscope is used. This project also introduces young learners to the internet and the capabilities of web browsers, search engines and databases. The editor board consists of professors from universities on both sides of the Atlantic.

Viscoelasticity: A type of deformation exhibiting the mechanical characteristics of viscous flow and elastic deformation.

Viscosity: The ratio of the magnitude of an applied shear stress to the velocity gradient that it produces; in other words: a measure of a noncrystalline material's resistance to permanent deformation.

Visible Spectrum: Visible light makes up only a small part of the *electromagnetic spectrum*. The visible light spectrum can be divided into different wavelenghts of light. The wavelength of the light determines the color of that light. The light spectrum goes from violet to red where red is the longest wavelength.

Vitamins (Engineering): In machine replication theory, vitamin parts are components of a self-replicating machine which the machine is incapable of producing itself, therefore these vital parts must be supplied from an external source.

Vitrification: During firing of a ceramic body, the formation of a liquid phase that becomes a glass-bonding matrix upon cooling.

1

Introduction to Research Methodology in Applied Sciences

INTRODUCTION

Methodology (also called manner) is defined as:

1. "the analysis of the principles of methods, rules, and postulates employed by a discipline";
2. "the systematic study of methods that are, can be, or have been applied within a discipline"; or
3. "a particular procedure or set of procedures."

Concept

It should be noted that the word "methodology" is frequently used when "method" would be more accurate. (This is a classic example of word inflation.) For example, "Since students were not available to complete the survey about academic success, we changed our methodology and gathered data from instructors instead". In this instance the methodology (gathering data via surveys, and the assumption that this produces accurate results) did not change, but the method (asking teachers instead of students) did. Methodology includes the following concepts as they relate to a particular discipline or field of inquiry:

1. a collection of theories, concepts or ideas;
2. comparative study of different approaches; and
3. critique of the individual methods

Methodology refers to more than a simple set of methods; rather it refers to the rationale and the philosophical assumptions that underlie a particular study. This is why scholarly literature often includes a section on the methodology of the researchers. This section does more than outline the researchers' methods (as in, "We conducted a survey of 50 people over a two-week period and subjected the results to statistical analysis", etc.); it might explain what the researchers' ontological or epistemological views are. Another key (though arguably imprecise) usage for methodology does not refer to research or to the specific analysis techniques. This often refers to anything and everything that can be encapsulated for a discipline or a series of processes, activities and tasks. Examples of this are found in software development, project management and business process fields. This use of the term is typified by the outline who, what, where, when, and why. In the documentation of the processes that make up the discipline, that is being supported by "this" methodology, that is where we would find the "methods" or processes. The processes themselves are only part of the methodology along with the identification and usage of the standards, policies, rules, etc. The tone or style of this article or section may not be appropriate for Wikipedia.Specific concerns may be found on the talk page. For example: Do researchers believe in the paradigm of Positivism, which holds that truth is *out there* waiting to be discovered? In this view, facts exist independently of any theories or human observation. This perspective dominates Western philosophical tradition, which provides the foundation of Western science.

Reality is assumed to be objective, that is, it exists outside our perception. In this paradigm, neither the search for truth nor truth itself is problematic: Truth is definite and ascertainable. Scientists conduct empirical experiments in laboratories and report what they have discovered as experts. Or is truth *constructed* (see Constructivism and Constructivist epistemology) within the minds of individuals and between people in a culture? In this view, facts *become* "facts" and are a construct of theories and points of view. This paradigm holds that both the nature of truth and the inquiry into that truth are problematic because truth is built (or *constructed*) from the ongoing processes of negotiation, revaluation and refinement of and between *individuals*. However, this is unrelated to perspectives outside the scientific community which attempt to equate research results with social and popular beliefs and belief systems.

Most sciences have their own specific scientific methods, which are supported by methodologies (i.e., rationale that support the method's validity). The social sciences are methodologically diverse using qualitative, quantitative, and mixed-methods approaches. Qualitative methods include the case study, phenomenology, grounded theory, and ethnography, among others. Quantitative methods include hypothesis testing, power analysis, metanalysis, observational studies, resampling, randomized controlled trials, regression analysis, multilevel modeling, and high-dimensional data analysis, among others.

Researchers in Natural and Applied Sciences

Researchers in natural and applied sciences describe and explain natural phenomena through the formal procedures of observation, description, hypothesis, prediction, and experiment (scientific method). The basis of scientific examination is the experiment, which provides for the measurement, classification, and explanation of observed phenomena. To establish their research methodologies, scientists must review existing scientific literature both to determine the pre-existence of data that could impact proposed research and to justify their research methodologies. Reference lists help to evaluate the authority and credibility of an scientific research. Researchers can use references to confirm a scientist's methodology and findings.

What is Wrong with "Technology as Applied Science?"

Scholars in science and technologies studies talk about a "pure science ideology" or "scientific ideology." Stereotyping applied science as a dull and mindless practice that generates no new knowledge, the ideology grossly distorts both pure and applied science. What is its origin?

A Paradox

Perhaps you have noticed a curious phenomenon. Many engineers and scientists identify technology with applied science. From the charter of the first engineering society to today, engineers talk proudly of application of science. Many such as Robert Thurston and Charles Steinmetz happily called engineering applied science. However, some engineers consider being identified with applied scientists an insult, as one insists: "engineering applies science but is not applied science." Why are the attitudes so different? Aeronautic engineer Walter Vincenti, who has published extensively in scholarly journals, suggested an answer. He observed that scholars "tend to think of it [engineering] as applied science. Modern engineers are seen as taking over their knowledge from scientists, and by some occasionally dramatic but probably intellectually uninteresting process, using this knowledge to fashion material artifacts." If applied science meant intellectual inferiority, then technology is definitely not applied science. But does it? Who say that it does?

Two Senses of "Applied Science"

Science generally means state of knowing or possessing knowledge that is sufficiently general, clearly conceptualized, carefully reasoned, systematically organised, critically examined, and empirically tested. According to subject matter, science can be analyzed into many sciences: natural sciences such as physics or biology, engineering sciences such as communication and control, social sciences such as economics, human sciences such as psychology.

Practicality of topics divides between basic and applied sciences. In the scientific and engineering community, the difference between them is one of focus and orientation, not intellectual quality, epistemological precedence, or historical priority. This is made clear by the U.S. National Science Foundation, which defines applied science as aiming at "gaining the knowledge or understanding to meet a specific, recognized need," treats it equally with basic science, and pours research funds into it. Research thrives in Divisions of Engineering and Applied Science of Caltech, Harvard, and many other universities. New knowledge fills numerous books and journals on applied mathematics, applied physics, applied mechanics, etcetera. The intellectual excitement and information fertility of applied science are widely acknowledged. It is in this proud sense that a carefully edited report with contributions from eighty engineers and scientists from academia, industry, and the government asserted: "*Applied science* is often regarded as a synonym for 'engineering'."

A different sense of "applied science" underlies the attack on engineering and technology as applied science. Here application of science is described as "more or less mechanical" and applied science "debased," "intellectual parasitism," "introducing no new knowledge," "a humdrum uncreative activity crucially dependent upon basic science," and low in "pecking order." This disparagement of applied science is called "the scientific ideology" or an "American ideology" by scholars who allege that it pervades western tradition, especially the American culture since at least mid-nineteenth century. The allegation was introduced in the 1970s and promoted ever since by sociological historian Edward Layton. It has been widely accepted in technology studies. What are the evidences of the allegation?

Is Applied Science Disdained in American Culture?

Is the disdain of applied science an American ideology? The United States spends more on applied than on pure research. America has a culture where Thomas Edison was a national hero and *Scientific American* a newsletter for patents, the inaugural editorial of *Science* extolled application, and the Land Grand Act specifically sponsored universities for applied oriented education. The preponderant practical attitude of Americans had struck European visitors such as Alexis de Tocqueville, who observed in 1835: "In America the purely practical part of the sciences is cultivated admirably, and people attend carefully to the theoretical portion immediately necessary to applications; in this way the Americans display a mind that is always clear, free, original, and fertile; there is almost no one in the United States who gives himself over to the essentially theoretical and abstract portion of human knowledge." Even in formal philosophy, America is known for its pragmatism distinct from British empiricism, French rationalism, and German idealism. Such a culture is unlikely to undervalue applied science.

Is snubbing application a prejudice of scientists? Nobel prizes in physics have been awarded to wireless telegraphy, automatic regulators, transistor, integrated circuit, electronic microscope, and fast photonics, which are applied science if anything is. Emphasis on application is even stronger in chemistry and biology, as is evident in the coziness between university biology departments and pharmaceutical companies. Even the purest of pure scientists deny that applied science is devoid of new knowledge.

Groundless Accusations

So where did "the scientific ideology" come from? Scholars referred to each other about it, but were not totally oblivious of its hearsay nature. One historian remarked: "The origin of this notion is not entirely clear. Certainly it is prominent in the rhetoric of the promoters of science from Francis Bacon and the seventeenth century academicians to James Conant and Vannevar Bush." Another admitted after two decades and numerous references to it in the history of technology: "Little attention has been paid to the history of this view [the scientific ideology] and why it (and similar beliefs) has been so pervasive in American culture." It is significant that he does not question the alleged pervasiveness even when his own historical research yields not examples but counterexamples.

The groundlessness of "the scientific ideology" is apparent from the piece of text most frequently offered as its certain and prominent evidence: Bush's *Science – the Endless Frontier*. Bush was an engineer whose own research was all applied. His article is posted approvingly in the website of the National Science Foundation, which takes great pain to put pure and applied sciences on equal footing. Written in 1945, it was a report to the U.S. president recommending a specific policy: the need to create public funding for basic research. In contrast to general treatises, requests for funding tend to focus sharply on the benefits of the proposed project. Omission does not imply disapproval; asking for too much would invite rejection. To win public support for basic research that has no apparent material benefits is not easy now and was more difficult then. Bush was careful to limit his objective. He did not ask funds for applied research, which had been supported by mission oriented agencies in the government, not to mention in the private sector for profit motives. He argued that basic research produces new knowledge but never suggested that it produces all knowledge so that that technology contains no knowledge. He argued that basic science is necessary but never suggested that it is sufficient of knowledge.

Consider Bush's sentence: "A nation which depends upon others for its new basic scientific knowledge will be slow in its industrial and weak in its competitive position in world trade, regardless of its mechanical skill." Layton quoted and accused it for implying the "intellectual parasitism" of applied science and denying "symbiotic relationship" between applied and basic sciences. The accusation has no justification, because the proposal nowhere asserts that basic research produces the *only* crucial knowledge. We can compare Bush's notion of basic research as "pace setter" to paratroops that stake out the ground. Suppose the military urges the creation of air born units, arguing that without them one would lose the rapid deployment edge, no matter how fast ground troops move. This in no way implies that ground troops are parasitic on paratroops, which will perish if not linked up with the main army. Bush did not denigrate application. Neither did other promoters of sciences as alleged. They argued for the *value of research without apparent applications*, not the *disvalue of research with applications*. Research requires much human and material resource. In attracting funds, pure science is disadvantageous because it promises no immediate return. Pure scientists working on a shoestring are more likely to explain the benefits of their works, as expressed in the title of Henry Rowland's "A plea for pure science." It appeared in 1883, ten years before the birth of *Physical Review*, when pure research was almost nonexistent in America. To distort such desperate pleas into a deprecation of application perverts the whole nature of science, pure and applied.

A Case of Muddled Thinking

When analyzed, alleged evidence of the prevalence of "the scientific ideology" turns out to be conceptual muddles that interpret *necessity* as *sufficiency*, *some* as *all*, "*A* is important" as *B* is worthless, "*A* is good" as *B* is bad, "*A* has something" as *B* has nothing. Applied science is stereotyped without any attempt to study its actual practice or analyze its technical contents. Counter examples are ignored. Confronted with growing insistence of numerous engineers to describe their practice as application of science, Layton shrugged: "it is enough to recognize that such claims [by engineers] are ideological in nature and not to be taken as literal descriptions." Such disregard of evidence is not uncommon in postmodernism – "interpretive flexibility" is a central tenet in social constructionism. A sociologist described the treatment of scientists by her postmodern colleagues: "a certain 'Besserwisser' approach prevails, with the sociologists smugly overruling the scientists. It was as if the sociologists were the self-appointed psychoanalysts of scientists, knowing their 'true' motives, unbeknownst to the scientists themselves."

Layton introduced "the scientific ideology" not as a positive doctrine but as a target of attack. Unfortunately, it is a wrong target. An elitist culture did exist in which "the idea of utility has long borne the stamp of vulgarity," as observed by historian Leo Marx. "*The* intellectual world" spurned the concept of technology until after 1918, more than half a century after the foundation of Massachusetts Institute of Technology. As late as 1959, when engineering research was wide spread, a scholar declared that no word existed for the improver of technology comparable to "scientist" as the improver of knowledge. This was the elitist culture that stood against the scientific culture in C. P. Snow's analysis of the gap between two cultures; its definition of "intellectual" excluded not only engineers but physicists and mathematicians. Snow's description was echoed in 2002 by Harvard's president Lawrence Summers, who criticized "a culture where it is unacceptable not to be able to name five plays by Shakespeare but where it is fine to not know the difference between a gene and chromosome." This culture – not the scientific culture – is the breeding ground of the misnamed "scientific ideology."

Bush, the alleged prime advocate of "the scientific ideology," actually advocated its negation: "In all associations between engineers and scientists, engineering is more a partner than a child of science." This thesis has long been a commonplace among engineers. However, Layton proposed it in 1970s as a novelty in technology studies, accompanied by the alleged prevalence of "the scientific ideology" in scientific culture and American culture at large. He argued for a valid old thesis with an invalid new reason. The falsity of his allegation was dimmed by the tendency of elitists to regard their small club as the whole world.

The false allegation is harmful because it attributes bigotry to the wrong people and distorts the whole picture. "The scientific ideology" hurts applied scientists and engineers. Its alleged prevalence adds harm to pure scientists and the American people who are thereby stereotyped as narrow-minded bigots. It creates animosity among engineers and scientists. By distorting legitimate arguments for basic science into an objectionable prejudice, it undermines support for basic research.

Three Aspects of Technology

Far from being opposite to culture, technology is an inalienable element of culture that permeates the fabric of our ways of life. Residing not only in high-tech goods and services but more importantly in human understanding, it influences how we do things, relate to each other, and organise our social institutions. Technology has three major aspects: goods and services, human activities that create these products, and capabilities that enable technical activities. The aspects are interrelated and mutually reinforcing. Activities in research, development, and production create not only consumer goods and services but also knowledge and skills, which supply the growth of technological ability. On the other side, people's demand for goods and services stimulate technological activities, some of its results are ploughed back as social investments in education, research, and infrastructure, which expand technological capability. Thus technology progresses under the "supply push" and "demand pull," influenced in each step by myriad factors such as natural resources, economic conditions, and consumer tastes.

(i) Technological products and infrastructures
(ii) Technological innovation and economic growth
(iii) Managing technological risks
(iv) General history of technology
(v) Research and development
(vi) Technology as a scientific capacity to produce

Technological Products and Infrastructures

High-tech goods and services permeate our daily life. Less conspicuous are various implements and infrastructures geared toward processes of production. Besides being capital investment, they embody certain human skills and experiences in hardware:

(i) plant layouts and operating procedures
(ii) machines for agriculture and manufacture
(iii) control mechanisms for automation
(iv) standards for technological systems and products
(v) public infrastructures for energy, communication, transportation, information processing, public health, and national defense.

Technology as a Scientific Capacity to Produce

What is technology, what does technology mean? One notion, which originated in the Greek *téchnç*, points to the rational ability to create and produce. This ability is primordial, for to produce the means of living and create meanings of life in work are vital to human existence. Modern technology grew out of ancient *téchnç* by developing its own reasoning and knowledge into science.

Embryonic Notion of Technology in Greek Philosophy

The ancient Greeks often discussed *epistçmç* and *téchnç* together, just as we now mention science and technology in one breath. Plato sometimes used the two terms interchangeably. Aristotle distinguished them more carefully.

Epistçmç had several meanings in ancient Greek. Broadly, it meant knowledge in general. Narrowly, it referred to a specific kind of knowledge, which is usually translated as science.

Téchnç is a state of capacity to produce with a true *logos*," Aristotle defined *Logos* was a central notion in Greek philosophy, broadly meaning reason and discourse. Because art had its own reasoning and discourse, it was knowledge, as distinct from opinion (*doxa*) and mere experience. Many arts existed, among others Aristotle cited architecture, medicine, and mathematics. Aristotle remarked that art originated from experiences but went well beyond mere empiricism. He explored the characteristics of *téchnç* in detail. Among other things, his explication addressed what we now call education, research, and the contents of technological knowledge .

Research: Aristotle said: "Art arises, when from many notions gained by experience one universal judgment about similar objects is produced." The ability to generalize and uncover principles behind diverse phenomena is also the hallmark of science. This ability is honed and practiced mostly in research. Graduate schools and industrial research laboratories first appeared, almost hand in hand, in Germany in the late nineteenth century. From the beginning, many, although far from all, research projects are applied oriented. Today, engineers stand shoulder to shoulder with natural scientists at the cutting edge of research.

Education: Aristotle said: "It is a sign of the man who knows, that he can teach, and therefore we think art more truly knowledge than experience is; for artists can teach, and men of mere experience cannot." In the old days, apprentices learned the skills of trade by working in workshops, where masters not so much taught via concepts as showed by their own practices. With the rise of scientific engineering, tacit know-how has been increasingly articulated, criticized, systematized, and developed, so that they can be promulgated in books and taught to student away from the workshops. Since the eighteenth century, when technological universities first appeared in France, apprenticeship has given way to education.

Contents of knowledge: Aristotle said: "Men of experience know that the thing is so, but do not know why, while artists know the 'why' and the cause of thing that is done." Not to accept what meets the eye unquestioningly but to seek explanations is another hallmark of science. Explanations are facilitated by universal judgments and general concepts, which give tongue to what are inarticulate in mere experiences. Aristotle also investigated what kinds of explanations – causes of things – were acceptable. He analyzed four kinds of cause: material cause, formal (structural) cause, efficient (dynamic) cause, and final (purposive) cause. Some historians of science asserted that of the four Aristotelian causes, only the efficient cause, which concerned forces, remained "scientific" after the Scientific Revolution. These historians were too much obsessed by the glamorous part of Newtonian mechanics to notice the many applied oriented researches that were going on. The other three causes continue to be studied and are very much alive in today's science and technology. Galileo started his scientific career investigating the material and structural causes of building construction. These topics had been developed by natural philosophers as well as civil engineers all through the eighteenth and nineteenth century, with conspicuous fruits such as the railroad bridges that symbolized the landscape of the industrial revolution, or the skyscrapers that dominate the skylines of modern cities. Stripped of its metaphysical trapping of finality, questions about functions of technological products are very important in today's engineering.

The Aristotelian definition of practical art is significant because it insists that *téchnç* contains its own *logos*. When the intrinsic *logos* of *téchnç* is systematically articulated and developed, it naturally grows into technology.

Internal and External Notions of "Technology"

Concatenations of *téchnç* and *logos* appeared in Latin writings with ambiguous meanings. According to the *Oxford English Dictionary*, the etymology of "technology" is systematic treatment. As such it can be viewed internally or externally.

In the external view, technology means the systematic discourse *about* practical art. Technology is the science about practical art just as entomology is the science about insects and geology about planet Earth. Here *logos* belongs to scholars who takes practical art and artists as their topics of investigation but is foreign to and not a part of the art or artists. It neglects the cognitive ability of the artists and concentrates on their products and social status. Appeared in the sixteenth century — French rhetorician Peter Ramus used *technologia* for systematic arrangement of all arts — this sense is mostly outdated. Today scholarly discourses about practical art or engineering are called not technology but technology *studies*, which include history, philosophy, and sociology of technology. Nevertheless, technology studies have a tendency to emphasize the external stance of seeing technology mainly as mindless physical or social systems. In many studies, technology is drained of science, engineering, and intellectual contents. Scientists and engineers are treated on the same status as catalysts and scallops in the "actor-network model," one of the most influential sociological models in science and technology studies.

The internal view inherits the Greek notion of *téchnç* containing its own *logos*, so that technology means the systematic reasoning *of* practical art itself. In this view, art and reasoning are not separate entities that later enter into a marriage. They are intertwined cognitive potentials inherent in every human being, because living in, coping with, and modifying the real world is primordial to all human life. Technology is the explicit rendition of reasoning inherent in practical art; the systematic abstraction of essentials; the articulation, generalization, refinement, and development of knowledge involved in productive and creative activities. Thus practical art — engineering and technology — became scientific not by imitation but by self development. This view was expressed by Galileo in *Two New Sciences*, one of his two major books: "in this department [the Venetian arsenal] all types of instruments and machines are constantly being constructed by many artisans, among whom there must be some who, partly by inherited experience and partly by their own observations, have become highly expert and clever in explanation."

Some seventeenth-century puritan theologians argued that what was nature to us was God's creation. Therefore they rejected the Aristotelian distinction between natural science and productive art and proposed *technologia* that encompassed both. Among the puritans was William Ames, whose ideas were influential in Massachusetts. In 1829, Boston botanist Jacob Bigelow observed that the word "technology," found in some old dictionaries, was revived among practical men. He delivered a series of lectures entitled *Elements of Technology*, in which gave a definition with Aristotelian ring: Technology is "the principle, processes, and nomenclatures of the more conspicuous arts, particularly those which involve application of science." He later sat on the board of trustees of Massachusetts Institute of Technology, the foundation of which in 1861 publicized the concept of technology.

Technology and Modern Technology

The internal view of technology spread in the nineteenth century. It has two connotations. In the broad sense, favored by anthropologists and historians, technology embraces all practical arts primitive and sophisticated. In a narrower sense, favored by engineers and scientists, technology includes only those practical arts that incorporate a significant body of explicitly articulated knowledge and explanation that is scientific in the modern sense.

Both internalist senses were used by Karl Marx, the first great economist to expound the deep relation between modes of production and human welfare. He wrote: "Technology reveals the active relation of man to nature, the direct process of the production of his life, and thereby it also lays bare the process of the production of the social relations of his life, and of the mental conceptions that flow from those relations." Containing man's relations both to nature and society and incorporating all skills and knowledge about material creation and production, technology in this sense has a very broad scope. However, Marx also observed that "right down to the eighteenth century, the different trades were called 'mysteries.'" Then, he continued, the veil of mystery was torn apart by "the modern science of technology." In this narrowed-down sense, technology is the science in which practical artists articulate and explain their own work.

Both the broad and narrow meanings of technology are currently used. For instance, the five-volume *A History of Technology* covers practical arts since antiquity, but its editors observe that "not until the nineteenth century did the term [technology] acquire a scientific content and come ultimately to be regarded as almost synonymous with 'applied science.'" This intrinsic relationship between technology and science.

is revealed in the organisation of many universities with School of Engineering and Applied Science.

Technology as Intellectual, Human, Physical, and Social Capital

In the internal view, technology is a scientific capacity to produce and create. A society's technological capacity is one of its major assets. It resides in four areas:

(i) *Intellectual capital*: factual knowledge, theories, patents, algorithms, science.

(ii) *Human capital*: understanding, skills, and practices of scientists, engineers, and other workers.

(iii) *Physical capital*: machines and their operating principles, plant layouts, infrastructures.

(iv) *Social capital*: organisation of educational, research, industrial, and other social institutions.

These capitals are products of technological activities: education, research, development, industry, and other productive works. Some products of these activities, notably high-tech goods and services, are consumed by people and most familiar to them as the essence of "technology." Not all products are consumed, however. Many are plowed back as social investments that expand technological capacities. Of the four kinds of technological capacity, science is explicitly articulated and can be promulgated rather easily. Other kinds of knowledge are more difficult to spread because they are tacit and embodied in living people, physical infrastructures, and social organisations. Transmission of tacit knowledge in "technology transfer" depends heavily on the travel or migration of engineers and managers, the establishment of firms or educational institutions, or the moving or building of physical plants. Tacit and embodied knowledge is the most valuable asset of technologically advanced nations, their greatest comparative advantage over catcher-ups, because it can only be patiently accrued in concrete beings as a major form of capital accumulation.

Concepts of System in Engineering

This talk explores three concepts of *system* in engineering: systems theory, systems approach, and systems engineering. They are exemplified in three dimensions of engineering: science, design, and management. Unifying the three system concepts is the idea of *function*: functional abstraction in theory, functional analysis in design, and functional requirements in management. Signifying what a system is *for*, function is a purposive notion absent in physical science, which aims to understand nature. It is prominent in engineering, which aims to transform nature for serving the wants and needs of people. The engineering system concepts are compared to the notion of system as a seamless web in postmodern technology studies. As Friedrich Nietzsche remarked: "*Being profound and seeming profound*. – Those who know that they are profound strive for clarity. Those who would like to seem profound to the crowd strive for obscurity. For the crowd believes that if it cannot see to the bottom of something it must be profound. It is so timid and dislikes going into the water."

Systems in Everyday Life, Technology Study, and Engineering

Systems are everywhere in our daily discourse, from the solar system to home entertainment systems, from water treatment to national security systems. Railway networks and electric power grids are systems, so is the internet and the world wide web. Then there are the more intangible political, social, and financial systems. "The system works," people say when things go smoothly; "the system fails," when troubles strike. The commonsense notion of system is familiar: the system is a whole comprising interrelated parts with significant complexity; the system is not merely the sum of its parts. There seems to be no restriction on whether the related parts are animate of inanimate, people of things, hardware or software, concrete or abstract. Nevertheless, their interrelations, although complex, should be susceptible to some rational understanding. A muddled mess or an incomprehensible chaos is at best a failed system, if one at all.

"System" is a buzzword in technology studies, although its significance beyond the commonsense notion is obscure. Systems are said to be heterogeneous, but the heterogeneity often turns out to be a jumbling miscellany and the system a sausage with medley indifferentiable stuffing. Perhaps the most prominent notion of "system" is expressed by the metaphor of a "seamless web." Introduced by Thomas Hughes, the prime promoter of "systems thinking," it conveys the notions of holism, perfection, and resistance to analysis. It is popular in postmodern scholarship, which is hostile to rationality.

Systems are central to engineering. Engineers are responsible for designing and building transportation, communication, and other systems that operate in the real world. Their systems concepts are clear. Here I explore three: systems theories, systems approach, and systems engineering. None comes close to a seamless web. The systems approach in engineering, with its emphasis on analysis and modularity, is opposite to the anti-analytic postmodern "systems thinking."

Systems versus Seamless Webs

In his book *Science of the Artificial*, Herbert Simon gives the parable of two watchmakers, each designs a watch with a hundred parts. In the first design, the hundred parts are so thoroughly interrelated that the watch totally falls apart if any one is removed. The watch is expensive because it must be assembled in one breath and cannot be repaired by replacing parts. The second watch has similar performances, but its parts are grouped into ten modules, which can be replaced if defective. Because it is simple to assemble and easy to modify, the second watchmaker is able to offer his products at a lower price and drive the first watchmaker out of business.

Simon's first watch design is akin to a seamless web; his second design, an engineering system. A seamless web is good if perfect, but perfection is more often than not illusory. Seamless webs are prone to disasters, because they can be unraveled by the tiniest of loose ends. The effect of a tiny flaw propagating unhindered and creating web-wide havoc is one of the root causes of "normal accidents," as Charles Perrow called it. To control such disastrous scenarios is a major reason for *modularity*. To limit potential damages, engineers are careful to introduce seams and modular boundaries into their systems. An electric power grid provides an example. Once electricity is fed into the grid, it flows automatically according to physical laws and the conditions of the entire grid. The risk of such seamless configuration is well known. Effects of a small mishap, such a lightning striking out a transformer, can cascade though the grid, leading to power failures in large regions. The 1996 Northwest power blackout and the 2003 Northeast blackout each cost damages in excess of a billion dollars. Engineers tolerated the seamless web not because they deemed it superior but because they could do little about its faults. Until very recently, they had no way to switch high-voltage currents on the grid in real time. Even so, they did try their best to install gates between regions for damage control. New England escaped the 2003 Northeast blackout because the gate designed to disengage it from the grid worked in time – it was saved by a seam.

A system can operate seamlessly without being a seamless web. An example is the internet, which is a patchwork of many networks: landline telephone networks, wireless computer connections, satellite links, and more. All participating networks use packet switching. Otherwise each has its peculiar internal operating principles. A basic design principle of the internet is to preserve as much as possible the autonomy of these internal principles, so that each network can be individually modified and improved. To tie disparate network together in the internet, engineers design routers and protocols at the interface between two networks, so that signals can pass smoothly between them. The routers are seams, good seams. The superiority of an engineering system lies not in seamlessness but in its good seams or good interfaces between its parts.

Besides the illusion of perfection, the gist of the seamless-web metaphor and associated "systems thinking" is the holistic aura that shields it from critical analysis. The resistance to analysis makes them look profound, but they are basically obscure and muddled, which are major critiques of postmodern studies. In stark contrast, the systematic approaches in science and engineering strive for clarity.

Being profound is different from seeming profound. Tackling with real-world complexity is different from using the word "complexity" to decorate simplistic ideas dreamed up in arm chairs. Simon's parable is intended to illustrate an approach for designing complex artificial systems that must operate in the real world, but its wisdom applies equally to research in natural science. In principle, the universe is a whole in which everything is connected to all others. Gravity and electromagnetism, the two forces that act between all things above the nuclear level, have infinite ranges. However, if we must treat the universe as a seamless web and grasp everything in it at once, our tiny brains would be so overwhelmed that we would fail to understand anything at all. None of our concepts would be valid, because concepts invariably make distinctions and "carve nature at its joints," as Plato said.

Science is successful partly because scientists are content to proceed one step at a time, to bite off what they can chew, and refrain from confusing grandiloquent such as seamlessness. Instead of trying to tackle the whole universe at once, scientists take things apart and examine bits and pieces, acknowledging their own limitations. The methods of Socrates were said to be division and collection; Galileo, resolution and composition. Descartes and Newton discusses analysis and synthesis. Engineers practice functional decomposition and physical integration in systems design.

Analysis clarifies. Analysis is also called reduction, and "reductionism" to scientists means the importance of analysis. However, "reductionism" has also become a philosophical dogma asserting that a system is *nothing but* its constituents, e.g., you are nothing but your genes or neurons. Ideological reductionism, which slights synthesis, has engendered much debate in the philosophy of science, debates that generate more heat than light.

Holism rejects analysis and sees only the whole. Reductionism rejects synthesis and sees only the parts. The systems approach in engineering integrates analysis and synthesis. It brings to relief the dictionary definition of a system as a whole with interrelated parts, emphasizing internal structure.

Systems Approach as Analysis-synthesis

Let us consider a familiar engineered system, an automobile. When you are driving it, it works as a unitary whole. Any trip to the garage will convince you that it is a system composed of many interrelated subsystems: power train, transmission, ignition, steering, braking, lubricating, suspension, and more. Each of these subsystems is in turn made up of many parts, for instance the clutch, stick shift, and gear box for transmission. The gear box in turn consists many components, and so on down to nuts and bolts. Cars are designed by engineers. Their systems approach is illustrated in many textbooks by the *Vee* model, originally due to Forsberg and

Mooz. The down stroke of the *Vee* represents functional analysis, the upward stroke physical synthesis.

When engineers want to design a car, they do not start with a bunch of nuts and bolts. They start with the car as a whole. Of course, the car does not yet exist. Thus they start with a conception of the intended car, more specifically, a set of *functional requirements* for it: what it is supposed to do, what performances are expected of it. To ascertain satisfactory functional requirements is usually an important and difficult task, especially when the system is very complex. We will return to it later in the context of systems engineering.

After design engineers have arrived at a satisfactory conception of the intended car, they proceed to *functional analysis*. They decompose the conceived car into functional subsystems with proper interfaces, e.g., a subsystem *for* power and a subsystem *for* transmission, and how the two are to work together. Then they further analyze a subsystem into its interrelated components, until they get manageable parts that can be specified to the last details. They have reached the bottom of the *Vee*. Turning the corner of the *Vee*, the thousands of parts are manufactured to specifications. They are then tested, brought together, and assembled into larger and larger subsystems, finally into a car ready for test drive. We are back at the top of the *Vee*, but this time we have a concrete system – a real car – instead of a mere conception of it.

Through functional decomposition, detailed design, and physical assembly, engineers know and specify the whole, its parts, and their interrelations clearly and at all compositional scales. The subsystems at intermediate levels are crucial for managing complex systems, for they enable engineers to introduce complex details one step at a time. In short, the *systems approach* integrates analysis and synthesis. It is most effective in treating complex phenomena, for it:

(i) encompasses both the holistic and modular views
  - grasps the arching features of the whole system
  - analyzes it into parts with proper interfaces
  - synthesizes knowledge about the parts to understand the whole

(ii) grasps the system and its details in many levels
  - decomposes a subsystem into sub-subsystems, and so on, to the last details
  - changes focus to view different levels so the mind is not overwhelmed by complexity

(iii) abstracts and hides information to focus on a task :

- simplifies the system by treating its parts as black boxes except their interfaces
- hiding information is *not* discarding it; a black box can be opened at will

(iv) makes a complex system more tractable

- a part can be studied or designed with minimal interference from other parts

(v) controls damage and improves safety

- confines most effects of a defect within a subsystem, preventing a system-wide collapse

The systems approach, in which one analyzes the details of parts in order to know the whole, works not only in engineering but also in natural science. Consider for example systems biology, which aspires to study organisms as wholes. The idea appeared in the 1960s, but lied dormant because the properties of the biological constituents remained in the dark. Meanwhile, biologists analyzed organisms into organs and tissues and cells and molecules. Now molecular biologists have deciphered the genome of many organisms, including humans. They have reached the bottom of the *Vee* and gained tremendous amount of knowledge. Yet they found it falls far short for understanding organisms. Then they turn to synthesis and investigate how genes function in cells and organisms as wholes. As they do so, systems biology springs alive. Several universities, including Harvard here, are establishing departments of systems biology. Four decades of analyzing organic constituents turn systems biology from philosophy into science.

Strategic Purviews of Systems Engineering

Analysis and synthesis focus on internal structures. A system in this focus is often, but not always, regarded as closed and isolated from the rest of the world. Idealization of closed systems is common in natural science; controlled experiments are designed to realize the ideals as much as possible. On the other hand, the ultimate purposes of engineering systems, be they cars or bridges, are to provide services to some external communities. Thus even when engineers focus on the internal structures of a system, they leave at least a crack at the door. The openings are represented in the system's *functions*, *input*, and *output*. Given a set of functional requirements as ends, the systems approach as analysis-synthesis searches for means to best serve the ends. Systems engineering goes one step further to engage in *analysis of ends* to determine what functions are required of the system they are charged to design and build. The ends are ultimately decided by various social groups that hold interests in the intended system – clients, as engineers briefly call them. To help their clients in defining feasible and desirable ends, systems engineers negotiate and form working partnerships with them. Systems engineering arose after World War II to design, develop, and manage complex technological systems with wide societal impacts. Its purview is strategic, taking into account not only a system's life cycle from womb to tomb, but also the people who are involved in various stages of the cycle. Among its missions are:

(i) ends analysis: requirements engineering,

(ii) life-cycle analysis: concurrent engineering,

(iii) multidisciplinary teamwork: organisation for development and management.

Functional Requirements

Many engineers avow that the most difficult task of a complex engineering project is to get the requirements right. The task depends crucially on the cooperation between systems engineers and their clients. For complex systems involving novel technologies, people are often uncertainty about what they want, or they are unrealistic in their expectations. When the clients divide into several groups, their desires often conflict. It is incumbent on systems engineers to help their clients to clarify their objectives: What exactly do you want? Can you afford it? If not, what options do you have?

Systems engineers consider both technical and contextual conditions. Consider an engineering project, the development of a passenger jetliner. (There are good accounts, by engineers and journalists, on the role of systems engineering in the development of the Boeing 777 jetliner in the 1990s). The major clients are the large airlines, each has its own requirements on range, speed, payload, price, fuel economy, and so on. Besides them, systems engineers also have to consult government aviation policies, environmental regulations, airport facilities, economic and demographic forecasts, and so on. To ensure that the designed airplane can be manufactured cost effectively, traveled on comfortably, operated safely, and maintained easily, systems engineers elicit opinions from manufacturers, passengers, pilots, flight attendants, and maintenance crews. They then have to make tradeoff among various requirements, for instance between ease of maintenance and lower manufacturing costs. Finally, having coordinated relevant requirements, they design into the airplane affordability, manufacturability, reliability, maintainability, user friendless, disposability, and a host of other -abilities – dispositional properties that they anticipate will function some time in its lifespan. They design *time* into *being*, which is the gist of concurrent engineering.

Stages of System Development

(i) elicitation of cradle-to-grave functional requirements from stake holders

(ii) definition of a system concept that satisfies the life-long requirements

(iii) successive functional modularization of the system concept

(iv) physical integration of components to build the system

An airplane, or your car, is an inanimate thing. But it is more than that, because it also carries interfaces with its intended users. The gentle shape of your car's seat, the clean layout of its dashboard, are all designed with you in mind. The philosopher Martin Heidegger once contemplated Van Gogh's painting of a pair of peasant's shoe and saw in it the meaning of human existence. Use and readiness-to-hand also shine in engineered systems. An airplane consists advanced materials, high performance engines, onboard computers, navigation and communications systems, and more. The development project of Boeing 777 alone involved some four thousand engineers with disparate expertise from many companies. Just to coordinate their efforts is a major management task for systems engineers. They are responsible for assembling experts in many areas, organising them into cohesive multidisciplinary teams, integrating their knowledge, and bringing them to bear on the project. Project management is facilitated by the systems approach of analysis-synthesis. In functional decomposition, systems engineers specify only the functional requirements of what a subsystem, for instance the onboard computer, is supposed to do. Then they let software engineers to figure out how to satisfy the requirements. In this way both parties can utilize their expertise maximally and yet still corporate tightly. They interact and negotiate on the requirements, but only where it counts, so that they do not suffer from micromanagement and counterproductive interferences.

Systems engineering combines technology development with strategic management, which plans ahead with long-term vision. Since the rise of large-scale industry and giant corporations, engineers had been among leaders of strategic management. They pioneered modern business administration in the nineteenth century and occupy many top executive offices today. Systems engineering attempts to articulate, rationalize, and develop best managerial practices, especially in high-technology areas. It originated in the Cold War and was revitalized in the 1980s, when American industry faced stiff commercial competition from Japan. The Japanese, especially Toyota Motors, are experts in systems engineering. So Americans analyzed Japanese practices and incorporated many of their innovations into systems engineering. The abstraction of general principles from one culture and apply it appropriately in another culture is a mark of scientific thinking, which transcends narrow cultural bounds. Systems engineering is thriving. MIT and Stanford both created departments for it most recently.

Functional Abstraction and Systems Theories

Systems engineering, which stands at the interface between engineering and management, is conspicuously practical and down to earth. In contrast, systems theories, which lie at the core of engineering science, are mathematical and rather abstract. This in no way implies that systems theories are impractical; they are practical in a general way. Connecting them to systems engineering is the notion of *function*, through which systems theories are applied to particular designs.

Adam Smith, whose *Wealth of Nations* appeared in the same year as his friend Watt's steam engine, observed a relation between machines and abstract systems: "Systems in many respects resemble machines. A machine is a little system, created to perform, as well as to connect together, in reality, those different movements and effects which the artist has occasion for. A system is an imaginary machine invented to connect together in fancy those different movements and effects which are already in reality performed." Smith's remark adumbrated the abstraction from concrete machineries prevalent in engineering systems theories. In a purposive context, a thing has two kinds of characteristic. The first are physical properties: its materials, structures, and motions. The second are functional characteristics: what it is for, what services it performs. *Systems theories abstract from physical properties and bring to relief functional characteristics*. Not surprisingly, systems abstraction is absent from physical sciences and peculiar to engineering, which aims to design systems that serve people. We can distinguish two broad types of concepts. Substantive concepts address *what are*, things and their properties. Functional concepts address *what for*. Functions tacitly point to a context, the larger environment in which a system operates and provides services. Functional concepts occur less in physics than in biology, especially evolutionary biology, where natural selection selects adaptable functions. Functional concepts are sort of controversial in natural sciences, because they connote some sense of purpose. Evolutionary biologists who evoke them often refer to engineering; there functional concepts are intuitive, prominent, and successful. Among functional concepts are dispositional properties, which indicate what a thing would do under certain circumstances. Properties such as solubility and flammability occur in physics. They are much more numerous in engineering, whose cradle-to-grave considerations cover properties such as affordability, reliability, durability, manufacturabiliy, and a host of other abilities. Many of such dispositional properties are kind of abstract and intangible. To treat them property engineers have to introduce concepts to define them clearly and performance metrics to measure them. Such concept formation is a kind of scientific thinking. Functions are paramount in engineering, because engineered systems are designed for service. Thus it is no surprise that they get the center stage of systems theory.

Information Theory

Examples of systems theories are control theory, information theory, theories for estimation and signal processing. Some systems theories, for example classical control, existed before WWII. But like elsewhere in engineering, a turning point occurred during the war. Mathematician Nobert Wiener introduced two concepts into engineering, probability and optimization, which revolutionized system theoretic thinking. His monograph was called "yellow peril" by engineers, because it had a yellow cover and because its difficult mathematics was overwhelming. But one generation later, engineer scientists became totally comfortable with abstract mathematics. Systems theories are highly mathematical, and their theorem-proof format has more the flavor of pure mathematics than the calculus and applied mathematics familiar in physical theories. Perhaps the most famous of systems theories is the information theory introduced by Claude Shannon. He opened his classic paper *A mathematical theory of communication*:

> "The fundamental problem of communication is that of reproducing at one point either exactly or approximately a message selected at another point. We wish to consider certain general problems involving communication systems. To do this it is first necessary to represent the various elements involved as mathematical entities, suitably idealized from their physical counterparts."

The paragraph highlights the essential characteristics of a systems theory:

(i) *Functionality*: the theory is *for the sake* of reliable communication. Reliability is a purposive notion. Shannon gave a brief definition of it here, and would introduce precise metric for it in the paper in terms of probability of errors.

(ii) *Abstraction*: the theory idealizes from physical properties.

(iii) *Generality*: the theory is concerned not with particular communication systems but with general principles underlying all kinds of reliable communication systems. Focuses on the general and the particular distinguish between engineering science and engineering design.

(iv) *Mathematical representation*: the functional relations among communication components are represented in mathematical terms.

Take for example signal processing, a widely applicable systems theory. A signal is something that carries information, and signal processing is the transformation of signals for efficient manipulation, transmission, or storage. Signals come in a variety of physical media: acoustic, mechanic, electromagnetic. Signal processors engage disparate physical mechanisms: electric, electronic, piezoelectric. When you speak on a phone, your information is carried in acoustic signals, which are immediately transformed into electromagnetic signals, which go through modulation, digitization, coding, multiplexing, demultiplexing, decoding, and other signal processing procedures before they are transformed back into acoustic signals heard by your friend on the other end.

Signal processing theory abstracts from most physical properties, retaining only a few essential features such as the wavelength of signals. It aims to capture, in mathematical terms, the *functions* of signal processors, how they transform the *forms* of signals, for instance the function of digitization transforms a signal from analog form to digital form. Because it captures the fundamental principles covering a wide variety of physical mechanisms, signal processing theory is applicable everywhere from telecommunications to scientific experiments.

Feedback Control as an Example of Functional Abstraction

Because systems theories abstract from physical properties, the functional relations they represent can be applied to systems with disparate physical make up. Thus signal processing theories apply equally to acoustic or electrical signals. Mathematical representations enable engineers to manipulate abstract forms, create novel functional relations, and realize them in appropriate physical media.

We can see how system theories work in the case of feedback control. Although the term "feedback control" was introduced in the 20th century, feedback devices had been made for many centuries. One famous example is Watt's flyball governor, which regulates the steam engine so that the flywheel operates in a steady pace. In systems abstraction, we forget all the physical mechanisms and concentrates on the functional relation between a plant, the flywheel in this particular case, and the controller, which is the flyball governor. The plant and the controlled is each represented by a mathematical expression, F and G.

Now let us add a twist, negative feedback, where the feedback control is *subtracted* instead of added to the input. Negative feedback was invented by Black for achieving low distortion amplification of electrical signals, especially for long distance telephony. Physically, it is totally different from mechanical system. However, we can still represent the amplifier as the plant, F, and a feedback control as G, the only difference is that we have a negative sign here. And we get a simple algebraic expression for the relation between the input and output through negative feedback. The problem for signal amplification is that the amplifier, F, is distortive. However, we can see that if the gain G of the controller is larger, so that FG is much greater than one, then the two Fs cancel out and the output is essentially independent of behavior of the amplifier. When you put in different specific forms of F and G, you can calculate the operational characteristics of a specific feedback control system. But even without the specifics, control theory can tell you a lot.

Systems in Engineering Science, Design, and Management

We have presented three notions of systems. They play major roles in three engineering activities. Systems theories with their systems abstraction are prominent in engineering science, which seek general functional principles. The systems approach as analysis-synthesis is widely practiced in engineering design of particular systems. Systems engineering strives to rationalize the management of large technical projects and their interfaces with society at large. Their domains, however, are not exclusive. Systems theories are routinely used in design and management. Analysis-synthesis is a time-honored approach in scientific research generally. The broad purviews of systems engineering are sipping into many development projects.

REFERENCES

Abernathy, W, J. 1978. *The Productivity Dilemma.* Baltimore: Johns Hopkins University Press.

Anderson, R. N. 1998. Oil production in the 21st century. *Scientific American*, 278(3): 86-90.

Appenzeller, T. and Norman, C. 1997. New eyes on hidden world. Introduction to a special issue on imaging technologies in *Science*, 276 (27 June): 1981-98.

Armstrong, N. 2000. The engineered century. www.greatachievements.org

Arora, A., Landau, R., and Rosenberg, N., eds. 1998. *Chemicals and Long-term Economic Growth.* New York: Wiley.

Ashburn, A. 1988. The machine-tool industry: the crumbling foundation. In *Is New Technology Enough?* Hicks, D. A. ed., Washington D.C.: American Enterprise Institute, pp.19-85.

Auyang, S. Y. 2004. *Engineering – An Endless Frontier.* Cambridge: Harvard University Press, Section 2.1.

Badamis, V. V. 1998. Home appliances get smart. *IEEE Spectrum*, 35(8): 36-40.

Ball, P. 1997. *Made to Measure: New Materials for the 21st Century.* Princeton: Princeton University Press.

Bell, R. and Bennett, P. A. 2000. IEC 61508 functional safety of electrical/electronic/programmable electronic safety related systems. *Computing and Control Engineering Journal*, 11(1): 3-5.

Bell, T. E. and Esch, K. 1987. The fatal flaws in flight 51-2. *IEEE Spectrum* (2): 36-51. Compare to Vaughan, D. 1996. *The Challenger Launch Decision.* Chicago: University of Chicago Press.

Bernal, J. D. 1971. *Science in History*, 4 volumes. Cambridge, MIT Press. (Emphasizes application of science).

Bigelow, J. 1829. *Elements of Technology.* Boston: Boston Press, pp.iii-iv.

Borwn, D. E. 2002. *Inventing America: From the Microwave to the Mouse.* Cambridge, MIT Press.

Branscomb, L. M. and Keller, J. H., eds. 1998. *Investing in Innovation.* Cambridge: MIT Press.

Bruce, J. P., Lee, H., and Haites, E. F., eds. 1995. *Climate Change 1995: Economic and Social Dimensions of Climate Change.* New York: Cambridge University Press, chapters 1 and 2 explains the approaches in assessing the risks of global warming.

Buchanan, R. A. 1985. The rise of scientific engineering in Britain. *British Journal for the History of Science*, 18: 218-33

Bull, S. R. 2001. Renewable energy today and tomorrow. *Proceedings of the IEEE*, 89: 1216-27.

Bush, V. 1965. The engineer. In *Listen to Leaders in Engineering*, A. Love and J. S. Childers, eds. (Tupper & Love, Atlanta, 1965), pp.1-15.

Cardwell, D. 1995. *The Norton History of Technology*. New York: Norton.

Chaisson, E. J, 1994. *The Hubble War*. Cambridge: Harvard University Press.

Crow, M. and Barry, B. 1998. *Limited by Design: R&D Laboratories in the U.S. National Innovation System*. New York: Columbia University Press.

Cusumano, M. A. and Selby, R. W. 1996. How Microsoft competes. *Research Technology Management*, 39(1): 26-30.

Dertouzos, M. L., Lester, R. K., and Solow, R. M. 1989. *Made in America: Regaining the Productivity Edge*. New York: Harper.

Douthwaith, B. 2002. *Enabling Innovation*, London: Zed Books. (agricultural machinery)

Edel, A. 1982. *Aristotle and His Philosophy*, Chapel Hill: The University of North Carolina Press.

Edel, *op cit*, p. 338.

Edgertpm, D. E. H. ed. 1996. *Industrial Research and Innovation in Business*. Cheltenham, UK: Elgar.

Edusi-Mensah, K. 1999. Critical issues in abandoned information systems development projects. *Communications of the ACM*, 40(9): 74-80.

Evan, W. M. and Manion, M. 2002. *Minding the Machine: Preventing Technological Disasters*. Upper Saddle River NJ: Prentice Hall.

Fielder, J. H. and Birsch, D. 1992. *The DC-10 Case: A Study in Applied Ethics, Technology, and Society*. Albany: State University of New York.

Foster, I. 2002. The Grid: a new infrastructure for 21st century science. *Physics Today*, February, 42-7.

Foster, K. R., Vecchia, P. and Repacholi, M. H. 2000. Science and the precautionary principle. *Science*, 288: 979-81.

Freeman, C. and Soete, L. 1997. *The Economics of Industrial Innovation*, 3rd ed. Cambridge: MIT Press.

Galilei, G. 1638. *Dialogues Concerning Two New Sciences*. New York: Dover; p.1.

General Accounting Office. 1998. Evolution and status of FAA's automation programme, GAO/T-RCED/AIMD-98-85.

Grahm, J. D. and Wiener, J. B. eds. 1995. *Risk vs. Risk: Tradeoffs in Protecting Health and the Environment*. Cambridge: Harvard University Press.

Green, R. 2000. Competition in generation: the economic foundation. *Proceedings of the IEEE*, 88: 128-39.

Hagonnet, P. and Silandes, S. ed. 1991. *Favorites of Fortune*. Cambridge, Harvard University Press.

Hayes, W. W., Chaker, A. A., and Hunt, C. 1999. Learning from disasters. *Civil Engineering Magazine* December, www.pubs.asce.org/ceonline/1299feat.html.

Heimann, C. F. L. 1997. *Acceptable Risk: Politics, Policy, and Risky Technologies*. Ann Arbor: University of Michigan Press.

Helpman, E. ed. 1998. *General Purpose Technologies and Economic Growth*, Cambridge, MIT Press.

Helpman, Elhanan, ed. 1998. *General Purpose Technologies*. Cambridge, MA: MIT Press.

Hicks, D. A. ed. 1988. *Is New Technology Enough?* Washington D.C.: American Enterprise Institute.

Hoffert, M. I. *et al*. 2002. Advanced technology path to global climate stability: energy for a greenhouse planet. *Science*, 298: 981-8.

Hoffrage, U., Lindsey, S., Hertwig, R., and Gigerenzer, G. 2000. Communicating statistical information. *Science*, 290: 2261-4.

Holdren, J. P. and Baldwin, S. F. 2001. The PCAST energy studies. *Annual Review of Energy and Environment*, 26:391-434.

International Energy Agency. 2000. *Electricity Information*. Paris: International Energy Agency.

Jezequel, J-M and Meyer, M. 1997. Design by contract: the lessons of Ariane, *IEEE Computer* 30(1): 129-30.

Johnstone, B. 2001. A bright future for displays. *Technology Review*, April, 81-8.

Katzer, J. R., Ramage, M. P., and Sapre, A. V. 2000. Petroleum refining poised for profound changes. *Chemical Engineering Progress*. July, 41-52.

Kline, R. 1995. Constructing "technology" as "applied science." *Isis*, 86: 194-221.

Landau, R. 1994. *Uncaging Animal Spirits: Essays in Engineering, Entrepreneurship, and Economics*. Cambridge: MIT Press.

Landes, D. S. 1969. *The Unbound Prometheus*. New York: Cambridge University Press.

Landes, Davis S. 1998. *The Wealth and Poverty of Nations: Why Some are So Rich and Some So Poor*. New York: Norton.

Landes, Davis S. 1998. *The Wealth and Poverty of Nations: Why Some are So Rich and Some So Poor*. New York: Norton.

Laudan, R. ed. 1984. *The Nature of technological Knowledge*. Dordrecht: Reidel, p.9.

Layton, E. T., Jr. 1976. American Ideologies of Science and Engineering. *Technology and Culture*, 17: 688-701.

Layton, E. T., Jr. 1991. A historical definition of engineering. In *Critical Perspectives on Nonacademic Science and Engineering*, ed. P. T. Durbin, Bethlehem: Lehigh University Press, pp. 60-79.

Lester, M. 2000. Communicate risk effectively. *Chemical Engineering Progress*, June: 79-83.

Leveson, H. G. and Turner, C. S. 1993. An investigation of the Therac-25 accidents. *IEEE Computer*, 25(7), 18-41.

Light, W. and Collins, B. L. 2000. Setting the standards. *Mechanical Engineering*. www.memagazine.org/backissues/febryary2000/features/setting/setting.htm.

Longstaff, T. A., Chittister, C., Pethia, R. Are we forgetting the risk of information technology? *IEEE Computer*, 33(12): 43-51.

Lovell, J. and Kluger, J. 1994. *Apollo 13*. Boston: Houghton Mifflin.

Mandelbaum, R. 2002. Reap the wild wind. *IEEE Spectrum*, 39(10): 34-9.

Marx, K. 1867. *Capital, I*. New York: Vintage Books, pp. 493; 616).

Marx, L. 1997. Technology: the emergence of a hazardous concept. *Social Research*, 64: 965-88.

Mokyr, J. 1990. *The Lever of Riches: Technological Creativity and Economic Progress*. New York: Oxford University Press.

Mokyr, J. 1990. *The Lever of Riches: Technological Creativity and Economic Progress*. New York: Oxford University Press.

Mokyr, Joel. 2002. *The Gifts of Athena: Historical Origins of the Knowledge Economy*. Princeton: Princeton University Press.

Mokyr, Joel. 2002. *The Gifts of Athena: Historical Origins of the Knowledge Economy*. Princeton: Princeton University Press.

Morgan, M. G. 1993. Risk analysis and management. *Scientific American*, July: 32-41.

Morton, D. 1999. Viewing television's history. *Proceedings of the IEEE*, 87: 1301-4.

Mowery, D. C. and Rosenberg, N. 1998. *Paths of Innovation*. New York: Cambridge University Press.

Multhauf, R. P. 1959. The scientist and the "improver of technology." *Technology and Culture* 1: 38-47.

Musson, A. E. and Robinson, E. 1969. *Science and Technology in the Industrial Revolution*. Toronto: University of Toronto Press.

Neef, D., Siesfeld, G. A., and Cefola, J. eds. 1998. *The Economic Impact of Knowledge*. Boston: Butterworth. Contains "Uncertainty and technological change" by N. Rosenberg and informative papers on the measurement and new economics of knowledge.

Neumann, P. G. 1995. *Computer-related Risks*. New York: ACM Press.

NSF, *Science and Engineering Indicators 2002*, pp.4-10. www.nsf.gov.

Nye, D. E. 1997. *American Technological Sublime*. Cambridge: MIT Press.

On the personal level, bloated self esteem is almost universal, as some eighty percent of Americans deem themselves above average. Smart people are especially prone to think themselves the best and brightest, whether they are pure or applied scientists. However, the issue here is not bickers in bars but the doctrinal denigration of a discipline.

Oz. E. 1994. When professional standard are lax: the CONFIRM failure and its lessons. *Communications of the ACM*, 37(10): 29-36.

Pacey, A. 1990. *Technology in World Civilization*. Cambridge: MIT Press.

Pakes, A. and Sokoloff, K. L. 1996. Science, technology, and economic growth. Introduction to a special issue in *Proceedings of National Academy of Science, USA*, 93: 12655.

Perrow, C. 1984. *Normal Accidents: Living with High Risk Technologies*. New York: Basic Book.

Peterson, D. J., LaTourrette, T., and Bartis, J. T. 2001. *New Forces at Work in Mining*. Santa Monica, CA: RAND.

Petroski, H. 1982. *To Engineer is Human: the Role of Failure in Successful Design*. New York: St. Martin's Press.

Pollard, S. 1989. *Britain's Prime and Britain's Decline*. London: Edward Arnold.

Pool, I de Sola, 1983. *Technologies of Freedom: On Free Speech in an Electronic Age*. Cambridge: Harvard University Press.

Ramage, J. 1997. *Energy: a Guidebook*. New York: Oxford University Press.

Ramakumar, R. 1993. Economic aspects of advanced energy technologies. *Proceedings of the IEEE*, 81: 318-27.

Ramo, S. 1988. Globalization of industry and implications for the future. In *Globalization of Technology*, ed. by J. H. Muroyama and H. G. Stevens. Washington, D.C.: National Academy Press, pp. 12-22.

Rhodes, R. 1999. *Visions of Technology*, New York: Simon & Schuster.

Rosenberg, N. 1976. *Perspectives on Technology*. New York: Cambridge University Press.

Rosenberg, N. 1982. *Inside the Black Box: Technology and Economics*. New York: Cambridge University Press.

Rosenberg, N. Landau, R. and Mowery, D. C. 1992. *Technology and Wealth of Nations*. Stanford: Stanford University Press.

Schurr, S. H., Burwell, C. C., Devine, W. D., and Sonenblum, S. 1990. *Electricity in the American Economy*. New York: Greenwood Press.

Scientific American, 1997. The Internet: fulfilling the promise. Special issue, March.

Scigliano, E. 2002. 10 technology disasters. *Technology Review*, June: 48-52.

See, for example, Bijker, W. E., Hughes, T. P., and Pinch, T. J. eds. 1987. *The Social Construction of Technology Systems*. Cambridge: MIT Press.

Segerstråle, U., ed. 2000. *Beyond the Science Wars*. New York: State University of New York Press, p.6.

Service, R. F. 2000. New tigers in the fuel cell tank. *Science*, 288: 1955-7.

Sherif, M. H. 2001. A framework for standardization in telecommunications and information technology. *IEEE Communications Magazine*, 39(4): 94-101.

Singer, C., Holy, E. J., and Holmyard, E. J., and Hall, A. R., eds. 1954. *A History of Technology*. Oxford: Oxford University Press.

Singer, C., Holy, E. J., and Holmyard, E. J., and Hall, A. R., eds. 1954. *A History of Technology*. Oxford: Oxford University Press, p. vii).

Snow, C. P. 1963. *The Two Cultures and a Second Look.* New York: Cambridge University Press.

Sobel, A. 1998. Television's bright new technology. *Scientific American*, May, 70-7

Srinivasan, S., Mosdale, R., Stevens, P. and Yang, C. 1999. Fuel cells: reaching the era of clean and efficient power generation in the twenty-first century. *Annual Review of Energy and Environment*, 24: 281-328.

Tenner, Edward. 1997. *Why Things Bite Back: Technology and the Revenge of Unintended Consequences.* New York: Knopf.

Tocqueville, A. de. 1835. *Democracy in America.* Chicago: University of Chicago Press (2000), Vol.2, p.43J.

V. Bush, Science – an endless frontier, www.nsf.gov/od/lpa/nsf50/vbush1945.htm.

Vincenti, W. G. 1990. *What Engineers Know and How They Know It: Analytical Studies from Aeronautical History.* Baltimore, MD: Johns Hopkins Press, p.3.

Waldrop, M. M. 2002. Grid computing. *Technology Review*, May, 31-7.

Williams, T. I. 1982. *A Short History of Twentieth Century Technology, 1900-1950.* Oxford: Oxford University Press.

Wilson, R. and Crouch, E. A. C, 2001. *Risk-Benefit Analysis*, 2nd ed. Cambridge: Harvard University Press.

2

Research Methodology in Engineering Physics and Optical Science

INTRODUCTION

Engineers apply the sciences of physics and mathematics to find suitable solutions to problems or to make improvements to the status quo. More than ever, Engineers are now required to have knowledge of relevant sciences for their design projects, as a result, they keep on learning new material throughout their career. If multiple options exist, engineers weigh different design choices on their merits and choose the solution that best matches the requirements. The crucial and unique task of the engineer is to identify, understand, and interpret the constraints on a design in order to produce a successful result. It is usually not enough to build a technically successful product; it must also meet further requirements. Constraints may include available resources, physical, imaginative or technical limitations, flexibility for future modifications and additions, and other factors, such as requirements for cost, safety, marketability, productibility, and serviceability. By understanding the constraints, engineers derive specifications for the limits within which a viable object or system may be produced and operated. Engineering is the discipline and profession of applying scientific knowledge and utilizing natural laws and physical resources in order to design and implement materials, structures, machines, devices, systems, and processes that realize a desired objective and meet specified criteria. The American Engineers' Council for Professional Development (ECPD, the predecessor of ABET) has defined engineering as follows:

"[T]he creative application of scientific principles to design or develop structures, machines, apparatus, or manufacturing processes, or works utilizing them singly or in combination; or to construct or operate the same with full cognizance of their design; or to forecast their behavior under specific operating conditions; all as respects an intended function, economics of operation and safety to life and property." One who practices engineering is called an engineer, and those licensed to do so may have more formal designations such as Professional Engineer, Chartered Engineer, or Incorporated Engineer. The broad discipline of engineering encompasses a range of more specialized subdisciplines, each with a more specific emphasis on certain fields of application and particular areas of technology. The *concept* of engineering has existed since ancient times as humans devised fundamental inventions such as the pulley, lever, and wheel. Each of these inventions is consistent with the modern definition of engineering, exploiting basic mechanical principles to develop useful tools and objects. The term *engineering* itself has a much more recent etymology, deriving from the word *engineer*, which itself dates back to 1325, when an *engine'er* (literally, one who operates an *engine*) originally referred to "a constructor of military engines." In this context, now obsolete, an "engine" referred to a military machine, *i. e.*, a mechanical contraption used in war (for example, a catapult). The word "engine" itself is of even older origin, ultimately deriving from the Latin *ingenium* (c. 1250), meaning "innate quality, especially mental power, hence a clever invention." Later, as the design of civilian structures such as bridges and buildings matured as a technical discipline, the term civil engineering entered the lexicon as a way to distinguish between those specializing in the construction of such non-military projects and those involved in the older discipline of military engineering (the original meaning of the word "engineering," now largely obsolete, with notable exceptions that have survived to the present day such as military engineering corps, *e. g.*, the U. S. Army Corps of Engineers).

History

The Acropolis and the Parthenon in Greece, the Roman aquaducts, Via Appia and the Colosseum, the Hanging Gardens of Babylon, the Pharos of Alexandria, the pyramids in Egypt, Teotihuacán and the cities and pyramids of the Mayan, Inca and Aztec Empires, the Great Wall of China, among many others, stand as a testament to the ingenuity and skill of the ancient civil and military engineers. The earliest civil engineer known by name is Imhotep. As one of the officials of the Pharaoh, Djosèr, he probably designed and supervised the construction of the Pyramid of Djoser (the Step Pyramid) at Saqqara in Egypt around 2630-2611 BC. He may also have been responsible for the first known use of columns in architecture.

An Iraqi Muslim by the name of al-Jazari helped pave the way for today's' modern machines when sometime in between 1174 and 1200 he built five machines to pump water for the kings of the Turkish Artuqid dynasty and their palaces. The double-acting reciprocating piston pump was instrumental in the later development of engineering in general because it was the first machine to incorporate both the connecting rod and the crankshaft, thus, converting rotational motion to reciprocating motion. Even today some toys still use the cam-lever mechanism found in al-Jazari's combination lock and automaton. Besides over 50 ingenuis mechanical devices, al-Jazari also developed and made innovations to segmental gears, mechanical controls, escapement mechanisms, clocks, robotics, and protocols for designing and manufacturing methods.

The first electrical engineer is considered to be William Gilbert, with his 1600 publication of De Magnete, who was the originator of the term "electricity". The first steam engine was built in 1698 by mechanical engineer Thomas Savery. The development of this device gave rise to the industrial revolution in the coming decades, allowing for the beginnings of mass production. With the rise of engineering as a profession in the eighteenth century, the term became more narrowly applied to fields in which mathematics and science were applied to these ends. Similarly, in addition to military and civil engineering the fields then known as the mechanic arts became incorporated into engineering.

Electrical Engineering can trace its origins in the experiments of Alessandro Volta in the 1800s, the experiments of Michael Faraday, Georg Ohm and others and the invention of the electric motor in 1872. The work of James Maxwell and Heinrich Hertz in the late 19th century gave rise to the field of Electronics. The later inventions of the vacuum tube and the transistor further accelerated the development of Electronics to such an extent that electrical and electronics engineers currently outnumber their colleagues of any other Engineering specialty. The inventions of Thomas Savery and the Scottish engineer James Watt gave rise to modern Mechanical Engineering. The development of specialized machines and their maintenance tools during the industrial revolution led to the rapid growth of Mechanical Engineering both in its birthplace Britain and abroad. Even though in its modern form Mechanical engineering originated in Britain, its origins trace back to early antiquity where ingenuous machines were developed both in the civilian and military domains. The Antikythera mechanism, the earliest known model of a mechanical computer in history, and the mechanical inventions of Archimedes, including his death ray, are examples of early mechanical engineering. Some of Archimedes' inventions as well as the Antikythera mechanism required sophisticated knowledge of differential gearing or epicyclic gearing, two key principles in machine theory that helped design the gear trains of the Industrial revolution and are still widely used today in diverse fields such as robotics and automotive engineering.

Chemical Engineering, like its counterpart Mechanical Engineering, developed in the nineteenth century during the Industrial Revolution. Industrial scale manufacturing demanded new materials and new processes and by 1880 the need for large scale production of chemicals was such that a new industry was created, dedicated to the development and large scale manufacturing of chemicals in new industrial plants. The role of the chemical engineer was the design of these chemical plants and processes. Aeronautical Engineering deals with aircraft design while Aerospace Engineering is a more modern term that expands the reach envelope of the discipline by including spacecraft design. Its origins can be traced back to the aviation pioneers around the turn of the century from the 19th century to the 20th although the work of Sir George Cayley has recently been dated as being from the last decade of the 18th century. Early knowledge of aeronautical engineering was largely empirical with some concepts and skills imported from other branches of engineering. Only a decade after the successful flights by the Wright brothers, the 1920s saw extensive development of aeronautical engineering through development of World War I military aircraft. Meanwhile, research to provide fundamental background science continued by combining theoretical physics with experiments. The first PhD in engineering (technically, *applied science and engineering*) awarded in the United States went to Willard Gibbs at Yale University in 1863; it was also the second PhD awarded in science in the U.S. In 1990, with the rise of computer technology, the first search engine was built by computer engineer Alan Emtage.

Branches

Engineering, much like science, is a broad discipline which is often broken down into several sub-disciplines. These disciplines concern themselves with differing areas of engineering work. Although initially an engineer will be trained in a specific discipline, throughout an engineer's career the engineer may become multi-disciplined, having worked in several of the outlined areas. Historically the main Branches of Engineering are categorized as follows:

- Aerospace Engineering - The design of aircraft, spacecraft and related topics.
- Chemical Engineering - The conversion of raw materials into usable commodities.
- Civil Engineering - The design and construction of public and private works, such as infrastructure, bridges and buildings.
- Electrical Engineering - The design of electrical systems, such as transformers, as well as electronic goods.
- Mechanical Engineering - The design of physical or mechanical systems, such as engines, powertrains, kinematic chains and vibration isolation equipment.

With the rapid advancement of Technology many new fields are gaining prominence and new branches are developing such as Computer Engineering, Software Engineering, Nanotechnology, Molecular engineering, Mechatronics etc. These new specialties sometimes combine with the traditional fields and form new branches such as Mechanical Engineering and Mechatronics and Electrical and Computer Engineering. For each of these fields there exists considerable overlap, especially in the areas of the application of sciences to their disciplines such as physics, chemistry and mathematics.

Computer Use

As with all modern scientific and technological endeavors, computers and software play an increasingly important role. As well as the typical business application software there are a number of computer aided applications (CAx) specifically for engineering. Computers can be used to generate models of fundamental physical processes, which can be solved using numerical methods. One of the most widely used tools in the profession is computer-aided design (CAD) software which enables engineers to create 3D models, 2D drawings, and schematics of their designs. CAD together with Digital mockup (DMU) and CAE software such as finite element method analysis allows engineers to create models of designs that can be analyzed without having to make expensive and time-consuming physical prototypes. These allow products and components to be checked for flaws; assess fit and assembly; study ergonomics; and to analyze static and dynamic characteristics of systems such as stresses, temperatures, electromagnetic emissions, electrical currents and voltages, digital logic levels, fluid flows, and kinematics. Access and distribution of all this information is generally organised with the use of Product Data Management software. There are also many tools to support specific engineering tasks such as Computer-aided manufacture (CAM) software to generate CNC machining instructions; Manufacturing Process Management software for production engineering; EDA for printed circuit board (PCB) and circuit schematics for electronic engineers; MRO applications for maintenance management; and AEC software for civil engineering. In recent years the use of computer software to aid the development of goods has collectively come to be known as Product Lifecycle Management (PLM).

Social Context of Engineering

Engineering is a subject that ranges from large collaborations to small individual projects. Almost all engineering projects are beholden to some sort of financing agency: a company, a set of investors, or a government. The few types of engineering that are minimally constrained by such issues are pro bono engineering and open design engineering. By its very nature engineering is bound up with society and human behavior. Every product or construction used by modern society will have been influenced by engineering design. Engineering design is a very powerful tool to make changes to environment, society and economies, and its application brings with it a great responsibility, as represented by many of the Engineering Institutions codes of practice and ethics. Whereas medical ethics is a well-established field with considerable consensus, engineering ethics is far less developed, and engineering projects can be subject to considerable controversy. Just a few examples of this from different engineering disciplines are the development of nuclear weapons, the Three Gorges Dam, the design and use of Sports Utility Vehicles and the extraction of oil. There is a growing trend amongst western engineering companies to enact serious Corporate and Social Responsibility policies, but many companies do not have these. Engineering is a key driver of human development. Sub-Saharan Africa in particular has a very small engineering capacity which results in many African nations being unable to develop crucial infrastructure without outside aid. The attainment of many of the Millennium Development Goals requires the achievement of sufficient engineering capacity to develop infrastructure and sustainable technological development. All overseas development and relief NGOs make considerable use of engineers to apply solutions in disaster and development scenarios. A number of charitable organisations aim to use engineering directly for the good of mankind: (i) Engineers Without Borders; (ii) Engineers Against Poverty; (iii) Registered Engineers for Disaster Relief; (iv) Engineers for a Sustainable World.

Problem Solving

Engineers use their knowledge of science, mathematics, and appropriate experience to find suitable solutions to a problem. Engineering is considered a branch of applied mathematics and science. Creating an appropriate mathematical model of a problem allows them to analyze it (sometimes definitively), and to test potential solutions. Usually multiple reasonable solutions exist, so engineers must evaluate the different design choices on their merits and choose the solution that best meets their requirements. Genrich Altshuller, after gathering statistics on a large number of patents, suggested that compromises are at the heart of "low-level" engineering designs, while at a higher level the best design is one which eliminates the core contradiction causing the problem. Engineers typically attempt to predict how well their designs will perform to their specifications prior to full-scale production. They use, among other things: prototypes, scale models, simulations, destructive tests, nondestructive tests, and stress tests. Testing ensures that products will perform as expected. Engineers as professionals take seriously their responsibility to produce designs that will perform as expected and will not cause unintended harm to the public at large. Engineers typically include a factor of safety in their designs to reduce the risk of unexpected failure. However, the greater the safety factor, the less efficient the design may be.

Cultural Presence

Engineering is a well respected profession. For example, in Canada it ranks as one of the public's most trusted professions. Sometimes engineering has been seen as a somewhat dry, uninteresting field in popular culture, and has also been thought to be the domain of nerds. For example, the cartoon character Dilbert is an engineer. One difficulty in increasing public awareness of the profession is that average people, in the typical run of ordinary life, do not ever have any personal dealings with engineers, even though they benefit from their work every day. By contrast, it is common to visit a doctor at least once a year, the chartered accountant at tax time, and, occasionally, even a lawyer. This has not always been so - most British school children in the 1950s were brought up with stirring tales of 'the Victorian Engineers', chief amongst whom were the Brunels, the Stephensons, Telford and their contemporaries. In science fiction engineers are often portrayed as highly knowledgeable and respectable individuals who understand the overwhelming future technologies often portrayed in the genre. The *Star Trek* characters Montgomery Scott, Geordi La Forge, Miles O'Brien, B'Elanna Torres, and Charles Tucker are famous examples. Occasionally, engineers may be recognized by the "Iron Ring"—a stainless steel or iron ring worn on the little finger of the dominant hand. This tradition began in 1925 in Canada for the Ritual of the Calling of an Engineer as a symbol of pride and obligation for the engineering profession. Some years later in 1972 this practice was adopted by several colleges in the United States. Members of the US Order of the Engineer accept this ring as a pledge to uphold the proud history of engineering. A Professional Engineer's name may be followed by the post-nominal letters PE or P.Eng in North America. In much of Europe a professional engineer is denoted by the letters IR, while in the UK and much of the Commonwealth the term Chartered Engineer applies and is denoted by the letters CEng.

Legislation

In most Western countries, certain engineering tasks, such as the design of bridges, electric power plants, and chemical plants, must be approved by a Professional Engineer or a Chartered Engineer or an Incorporated Engineer. Laws protecting public health and safety mandate that a professional must provide guidance gained through education and experience. In the United States, each state tests and licenses Professional Engineers. In much of Europe and the Commonwealth professional accreditation is provided by Engineering Institutions, such as the Institution of Civil Engineers from the UK. The engineering institutions of the UK are some of the oldest in the world, and provide accreditation to many engineers around the world. In Canada the profession in each province is governed by its own engineering association. For instance, in the Province of British Columbia an engineering graduate with 4 or more years of experience in an engineering-related field will need to be registered by the Association for Professional Engineers and Geoscientists [(APEGBC)] in order to become a Professional Engineer and be granted the professional designation of P.Eng. The federal US government, however, supervises aviation through the Federal Aviation Regulations administrated by the Dept. of Transportation, Federal

Aviation Administration. Designated Engineering Representatives approve data for aircraft design and repairs on behalf of the Federal Aviation Administration. Even with strict testing and licensure, engineering disasters still occur. Therefore, the Professional Engineer, Chartered Engineer, or Incorporated Engineer adheres to a strict code of ethics. Each engineering discipline and professional society maintains a code of ethics, which the members pledge to uphold. Refer also to the Washington accord for international accreditation details of professional engineering degrees.

Relationships with Other Disciplines

There exists an overlap between the sciences and engineering practice; in engineering, one applies science. Both areas of endeavor rely on accurate observation of materials and phenomena. Both use mathematics and classification criteria to analyze and communicate observations. Scientists are expected to interpret their observations and to make expert recommendations for practical action based on those interpretations. Scientists may also have to complete engineering tasks, such as designing experimental apparatus or building prototypes. Conversely, in the process of developing technology engineers sometimes find themselves exploring new phenomena, thus becoming, for the moment, scientists. In the book *What Engineers Know and How They Know It*, Walter Vincenti asserts that engineering research has a character different from that of scientific research. First, it often deals with areas in which the basic physics and/or chemistry are well understood, but the problems themselves are too complex to solve in an exact manner. Examples are the use of numerical approximations to the Navier-Stokes equations to describe aerodynamic flow over an aircraft, or the use of Miner's rule to calculate fatigue damage. Second, engineering research employs many semi-empirical methods that are foreign to pure scientific research, one example being the method of parameter variation. As stated by Fung et al. in the revision to the classic engineering text, Foundations of Solid Mechanics,

> "Engineering is quite different from science. Scientists try to understand nature. Engineers try to make things that do not exist in nature. Engineers stress invention. To embody an invention the engineer must put his idea in concrete terms, and design something that people can use. That something can be a device, a gadget, a material, a method, a computing programme, an innovative experiment, a new solution to a problem, or an improvement on what is existing. Since a design has to be concrete, it must have its geometry, dimensions, and characteristic numbers. Almost all engineers working on new designs find that they do not have all the needed information. Most often, they are limited by insufficient scientific knowledge. Thus they study mathematics, physics, chemistry, biology and mechanics. Often they have to add to the sciences relevant to their profession. Thus engineering sciences are born."

Medicine and Biology

The study of the human body, albeit from different directions and for different purposes, is an important common link between medicine and some engineering disciplines. Medicine aims to sustain, enhance and even replace functions of the human body, if necessary, through the use of technology. Modern medicine can replace several of the body's functions through the use of artificial organs and can significantly alter the function of the human body through artificial devices such as, for example, brain implants and pacemakers. The fields of Bionics and medical Bionics are dedicated to the study of synthetic implants pertaining to natural systems. Conversely, some engineering disciplines view the human body as a biological machine worth studying, and are dedicated to emulating many of its functions by replacing biology with technology. This has led to fields such as artificial intelligence, neural networks, fuzzy logic, and robotics. There are also substantial interdisciplinary interactions between engineering and medicine. Both fields provide solutions to real world problems. This often requires moving forward before phenomena are completely understood in a more rigorous scientific sense and therefore experimentation and empirical knowledge is an integral part of both. Medicine, in part, studies the function of the human body.

The human body, as a biological machine, has many functions that can be modeled using Engineering methods. The heart for example functions much like a pump, the skeleton is like a linked structure with levers, the brain produces electrical signals etc. These similarities as well as the increasing importance and application of Engineering principles in Medicine, led to the development of the field of biomedical engineering that utilizes concepts developed in both disciplines. Newly emerging branches of science, such as Systems biology, are adapting analytical tools traditionally used for engineering, such as systems modeling and computational analysis, to the description of biological systems.

Art

There are connections between engineering and art; they are direct in some fields, for example, architecture, landscape architecture and industrial design (even to the extent that these disciplines may sometimes be included in a University's Faculty of Engineering); and indirect in others. The Art Institute of Chicago, for instance, held an exhibition about the art of NASA's aerospace design. Robert Maillart's bridge design is perceived by some to have been deliberately artistic. At the University of South Florida, an engineering professor, through a grant with the National Science Foundation, has developed a course that connects art and engineering. Among famous historical figures Leonardo Da Vinci is a well known Renaissance artist and engineer, and a prime example of the nexus between art and engineering.

Engineering Physics

Engineering physics (EP) is an academic degree, available mainly at the levels of B.Sc., M.Sc. and Ph.D. Unlike other engineering degrees (such as aerospace engineering or electrical engineering), EP does not necessarily include a particular branch of science or physics. Instead, EP is meant to provide a more thorough grounding in applied physics of any area chosen by the student (such as optics, nanotechnology, control theory, aerodynamics, or solid-state physics). This is why in some countries only the B.Sc. part of the degree is called a degree in Engineering Physics. Engineering physics degrees are respected degrees taught in many countries. It is notable that in many languages the term for Engineering Physics would be directly translated into English as "technical physics". More recently, as an apparent attempt to stress the interdisciplinary nature of such degrees, some institutions now use the term Engineering science.

Optics

Optics is the science that describes the behavior and properties of light and the interaction of light with matter. Optics explains optical phenomena. The field of optics usually describes the behavior of visible, infrared, and ultraviolet light; however because light is an electromagnetic wave, similar phenomena occur in X-rays, microwaves, radio waves, and other forms of electromagnetic radiation and analogous phenomena occur with charged particle beams. Optics can largely be regarded as a sub-field of electromagnetism. Some optical phenomena depend on the quantum nature of light relating some areas of optics to quantum mechanics. In practice, the vast majority of optical phenomena can be accounted for using the electromagnetic description of light, as described by Maxwell's Equations. The field of optics has its own identity, societies, and conferences. The pure science aspects of the field are often called optical science or optical physics. Applied optical sciences are often called optical engineering. Applications of optical engineering related specifically to illumination systems are called illumination engineering. Each of these disciplines tends to be quite different in its applications, technical skills, focus, and professional affiliations. More recent innovations in optical engineering are often categorized as photonics or optoelectronics. The boundaries between these fields and "optics" are often unclear, and the terms are used differently in different parts of the world and in different areas of industry. Because of the wide application of the science of "light" to real-world applications, the areas of optical science and optical engineering tend to be very cross-disciplinary. Optical science is a part of many related disciplines including electrical engineering, physics, psychology, medicine (particularly ophthalmology and optometry), and others. Additionally, the most complete description of optical behavior, as known to physics, is unnecessarily complicated for most problems, so particular simplified models are used. These limited models adequately describe subsets of optical phenomena while ignoring behavior irrelevant and/or undetectable to the system of interest.

Classical Optics

Before quantum optics became important, optics consisted mainly of the application of classical electromagnetism and its high frequency approximations to light. Classical optics divides into two main branches: geometric optics and physical optics.

Geometric optics, or ray optics, describes light propagation in terms of "rays". Rays are bent at the interface between two dissimilar media, and may be curved in a medium in which the refractive index is a function of position. The "ray" in geometric optics is an abstract object which is perpendicular to the wavefronts of the actual optical waves. Geometric optics provides rules for propagating these rays through an optical system, which indicates how the actual wavefront will propagate. Note that this is a significant simplification of optics, and fails to account for many important optical effects such as diffraction and polarization.

Geometric optics is often simplified even further by making the paraxial approximation, or "small angle approximation." The mathematical behavior then becomes linear, allowing optical components and systems to be described by simple matrices. This leads to the techniques of Gaussian optics and *paraxial raytracing*, which are used to find first-order properties of optical systems, such as approximate image and object positions and magnifications. Gaussian beam propagation is an expansion of paraxial optics that provides a more accurate model of coherent radiation like laser beams. While still using the paraxial approximation, this technique partially accounts for diffraction, allowing accurate calculations of the rate at which a laser beam expands with distance, and the minimum size to which the beam can be focused. Gaussian beam propagation thus bridges the gap between geometric and physical optics.

Physical optics or wave optics builds on Huygen's principle and models the propagation of complex wavefronts through optical systems, including both the amplitude and the phase of the wave. This technique, which is usually applied numerically on a computer, can account for diffraction, interference, and polarization effects, as well as aberrations and other complex effects. Approximations are still generally used, however, so this is not a full electromagnetic wave theory model of the propagation of light. Such a full model would (at present) be too computationally demanding to be useful for most problems, although some small-scale problems can be analyzed using complete wave models.

Topics Related to Classical Optics

- Aberrations

- Coherence
- Diffraction
- Dispersion
- Distortion
- Fabrication and testing (optical components)
- Fermat's principle
- Fourier optics
- Geometric optics of:
  - Lenses
  - Mirrors
  - Optical instruments
  - Prisms
- Gradient index optics
- Interferometry
- Optical lens design
- Optical resolution
- Polarization
- Ray (optics)
- Ray tracing (physics)
- Reflection
- Refraction
- Scattering
- Spectrum
- Wave

Modern Optics

Modern optics encompasses the areas of optical science and engineering that became popular in the 20th century. These areas of optical science typically relate to the electromagnetic or quantum properties of light but do include other topics.

Topics Related to Modern Optics

- Adaptive optics
- Circular dichroism
- Crystal optics

- Diffractive optics
- Fiber optics
- Waveguide (optics)
- Holography
- Integrated optics
- Jones calculus
- Lasers
- Lens flare
- Microlens
- Non-imaging optics
- Nonlinear optics
- Optical pattern recognition
- Optical processors
- Optical vortex
- Photometry
- Photonics
- Quantum optics
- Radiometry
- Statistical optics
- Thin-film optics
- X-ray optics

Other Optical Fields

- Abbe number
- Color science
- Image processing
- Information theory
- Lighting
- Machine vision
- Optical communication
- Optical computers
- Optical data storage
- Optical feedback

- Pattern recognition
- Photography (science of)
- Radiative heat transfer
- Thermal physics
- Visual system

Everyday Optics

Optics is part of everyday life. Rainbows and mirages are examples of optical phenomena. Many people benefit from eyeglasses or contact lenses, and optics are used in many consumer goods including cameras. Superimposition of periodic structures, for example transparent tissues with a grid structure, produces shapes known as moiré patterns. Superimposition of periodic transparent patterns comprising parallel opaque lines or curves produces line moiré patterns.

Optical Engineering

Optical engineering is the field of study which focuses on applications of optics. Optical engineers design components of optical instruments such as lenses, microscopes, telescopes, and other equipment that utilize the properties of light. Other devices include optical sensors and measurement systems, lasers, fiber optic communication systems, optical disc systems (e.g. CD, DVD), etc. Since optical engineers want to design and build devices that make light do something useful, they must understand and apply the science of optics in substantial detail, in order to know what is physically possible to achieve (physics and chemistry). But they also must know what is practical in terms of available technology, materials, costs, design methods, etc. As with other fields of engineering, computers are important to many (perhaps most) optical engineers. They are used with instruments, for simulation, in design, and for many other applications. Engineers often use general computer tools such as spreadsheets and programming languages, and they also make frequent use of specialized optical software designed specifically for their field. Optical engineering metrology uses optical methods to measure micro-vibrations with instruments like the laser speckle interferometer or to measure the properties of the various masses with instruments measuring refraction. An optical instrument either processes light waves to enhance an image for viewing, or analyzes light waves (or photons) to determine one of a number of characteristic properties.

Image Enhancement

The first optical instruments were telescopes used for magnification of distant images, and microscopes used for magnifying very tiny images. Since the days of Galileo and Van Leeuwenhoek, these instruments have been greatly improved and extended into other portions of the electromagnetic spectrum. The binocular device is a generally compact instrument for both eyes designed for mobile use. A camera could be considered a type of optical instrument for storing an image.

Analysis

Another class of optical instrument is used to analyze the properties of light or optical materials. They include:

- Interferometer for measuring the interference properies of light waves
- Photometer for measuring light intensity
- Polarimeter for measuring dispersion or rotation of polarized light
- Reflectometer for measuring the reflectivity of a surface or object
- Refractometer for measuring refractive index of various materials, invented by Ernst Abbe
- Spectrometer or monochromator for generating or measuring a portion of the optical spectrum, for the purpose of chemical or material analysis.
- Autocollimator which is used to measure angular deflections.

Optical Engineering Fact Sheet

The demand for engineers with a background in electro-optics and photonics has grown as result of the increased use of optics in the field of engineering. These engineers design optoelectronic circuits, signal sources, detectors and transmission media. The optical engineering option in the Department of Electrical and Computer Engineering prepares the engineer for various career opportunities.

Cooperative Education Programme

The Cooperative Education Programme allows students to alternate classroom study with a series of paid professional work experiences related to optical engineering. These experiences increase in complexity as the student's background increases. The programme provides opportunity for pre-graduation experience in the profession, exploration of several career opportunities, money for education, an enriched degree and enhanced opportunities for employment following graduation.

The Programme

The optical engineering option was developed jointly with the Department of Physics. Many technical disciplines now use optics. Medicine uses laser surgery and optical diagnostics. Communications is expanding optical fiber communication. Image processing is using optical techniques. The optical engineering option prepares future engineers for such areas as quantum theory; coherent/incoherent, polarized/

non-polarized light; geometric, physical and Fourier optics; holography; and image processing and acquisition.

High School Preparation

High school students should attempt to complete one unit of physics, four units of mathematics and one unit of chemistry. Students without these courses may take them in special programmes at North Dakota State University.

Career Opportunities

NDSU electrical engineering graduates are working all over the world in a variety of exciting jobs. They work in research, design, sales, manufacturing, testing, installation, development and teaching. Many graduates find that an engineering education provides excellent training for fields other than engineering such as business, medicine or law. Those interested in research and teaching usually go on to graduate school for further study.

Research and Graduate Study

Graduate study leading to the M.S. and Ph.D. degrees in electrical engineering is offered in the department. Further details are available in the Graduate Bulletin.

The Facilities

The Electrical Engineering Building is part of the engineering and architecture complex. The building contains specialized laboratories and equipment. Numerous grants and donations from the National Science Foundation and private industry have provided valuable equipment. Laboratories along with department and University computer capabilities support education and research. The ECE department shares the Undergraduate Optics Teaching Laboratory in South Engineering, with the physics department.

Financial Aid

The NDSU Office of Student Financial Services will make every effort to provide adequate financial assistance to all students demonstrating financial need.

Optical Engineering Field

Researching Optical and electron optical engineering which are the key technologies in various fields such as ophthalmic medical care, measurement, semiconductors, and the IT industry.

Ophthalmic Diagnostic Technology

Developing the technological seeds in the future for TOPCON ophthalmic products.

- Refraction Examination Technology

  Development of a next-generation wavefront sensor with an efficient and automatic screening function

- Retinal Inspection Technology

  Development of a retinal camera that incorporates a new diagnostic method with adaptive optics and spectroscopic imaging.

  [Related product: Ophthalmic & Medical Instruments] Wave Front Analyzer KR-9000PW

Optical Technology

Strengthening the basic optical technology that is essential to Topcon products.

- Electron Optical Simulation

  The behavior of electrons in devices like electron microscopes is analyzed with high accuracy.

- Optical Simulation

  Simulations of light scattered by particles

- Optical Thin Film Technology Research

Optical Systems for Information Technology

Challenging to enter into new IT optical system fields.

- Design of optical systems for projectors
- Design of camera lenses for compact imaging devices

  [Related product: Optical Devices]

- Optical Engine for Projectors

Semiconductor Measurement Technology

Challenging to establish three-dimensional measurement of semiconductor microstructure.

- T-MOL(Tilting and Moving Objective Lens) Technology

Optical System

Basic Constraints

Aperture size and scan angle are directly related by the Optical (LaGrange) Invariant which states that the product of the field angle (tangent) and aperture is constant. Aperture size and resolution are proportional, and are usually related by the Rayleigh Criterion:

$$h = 2.44\ l\ (f/\#)$$

where h is the resolvable spot size (diameter) and f/# (f-number) is the imaging element diameter divided by the distance to focus.

In a typical retinal scanning system, a telescope is used to form a reduced "image" of the scanner at the eye. This is not the image seen by the user, but an exit pupil or aperture stop of the system in image space. By forming an exit pupil smaller than the scanner aperture, the scan angle is effectively amplified by a proportional amount. In other words, the ratio of the size of the aperture stop image (exit pupil) to the original scanner is inversely proportional to the magnification of the aerial image, in accordance with the Optical Invariant. However, this smaller exit pupil can lead to two problems: difficulty in making sure the light still enters the eye, and reduced resolution due to diffractive spreading as given by the above equation. Wide FOV polychromatic eyepiece design is non-trivial — adding light weight and form factor constraints makes it even more challenging. Here the small instantaneous ray bundle size helps considerably. For instance, with the fast (small f-number) eyepiece only the aberrations across one beam width will degrade the image, rather than over the entire aperture.

System Design Considerations

An important limit on field-of-view for any pupil-forming system is eye relief. The FOV can be defined by the (half-)angle formed by the chief or principle ray with the optical axis. This implies that its tangent is inversely proportional to eye relief, defined as the distance from the final element to the exit pupil, for an eyepiece of given focal length. Therefore a wider FOV system will less eye relief. Note that inadequate eye relief (less than 20 mm) may prohibit the use of eyeglasses, and even more eye relief may be needed for a wide FOV system. This is because the exit pupil must be closer to the center of the eye's rotation to permit viewing the edges of the image. Pupil distortion is another concern. If the center of the exit pupil is farther from the eyepiece than the edges of the pupil, the eye must be moved closer to the eyepiece when viewing the periphery of the image. This is clearly unacceptable for a head-mounted display.

PATENTS: Optical Engineering Advances for Astronomy

Innovations in astronomy have been applied to fields ranging from medicine to military operations. For example, to compensate for image distortions caused by atmospheric effects, adaptive optics techniques have been developed by astronomers and optical engineers. Elements of this technology have found their way into ophthalmic instruments designed to image the retina of the eye. The images are of such high quality that aberrations of the eye can be measured with very high precision. With this instrumentation, it is possible to specify precise parameters for making corrective lenses or performing corrective surgery. Various eye diseases can also be diagnosed with greater confidence. This advancement in ophthalmology is only one of many examples of the technological progeny born from the synergy of optical engineering and astronomy. Five recent U. S. Patent applications exemplify the important contributions from the astronomy field.

Optical Detectors

Optical detectors for sensing and imaging light sources in multiple spectral bands are required by applications ranging from astronomy to medicine. Such detectors are particularly useful to astronomy since different regions of the electromagnetic spectrum reveal different types of phenomena in the universe. Often, complete understanding is possible only if the entire spectrum is examined. US patent application discloses a design for an optical detector of infrared, sub-millimeter and high energy radiation. In the art of light detection, detectors with the highest sensitivity are, essentially, a type of calorimeter. As light shines on the detecting medium, photons are absorbed and the energy of absorption goes into heating the material. The resulting rise in temperature can be translated into (voltage) light intensity or even photon counts. For the absorption of photons having energies of around 1 KeV, the temperature rise is sufficient to detect a single photon. The sensitivity of calorimetric detectors depends strongly on the heat capacity (thermal mass) of the detecting medium. The lower the heat capacity, the better the sensitivity. One method of reducing the heat capacity is to cool the detector with liquid helium. In the temperature regime of liquid helium, the heat capacity of the detecting medium is proportional to the cube of the absolute temperature. Thus for temperatures of less than 1 Kelvin, the heat capacity can become very small. For many applications, the light intensity is high enough that cryogenic cooling is not necessary. Even then, it is essential that the heat capacity of the detecting medium be minimized. The detector design disclosed by improves the state of the art by reducing the heat capacity in a novel way. The detecting medium is filled with microscopic "photoluminescent temperature probes," each with a mass on the order of 10^{-11} grams. Such a small mass aids in keeping the heat capacity low. Incident light from a source to be imaged causes the temperature probes to fluoresce. For a given intensity and wavelength of incident radiation, the generated photoluminescence is a unique indicator of temperature. The photoluminescent light can be sensed by a low noise photo-electronic device which allows an image of the source to be constructed. This detection scheme has the additional advantage of circumventing electrical noise and Joule heating.

Object Shape

The precise shapes of mirrors and lenses used in telescopes and cameras place stringent demands on manufacturing processes and quality assurance. Interferometric techniques are often used to assess the surface geometry of optical elements. A novel method for determining the shapes of optical surfaces is disclosed in patent application. Instead of using interferometric principles, this proposed method employs the chromatic dispersion of a light source into various angles of incidence onto a surface whose geometry is to be measured. Different wavelengths emerge from the source and are associated with different rays of light having slightly different angles of incidence. Each wavelength is reflected into different angles depending on the surface geometry and the angle of incidence. The detected angular distribution of the reflected light of given wavelengths can then be used to determine the surface geometry.

X-ray Imaging System

High resolution x-ray images are critical to many fields including medicine, dentistry, airport security and astronomy. For astronomy, x-rays are of interest because they are radiated from high energy processes such as accretion disks around black holes. An invention that claims to provide high image resolution and detection efficiency of x-ray sources is described in patent application. This imaging system can be used for x-rays ranging in energy from 1 to 20 KeV. It is consists of three main components: a scintillator, an optical system and a CCD camera. The principles of operation are as follows: x-rays emitted from a source cause excitations in the scintillator of a detector. The scintillating material de-excites by radiating light in the visible spectrum. A substrate is spaced between the scintillator and lens system. The lens system includes an objective lens and a tube lens. Light is imaged onto a CCD detector by the lens system. The scintillator and lenses function together as an optical system which gives rise to magnifications ranging from 500 to 1000. This level of magnification enables image resolutions on the order of 1 μm for typical CCD pixel sizes. Quantum efficiencies on the order of 95% are claimed.

Focusing and Collimating Telescopes

Over the years, amateur astronomers have made significant contributions to astronomy including the discovery of comets, asteroids and supernovae. Patent application US 2006/0132908 A1 describes an apparatus and method used to focus and collimate small telescopes. Since portable telescopes are usually transported to the observing site, there is a risk that the optical alignment may suffer from unintended jolts. Consequently, these telescopes are in need of frequent collimation. The process of collimation can be a tedious, time consuming procedure. In addition to the necessity of precise collimation, image quality depends on proper focusing.

The invention disclosed in US 2006/0132908 A1 purports to automate the focusing and/or collimation adjustments. The automation is accomplished by control electronics, motorized components, and inputs such as physical specifications of the optical elements, imaging devices such as CCD cameras and even information about a particular user.

Actuator Arrays for Adaptive Optics

The theoretical angular resolution of an optical system such as a telescope is limited by diffraction. This limit is given by the well known Rayleigh criterion, where the angular resolution á is in radians, ë is the wavelength and *d* is the aperture diameter. For astronomical telescopes, this limit cannot be achieved due to atmospheric turbulence and air currents. The result is excessive blurring of images. Less than ideal angular resolution amounts to a loss of information. For example, atmospheric effects might not allow a binary star system to be resolved into two stars and so it appears as a single star-like object. Adaptive optics solutions can compensate for atmospheric effects, leading to sharper images. In some cases, the mitigation of atmospheric effects may allow the optical system to approach its theoretical diffraction limit. By changing the effective shape of an optical surface such as a deformable or segmented mirror, wavefront distortions induced by the atmosphere are counteracted. A bright "reference beacon" (such as a star) near the object to be imaged is used to quantify the wavefront distortions. This allows "corrected shapes" to be derived in real time with subsequent rapid mechanical actuations applied to the optical surface. A novel system of actuator arrays for an adaptive optics system is disclosed in patent application. The actuator arrays in this invention are intended for deformable surfaces. The actuator arrays are arranged in "braking groups" and "force-altering groups." Precise control of these groups can mitigate atmospherically induced aberrations.

Optical Engineering Challenges of the Virtual Retinal Display

This paper presents an overview of the VRD project at the HIT lab from an optical systems designer's viewpoint, followed by details of some system components, design criteria, and specific subproject developments — primarily in optical imaging. Due to both breadth and patent considerations it is necessary to mention some aspects of the project in passing only.

System Overview

The VRD can be considered a portable system that creates the perception of an image by scanning a beam of light directly into the eye. Most displays directly address a real image plane (typically a CRT or matrix-addressed LCD) which might be relayed to form a larger, more distant image for a head-mounted display (HMD). The VRD uses a scanned, modulated light beam to treat the retina as a projection screen, much as a laser light show would use the ceiling of a planetarium. The closest previously existing device would be the scanning laser opthalmoscope (SLO) which scans the retina to examine it; the SLO is designed to capture light returning from the eye whereas the VRD is designed as a portable display. Another class of related systems are "Maxwellian-view" systems used in psychophysical research. The VRD has several advantages over CRTs, LCD, and other addressable-screen displays:

- Resolution is limited by beam diffraction and optical aberrations, not by the size of an addressable pixel in a matrix. Very high resolution images are therefore possible without extensive advances in micro-fabrication technology. Also, the VRD does not suffer from pixel defects.
- The display can be made as bright as desired simply by controlling the intensity of the scanned beam. This makes it much easier to use the display in "see-though" configuration on a bright day.
- The scanning technology in the current display requires only simple, well understood manufacturing technology and can therefore be manufactured inexpensively.
- Because the light is projected into the eye and the scanner is electro-mechanically efficient, the display uses very little power.
- In theory, the VRD allows for accommodation to be modulated pixel by pixel as the image is being scanned.

All components in the VRD are small and light, making them ideal for use in a portable display.

The VRD display concept was initially conceived by Dr. Thomas A. Furness as a means of eliminating large aperture optics and expensive high-resolution addressable images sources such as CRTs. Soon after joining the HIT Lab in 1991, Joel Kollin realised a key feature about the VRD — movements of the eye would not result in perceived movement in the image. Therefore, eye tracking would not be necessary beyond that what might be needed to ensure that the light beam entered the eye. He then designed and constructed the original bench-mounted VRD, using an acousto-optic device as the horizontal scanner. Electronics largely designed and built by Bob Burstein then allowed it to be driven directly by a DEC workstation, although it was still significantly lower in both contrast and resolution than a standard SVGA display and offered an image only in uncalibrated shades of red. We subsequently began work on patenting the display and brought on board David Melville to engineer the mechanical design, especially a new scanning system. In 1993, a newly formed corporation, MicroVision Inc., licensed the VRD technology and signed a 4 year, $5.1 million development contract with the University. Rich Johnston was hired specifically to manage the VRD and other hardware products of the Lab. By forming relationships with other researchers in the College of Engineering, he has orchestrated a programme to solve the challenges and bottlenecks of the project. In late 1993 and 1994, Mike Tidwell redesigned the VRD to maximize the resolution possible with the A-O scanner while David Melville designed a new Mechanical Resonant Scanner (MRS) which would be capable of the high rates of horizontal scanning without the costs and other limitations of the A-O devices. The MRS was then utilized in full-color inclusive and "see-through" systems.

Subsystems

In the VRD a light source is modulated with image information, either by direct power ("internal") modulation or by an external modulator. The light is passed through an x-y scanning system, currently the MRS and a galvanometer. Light from the scanner pair enters an optical system, which in present implementations of the VRD forms an aerial image and then uses and eyepiece to magnify and relay this image to infinity.

Light Sources

Coherence and Source Size

According to conventional additive color theory, any color can be represented as a mixture of three appropriately chosen primaries. The three ideal VRD light sources would be monochromatic for maximum possible color saturation. The ideal colors would be near the corners of the CIE chromaticity chart but not too far in the blue or red as the nominal gains in addressable color space would be more than offset by sensitivity decrease in the eye. Spatial coherence is also important — larger source spots will correspond to larger spots on the retina, decreasing resolution. The primary cause of the real (if sometimes exaggerated) hazards of laser light are the result of spatially coherent light focusing to a small area on the retina, causing highly localized heating and ablation of tissue. In the VRD the spot is traveling in two directions and even when stationary is not at a power level that would cause damage. We are working with ophthalmologists and will publish a definitive article on this in the near future. Incidentally, polychromatic sources can be shown to form spots comparable to monochromatic ones of the same spatial extent. Therefore spatial coherence is responsible for the small spot size which leads to both high resolution and (given enough power) retinal hazard. To achieve the desired resolution, all current VRD prototypes have used lasers for their superior spatial coherence characteristics. In order to use a point source such as an LED, the image of the source should be smaller than the diffraction limit of the scanner. Using the lens magnification, one can determine the maximum source size that can be used before degrading the diffraction limited spot size at the image plane. The angular divergence of the source is effectively limited by treating the scanner as a stop. Light which does not hit the mirror does not contribute to the image plane spot size. From this geometric argument we can derive an equivalent point source size between 4 and 5 microns for a VGA resolution image in our current system. For a system where the scanner is illuminated with a collimated Gaussian beam, similar arguments can be made to determine the required divergence and beam waist from the equations for image plane spot size.

Scanners

The horizontal scanning mechanism of the VRD must be capable of both relatively high scan rates (15 kHz-90+ kHz) and high resolution (500-2000+ pixels) for NTSC to HDTV formats, respectively. To date we have built SVGA format systems (80 kHz) in monochrome/greyscale using a A-O scanner and 30 kHz in full-color with a mechanical resonant one.

Devices

Red laser diodes have more than adequate modulation for our current needs but suffer from contrast problems due to effects of extinguishing and re-establishing the lasing action. When the current drops below the lasing threshold the laser acts like an LED, exhibiting reduced optical power and coherence but still glowing. This can be seen as a bend in the current vs. optical power curve. We presently adjust the range on this curve to obtain satisfactory image contrast. External A-O devices are used to modulate the gas lasers currently used as blue and green sources. We intend to switch to solid-state lasers in the green and blue in the very near future as they become commercially available. Work is proceeding on the use of LEDs as the VRD light source. LEDs can be directly modulated, are inexpensive, and are available in a wide range of colors. The spatial coherence and modulation bandwidth of available visible LEDs is below the requirements for high-resolution displays. We are working with LED manufacturers to eliminate these issues.

Acousto-Optic Scanners

High-speed A-O scanners require a highly anamorphic beam and expensive drive electronics. In addition, they suffer from light loss, small deflection angles, variations in diffraction efficiency and non-linear chromatic aberration. For these reasons we now use the more commercially viable mechanical devices.

Resonant Scanners

Mechanical resonant scanners are free from chromatic aberration, extremely efficient, small and inexpensive to produce. The MRS will be discussed at length in a future paper, but certain issues involved with all resonant scanners might be noted here as they directly affect the optical design. By their nature, resonant scanners are very efficient as they convert potential energy to kinetic and back again, in a manner similar to a pendulum. Because of their sinusoidal scan, it is highly desirable to use resonant devices as bi-directional scanners. At the current time the MRS is capable of roughly +/- 12 degrees at 3 mm clear aperture at 15kHz bi-directional (i.e. 30 kHz effective scan rate.) We expect this will soon improve to greater than +/- 20 degrees with the next generation of driver circuitry. Larger scan angles mean less magnification is necessary, leading to larger exit pupils and a smaller system. We are still researching other scanning technologies, especially those which might have advantages that outweigh the low cost and high efficiency of the MRS. Currently we are using a galvanometer for the vertical scanner while a less expensive solution is being developed.

Holographic Optical Elements

Holographic Optical Elements (HOEs) are diffractive optical elements that are constructed holographically i.e. by interfering two beams of light. Typically one beam resembles the "playback" beam that will illuminate the HOE in the final system. The second beam corresponds to the "image" beam desired to exit the HOE upon playback. In practice, the construction beams can differ from this paradigm since there is considerable variation in the playback beam, especially in a wide field scanning system. In any case, most HOEs can be approximated as holograms of point sources or collimated beams of light, such that light from one source is imaged into the other.

Characteristics

The diffractive power of the HOE leads to several interesting possibilities as well as a new set of constraints. For instance, "curved" mirrors can be made on a flat substrate by interfering expanding and contracting beams of light from different sides of the HOE plate. This can be accomplished by simply placing the HOE plate between a spatial filter (beam expander) aperture and a concave mirror, with the beam reflecting from the mirror converging back to the aperture. The interference fringes thus recorded will resemble an actual mirror, as the fringes formed are normal to the intersection between the crossed construction beams. More specifically, they will be the same "speed" (f/#) as the construction mirror but with a focal length given by the distance between the HOE and the aperture.

The HOE would be considered a non-conformal reflection HOE, meaning the fringes are not conformal or parallel to the surface. The playback beam will reflect off the HOE since the construction beams impinge from different sides, causing the interference fringes to be formed roughly perpendicular to the propagation directions. If the HOE is recorded on a curved substrate so that the fringes conform to the surface, it would act as a multi-layer coated mirror. A HOE of this type can reflect nearly all of the light whose propagation vector component k was twice that of the fringe spacing — this is known as the Bragg condition. The Bragg condition is the combination of wavelength and angle that causes the impinging and diffracted light of the HOE to be in phase with each other. Not surprisingly, the wavelength and angle of the construction beams will determine the Bragg condition of the HOE fringes, although this can be modified after recording by chemical or physical distortion of the fringes. For a diffuse and/or polychromatic illumination source, those rays meeting the Bragg condition will be diffracted much more strongly — this is known as Bragg selection. We say that holograms with Bragg selection are "thick", meaning they have significant structure inside the plane of the hologram, which may be less than 7 microns but still contain 10 or more fringes to form a "multilayer stack". Reflection holograms are by definition thick, whereas transmission holograms can be thick or thin depending on the exposure geometry and choice of material. Embossed or surface relief holograms, such as those found on credit cards, are thin holograms and therefore have little or no Bragg selection. They are colorful because they are "rainbow" or Benton holograms, which are vertically dispersive transmission holograms mounted in front of a mirror. Thick reflection and transmission holograms can approach 100% diffraction efficiency (at least for a point-source hologram), whereas thin transmission holograms are limited to 33.9% maximum theoretical efficiency.

Besides a decrease in the bulk and weight, HOEs have several other advantages over conventional elements due to Bragg selection. For a see-through system, the wavelength used by the display can be selectively reflected from the HOE which also tends to reject outside light of the same color. This means higher contrast relative to a broadband beamsplitter for a given brightness and/or transmissivity for the system as a whole, although the outside light may be color shifted as a result. Also, the HOE can multiplex functions by acting differently for beams impinging from different directions or with different wavefronts. For example, light might pass through the HOE virtually undisturbed, be reflected from a beamsplitter, and then be magnified by the HOE. This is a system being tested by HITL as described below. A more complex system might act as a prism for one wavefront and a lens for another.

A reflection hologram for a full-color system can be accurately recorded by three separate exposures at chosen red, green, and blue laser wavelengths. Each set of fringes is Bragg selective for a narrow bandwidth — usually around the exposure wavelength, although this can be shifted and the bandwidth broadened. Since each color is independently exposed, it is possible to modify the exposure geometry to minimize chromatic aberrations or to combine spatially separate color images. Each exposure uses up some potential refractive index modulation, but this limitation can be circumvented by copying the HOE. This is often accomplished by placing the copy hologram in contact with the master and exposing it to the playback beam. The resulting image beam from the master interferes with the playback beam to form nearly identical fringes in the copy hologram. Computer generated diffractive optical elements can also be "contact copied" in this manner.

In general, HOEs also allow greater freedom in an optical system since diffractive optical elements cause chromatic dispersion opposite in sign to refractive elements. Diffractive power can be added to a refractive and reflective element by incorporating diffractive features on a lens or mirror surface. Thin holograms or other diffractive devices can be pressed onto the surface of molded or cast parts. Thick holograms can be placed on curved reflectors or lenses by coating the surface with photopolymer or gelatin and exposing. Conformal exposure increases expenses quite a bit — from perhaps $5 to $50, whereas complex lenses and reflectors can be molded for under $5 in large quantity.

Thick HOEs have some other disadvantages besides cost. Bragg selection can limit the field of the HOE, with efficiency and FOV decreasing away from the Bragg condition. At the same time, insufficient Bragg selection can lead to significant dispersion in a non-monochromatic source such as an LED, and even cross-talk between the different color exposures. Also, flare from bright ambient light could be diffracted into the eye by a reflection HOE acting as a transmission hologram. This is more of a problem for non-conformal holograms, where the fringes can be perpendicular to the plane of the hologram at the surface, allowing for significant diffractive transmission. Proper design and the use of baffles can help minimize flare. Also, non-conformal holograms can lead to distortion, since the HOE might intersect the scanned beam at a different point a curved mirror would.

HITL HOE Prototype

After constructing several promising HOEs in DuPont photopolymer to test Bragg selection and image quality, a VRD system incorporating a HOE was designed and built. In this system, light from the MRS/objective system is transmitted undisturbed at a shallow angle through a reflective HOE and is reflected from a beamsplitter. (Light transmitted through the beamsplitter on this first pass simply passes off to the side of the viewer's eye.) The reflected light now impinges on the HOE with the optical axis of the HOE co-linear with the center scan beam (i.e. on-axis). Light reflected from the HOE is now collimated and the aerial image is relayed to infinity. For this particular implementation we tilt the HOE vertically so that the specular reflection of the scanner off of the HOE substrate misses the eye. This leads to a small amount of keystoning in the image, and might be avoided by the use of anti-reflective (AR) substrate and/or polarizing elements instead of tilting.

Experimental Results

Our first VRD system incorporating HOEs was designed using ZEMAX and exposed onto DuPont OmniDex 706 film. We started by constructing simple, nearly on-axis non-conformal 35mm focal length, f/0.8 mirrors by two different methods. At first we used a two-beam exposure at 532nm with back to back singlets to converge an expanded, spatially filtered beam to a point near the pinhole of another spatial filter. This method allows for more flexibility for future experiments with off-axis systems, but has a few drawbacks. First there is distortion introduced by the singlet pair — we cannot be measure this or predict it using ZEMAX directly but it is fairly obvious barrel distortion which accentuates rather than correcting the sinusoidal distortion. Also we noticed that there were several "false foci" recorded on the HOE — these were from stray surface reflections and manifested themselves as extra exit pupils with distorted images. These will presumably be reduced or eliminated by anti-reflective coatings on the optics and plate.

We then made a simple one-beam "Denisyuk" HOE by using a mirror to reconverge light to the spatial filter, as shown in the previous setup, Bragg angle can be altered by varying the conjugates from the nominal 1:1 ration. Stray reflections were reduced, with only the specular highlight from the scanner being apparent. This system also makes it easier to construct multiple color HOEs by sequential exposure in different wavelengths. So far the results obtained for a two-color HOE recorded on DuPont 700HD 15-20 full-color reflection film have been disappointing, but we have just begun experimenting with this material. Exposure times are very long — 10-12 minutes for red (633nm He-Ne) followed by 3-4 minutes for the much stronger green (532nm doubled Nd-YAG). Once we have obtained better results and have optimized recording conditions, we plan to try three-color exposures with blue for a full-color VRD system.

A testing system now under construction will enable us to quantitatively measure system MTF, spot size, resolution and contrast. We can therefore only offer preliminary results based on test patterns which are observed visually. For the single color (green) HOEs we were able to resolve the full resolution of 640 by 480 pixels except for extreme left and right edges of the display, which are compressed by the sinusoidal distortion. This was determined by displaying gratings of alternating off and on pixels in the vertical and horizontal directions. Cosmetically, the holograms show surface defects incurred during lamination and striated variations in diffraction efficiency. The two-color HOEs were much dimmer and noisier than the green ones in the VRD setup, possibly due to errors in the Bragg selection, long exposure times necessary because of limited He-Ne power, and mechanical properties of the material.

Diffraction efficiency is probably also reduced by the current lasers used in the VRD — 543nm He-Ne for the green and 650nm (nominal) red laser diode. Baking the holograms seems to make them brighter in white light but not in the system, leading us to believe that efficiency is not improving much for our choice of off-peak wavelengths. Successful use of HOEs will require careful control over the peak Bragg wavelength and/or broad spectral bandwidths to match the source. LEDs are fairly well-matched to the bandwidth exhibited by DuPont photopolymer holograms if the peak wavelengths are close. In the next year we hope to add a wet darkroom and environmental controls to our optics facility which will make it much easier to try other materials such as those made by Polaroid. Recently we have also constructed a "VRD simulator" which allows us to examine optical subsystems (eyepieces) of the VRD without requiring access to the scanner and being limited in optical power or wavelength. The basic concept is to take light from a slide transparency and project it aerially as a real image in front of a apertured projection lens. The aperture of the projection lens corresponds to the stop in the system, simulating a scanner aperture and resulting pupil size. The distance from the projection lens to the image and the focal length determines the size and field angle of the aerial image, which is then re-imaged by the tested system which also forms an image of the projection aperture to the eye. The image can be made as bright as desired to test inefficient systems prior to optimization, and the chromatic response to a white-light source or various filtered colors can also be tested. This is especially useful for testing HOEs with Bragg condition problems. It is not currently capable of simulating distortion other than what is introduced by the projection optics.

The Virtual Retinal Display has significant performance and ergonomic advantages, especially for portable displays. Subsystems and issues currently being addressed at the HIT Lab include: light source development, scanning technology, optical system engineering and compact eyepieces. In particular, holographic optical elements are a promising means of providing see-through eyepieces in a small form factor with unique advantages.

Materials

While the first holograms and HOEs were recorded on silver halide material, (aerial photography plates and films) the high efficiencies mentioned above require nearly perfect phase materials. Silver halide holograms can be "bleached" to change their amplitude variation into phase retardance, but this is usually at the expense of increasing the film grain noise inherent in the material. Dichromated gelatin (DCG) is the traditional recording medium for HOEs as it is nearly noiseless and very efficient. Unfortunately, DCG is also toxic, fragile, usually mounted on glass, and requires tight process control and a perfect seal against moisture and humidity. More recently, photopolymers have become available as a more durable and easier alternative. DuPont has produced a family of products (Omnidex) which require no wet processing, only flooding with white or UV light after exposure and heating to raise the diffraction efficiency. While Omnidex does not match the high index of refraction variation and efficiency of dichromated gelatin, it does meet the requirements of many HOE applications and is relatively impervious to environmental stress including heat and water. Polaroid also has a family of materials which offer some interesting variations in reflection bandwidth and refractive index modulation. It should be noted that all of these materials require significantly more light to expose than silver halide products. Because conventional silver-based films and plates have a grain structure to amplify the exposure, since each grain is activated as a unit. While silver halide is more sensitive (since it takes fewer photons to expose an area of film), this grain amplification effect adds noise and scatter, making silver materials less desirable for technical applications.

REFERENCES

A.M. Weber, W.K. Smothers, T.J. Trout, and D.J. Mickish, "Hologram recording in DuPont's new photopolymer materials," Practical Holography IV, SPIE Vol. 2152, 1990.

Block, S.M. (1990). "Optical tweezers: a new tool for biophysics". in *Noninvasive Techniques in Cell Biology*. Modern Cell Biology Vol. 9: 375-401. S. Grinstein and K. Foskett (eds.). New York, Wiley-Liss.

Conibear, P.B. and Bagshaw, C.R. (2000). "A comparison of optical geometries for combined flash photolysis and total internal reflection fluorescence microscopy." *Journal Of Microscopy-Oxford* **200**: 218-229.

J. Smith, S. Montague, and J. Sniegowski, SPIE Micromachining and Microfabrication '95, vol. 2639, pp. 64-73, Oct. 1995.

Knight, A.E. and Molloy, J.E. (2000). "Muscle, myosin and single molecules". In "Molecular Motors" *Essays In Biochemistry* Vol. **35** (S. J. Higgins and G. Banting, Eds.). London, Portland Press.

M. Tidwell, R.S. Johnston, D. Melville, and T.A. Furness, "The virtual retinal display — a retinal scanning imaging system," Virtual Reality World '95 Conference Documentation, IDG Conferences. pp. 325-333, 1995.

M.P. de Boer, A. H. Heuer, S. J. Jacobs, and E. Peeters, eds., Mater. Res. Soc. Proc. Vol. 605. 2000, Materials Research Society: Warrendale, PA. 314 pages.

M.P. de Boer, N. F. Smith, N. D. Masters, M. B. Sinclair, and E. J. Pryputniewicz, in *Mechanical properties of structural thin films, STP 1413*, S. B. Brown and.C.L. Muhlstein, Editors. 2001, ASTM: West Conshohocken, PA. p. 85-95.

Molloy, J.E. (1998). "Optical chopsticks: Digital synthesis of multiple optical traps." *Meth. Cell Biol.* **55**: 205-216.

R. H. Webb, G. W. Hughes, and F. C. Delori, "Confocal scanning laser ophthalmoscope," Appl. Opt., Vol. 26, No. 8, pp. 1492-1499, 1987.

Sheetz, M.P., Ed. (1998). Laser Tweezers in Cell Biology. *Methods in Cell Biology*. San Diego, Academic Press.

Visscher, K., Gross, S.P. and Block, S.M. (1996). "Construction of multiple-beam optical traps with nanometer-resolution position sensing." *IEEE Journal Of Selected Topics In Quantum Electronics* **2**(4): 1066-1076.
Visscher, K., Gross, S.P. and Block, S.M. (1996). "Construction of multiple-beam optical traps with nanometer-resolution position sensing." *IEEE Journal Of Selected Topics In Quantum Electronics* **2**(4): 1066-1076.

3

Research Methodology in Electronic Science

INTRODUCTION

The field of electronics comprises the study and use of systems that operate by controlling the flow of electrons (or other charge carriers) in devices such as thermionic valves (vacuum tubes) and semiconductors. The design and construction of electronic circuits to solve practical problems is an integral technique in the field of electronics engineering and is equally important in hardware design for computer engineering. All applications of electronics involve the transmission of either information or power. Most deal only with information. The study of new semiconductor devices and surrounding technology is sometimes considered a branch of physics. This article focuses on engineering aspects of electronics. Other important topics include electronic waste and occupational health impacts of semiconductor manufacturing. Electronic systems are used to perform a wide variety of tasks. The main uses of electronic circuits are: (i) The controlling and processing of data. (ii) The conversion to/from and distribution of electric power. Both these applications involve the creation and/or detection of electromagnetic fields and electric currents. While electrical energy had been used for some time prior to the late 19th century to transmit data over telegraph and telephone lines, development in electronics grew exponentially after the advent of radio. One way of looking at an electronic system is to divide it into 3 parts:

1. Inputs – Electronic or mechanical sensors (or transducers). These devices take signals/information from external sources in the physical world (such as antennas or technology networks) and convert those signals/information into current/voltage or digital (high/low) signals within the system.

2. Signal processors – These circuits serve to manipulate, interpret and transform inputted signals in order to make them useful for a desired application. Recently, complex signal processing has been accomplished with the use of Digital Signal Processors.
3. Outputs – Actuators or other devices (such as transducers) that transform current/voltage signals back into useful physical form (e.g., by accomplishing a physical task such as rotating an electric motor).

For example, a television set contains these 3 parts. The television's input transforms a broadcast signal (received by an antenna or fed in through a cable) into a current/voltage signal that can be used by the device. Signal processing circuits inside the television extract information from this signal that dictates brightness, colour and sound level. Output devices then convert this information back into physical form. A cathode ray tube transforms electronic signals into a visible image on the screen. Magnet-driven speakers convert signals into audible sound.

Electronic Devices and Components

An electronic component is any indivisible electronic building block packaged in a discrete form with two or more connecting leads or metallic pads. Components are intended to be connected together, usually by soldering to a printed circuit board, to create an electronic circuit with a particular function (for example an amplifier, radio receiver, or oscillator). Components may be packaged singly (resistor, capacitor, transistor, diode etc.) or in more or less complex groups as integrated circuits (operational amplifier, resistor array, logic gate etc). Active components are sometimes called *devices* rather than components.

Types of Circuits

Analog Vircuits

Most analog electronic appliances, such as radio receivers, are constructed from combinations of a few types of basic circuits. Analog circuits use a continuous range of voltage as opposed to discrete levels as in digital circuits. The number of different analog circuits so far devised is huge, especially because a 'circuit' can be defined as anything from a single component, to systems containing thousands of components. Analog circuits are sometimes called linear circuits although many non-linear effects are used in analog circuits such as mixers, modulators, etc. Good examples of analog circuits include vacuum tube and transistor amplifiers, operational amplifiers and oscillators. Some analog circuitry these days may use digital or even microprocessor techniques to improve upon the basic performance of the circuit. This type of circuit is usually called 'mixed signal'.

Sometimes it may be difficult to differentiate between analog and digital circuits as they have elements of both linear and non-linear operation. An example is the comparator which takes in a continuous range of voltage but puts out only one of two levels as in a digital circuit. Similarly, an overdriven transistor amplifier can take on the characteristics of a controlled switch having essentially two levels of output.

Digital Circuits

Digital circuits are electric circuits based on a number of discrete voltage levels. Digital circuits are the most common physical representation of Boolean algebra and are the basis of all digital computers. To most engineers, the terms "digital circuit", "digital system" and "logic" are interchangeable in the context of digital circuits. In most cases the number of different states of a node is two, represented by two voltage levels labeled "Low" and "High". Often "Low" will be near zero volts and "High" will be at a higher level depending on the supply voltage in use. Computers, electronic clocks, and programmable logic controllers (used to control industrial processes) are constructed of digital circuits. Digital Signal Processors are another example.

Building-blocks:

- logic gates
- Adders
- Binary Multipliers
- flip-flops
- counters
- registers
- multiplexers
- Schmitt triggers

Highly integrated devices:

- microprocessors
- microcontrollers
- Application specific integrated circuit(ASIC)
- Digital signal processor (DSP)
- Field Programmable Gate Array (FPGA)

Mixed-signal Circuits

Mixed-signal circuits refers to integrated circuits (ICs) which have both analog circuits and digital circuits combined on a single semiconductor die or on the same circuit board. Mixed-signal circuits are becoming increasingly common. Mixed circuits contain both analog and digital components. Analog to digital converters and digital to analog converters are the primary examples. Other examples are transmission gates and buffers.

Heat Dissipation and Thermal Management

Heat generated by electronic circuitry must be dissipated to prevent immediate failure and improve long term reliability. Techniques for *heat dissipation* can include heatsinks and fans for air cooling, and other forms of computer cooling such as water cooling. These techniques use convection, conduction, & radiation of heat energy.

Noise

Noise is associated with all electronic circuits. Noise is generally defined as any unwanted signal that is not present at the input of a circuit. Noise is not the same as signal distortion caused by a circuit.

Electronics Theory

Mathematical methods are integral to the study of electronics. To become proficient in electronics it is also necessary to become proficient in the mathematics of circuit analysis. Circuit analysis is the study of methods of solving generally linear systems for unknown variables such as the voltage at a certain node or the current though a certain branch of a network. A common analytical tool for this is the SPICE circuit simulator. Also important to electronics is the study and understanding of electromagnetic field theory.

Computer Aided Design (CAD)

Today's electronics engineers have the ability to design circuits using premanufactured building blocks such as power supplies, semiconductors (such as transistors), and integrated circuits. Electronic design automation software programmes include schematic capture programmes and pcb design programmes. Popular names in the EDA software world are MultiSIM, Cadence (ORCAD), Eagle PCB and Schematic, Mentor (PADS PCB and LOGIC Schematic), Altium (Protel), and many others. The programmes can cost a few hundred dollars up to tens of thousands, depending upon complexity. For example, some programmes can automatically "route" a PCB with surprising accuracy, while some programmes can perform thermal and electrical analysis.

Electronic Test Equipment

Electronic test equipment is used to create stimulus signals and capture responses from electronic Devices Under Test (DUTs). In this way, the proper operation of the DUT can be proven or faults in the device can be traced and repaired.

Practical electronics engineering and assembly requires the use of many different kinds of electronic test equipment ranging from the very simple and inexpensive (such as a test light consisting of just a light bulb and a test lead) to extremely complex and sophisticated such as Automatic Test Equipment.

Construction Methods

Many different methods of connecting components have been used over the years. For instance, in the beginning point to point wiring using tag boards attached to chassis were used to connect various electrical innards. Cordwood construction and wire wraps were other methods used. Most modern day electronics now use printed circuit boards (made of FR4), and highly integrated circuits. Health and environmental concerns associated with electronics assembly have gained increased attention in recent years, especially for products destined to the European Union, with its Restriction of Hazardous Substances Directive (RoHS) and Waste Electrical and Electronic Equipment Directive (WEEE), which went into force in July 2006.

Main Branches

- Digital electronics
- Analogue electronics
- Microelectronics
- Fuzzy electronics
- Circuit Design
- Integrated circuit
- Optoelectronics
- Semiconductor
- Semiconductor device

Analogue Electronics

Analogue electronics are those electronic systems with a continuously variable signal. In contrast, in digital electronics signals take only one of two different levels. The term "analogue" describes the proportional relationship between a signal and a voltage or current that represented the signal.

Description of Analogue Signals

An analogue signal uses some property of the medium to convey the signal's information. For example, an aneroid barometer uses angular position as the signal to convey pressure information. Electrical signals may represent information by changing their voltage, current, frequency, or total charge. Information is converted from some other physical form (such as sound, light, temperature, pressure, position) to an electrical signal by a transducer. The signals take any value from a given range, and each unique signal value represents different information. Any change in the signal is meaningful, and each level of the signal represents a different level of the phenomenon that it represents. For example, suppose the signal is being used to represent temperature, with one Volt representing one degree Celsius. In such a system 10 Volts would represent 10 degrees, and 10.1 Volts would represent 10.1 degrees.

Another method of conveying an analogue signal is to use modulation. In this, some base carrier signal has one of its properties altered: amplitude modulation (AM) involves altering the amplitude of a sinusoidal voltage waveform by the source information, frequency modulation (FM) changes the frequency. Other techniques, such as changing the phase of the carrier signal are also used. In an analogue sound recording, the variation in pressure of a sound striking a microphone creates a corresponding variation in the current passing through it or voltage across it. An increase in the volume of the sound causes the fluctuation of the current or voltage to increase proportionally while keeping the same waveform or shape. Mechanical, pneumatic, hydraulic and other systems may also use analogue signals.

Inherent Noise

The primary disadvantage of analogue signalling is that any system has noise; that is, random disturbances or variations in it. Since all variations of an analogue signal are significant, any disturbance is equivalent to a change in the original signal and so appears as noise. As the signal is copied and re-copied, or transmitted over long distances, these random variations become dominant and lead to signal degradation. Electrically these disturbances are reduced by shielding, and using low noise amplifiers. The effects of random noise can make signal loss and distortion impossible to recover, since amplifying the signal to recover attenuated parts of the signal often generates more noise and amplifies the noise as well.

Analogue vs. Digital Electronics

Since the information is encoded differently in analogue and digital electronics, the way they process a signal is consequently different. All operations that can be performed on an analogue signal such as amplifcation, filtering, limiting, and others, can also be duplicated in the digital domain. The first electronic devices invented and mass produced were analogue. The use of microelectronics has reduced the cost of digital techniques and now make digital methods feasible. The main differences between analogue and digital electronics are listed below:

Noise

Because the way information is encoded in analogue circuits, they are much more susceptible to noise than digital circuits, since a small change in the signal can represent a significant change in the information present in the signal and can cause the information present to be lost. Since digital signals take only one of two different values, a distrubance would have to be about one-half the magnitude of the digital signal to cause an error; this property of digital circuits can be exploited to make signal processing noise-resistant. In digital electronics, because the information is quantized, as long as the signal stays inside a range of values, it represents the same information. Digital circuits use this principle to regenerate the signal at each logic gate, lessening or removing noise.

Design Difficulty

Digital systems are much easier and smaller to design than comparable analogue circuits. This is one of the main reasons why digital systems are more common than analogue. An analogue circuit must be designed by hand, and the process is much less automated than for digital systems. Also, because the smaller the integrated circuit (chip) the cheaper it is, and digital systems are much smaller than analogue, digital is cheaper to manufacture.

Precision

A number of factors affect how precise a signal is, mainly the noise present in the original signal and the noise added by processing. See Signal to Noise Ratio. Fundamental physical limits such as the shot noise in components limits the resolution of analog signals. In digital electronics additional precision is obtained by using additional digits to represent the signal; the practical limit in the number of digits is determined by the performance of the analog to digital converters, since digital operations can usually be performed without loss of precision.

Digital Electronics

Digital electronics are those electronics systems that use a digital signal instead of an analog signal. Digital electronics are the most common representation of Boolean algebra and are the basis of all digital circuits for computers, mobile phones, and numerous other consumer products. The most common "fundamental unit" of digital electronics is the logic gate. By combining numerous logic gates (from tens to hundreds of thousands) more complex systems can be created. The complex system of digital electronics is collectively referred to as a digital circuit. To most electronic engineers, the terms "digital circuit", "digital system" and "logic" are interchangeable in the context of digital circuits.

Advantages

The usual advantages of digital circuits when compared to analog circuits are:

- Digital systems interface well with computers and are easy to control with software. It is often possible to add new features to a digital system without changing hardware, and to do this remotely, just by uploading new software. Design errors or bugs can be worked-around with a software upgrade, after the product is in customer hands.
- Information storage can be much easier in digital systems than in analog ones. In particular, the great noise-immunity of digital systems makes it possible to store data and retrieve it later without degradation. In an analog system, aging and wear and tear will degrade the information in storage, but in a digital system, as long as the wear and tear is below a certain level, the information can be recovered perfectly.

Robustness

One of the primary advantages of digital electronics stems from it simply being digital: robustness. The robustness stems from the fact that if the noise is less than the noise margin then the system performs as if there were no noise at all. This is a necessary and sufficient property for a circuit to be considered digital. However, if the noise exceeds this level, the circuit can give unexpected and undesired results — perhaps catastrophic incorrect results. Digital signals can thus be regenerated to achieve lossless data transmission, within certain limits. Analog signal transmission and processing, by contrast, always introduces noise. Theoretically, there is no data-loss when copying digital data. This is a great advantage over analog systems, which faithfully reproduce every bit of noise that makes its way into the signal.

Disadvantages

Digital circuits use more energy than analog circuits to accomplish the same calculations and signal processing tasks, thus producing more heat as well. In portable or battery-powered systems this can be a major limiting factor, but in a situation where power is plentiful, a digital system is often preferred because of all the advantages listed above, especially that of (re-)programmability and ease of upgrading without requiring hardware changes. A particular example is the cellular telephone, which being a battery-powered portable device, uses a low-power analog front-end to acquire and tune in the radio signal from the base station. The base station, being in a fixed location with access to the power grid, can afford to use power-hungry software-defined (digital) radio techniques that digitize the signal essentially at the antenna (after wideband filtering and downconversion to intermediate frequency) and performs all channelization and demodulation via software-driven calculations. Such base stations can be reprogrammed, potentially via remote control, to process the signals used in future cellular standards as those standards become available. Digital circuits are sometimes more expensive, especially in small quantities. The world in which we live is analog, and signals from this world such as light, temperature, sound, electrical conductivity, electric and magnetic fields, and phenomena such as the flow of time, are for most practical purposes continuous and thus analog quantities rather than discrete digital ones. For a digital system to do useful things in the real world, translation from the continuous realm to the discrete digital realm must occur, resulting in quantization errors. This problem can usually be mitigated by designing the system to store enough digital data to represent the signal to the desired degree of fidelity. The Nyquist-Shannon sampling theorem provides an important guideline as to how much digital data is needed to accurately portray a given analog signal.

Analog Issues in Digital Circuits

Digital circuits are made from analog components, and care has to be taken in design so that the analog nature of these underlying components don't dominate over the desired digital behavior. In particular, attention must be paid to all noise and timing margins, to parasitic inductances and capacitances, to proper filtering of power and ground connections, to electromagnetic coupling amongst datalines, and many other details. Inattention to these can cause intermittent problems such as "glitches", vanishingly-fast pulses that may trigger some logic but not others, "runt pulses" that do not reach valid switching (threshold) voltages, or unexpected ("undecoded") combinations of logic states. A corollary of the fact that digital circuits are made from analog components is the fact that digital circuits are slower to perform calculations than analog circuits that occupy a similar amount of physical space and consume the same amount of power. However, the digital circuit will perform the calculation with much better repeatability, due to the high noise immunity of digital circuitry.

Fragility

Digital systems can be fragile, in that if a single piece of digital data is lost or misinterpreted, the meaning of large blocks of related data can completely change. This problem can be mitigated by designing the digital system for robustness. For example, a parity bit or other error-detecting or error-correcting code can be inserted into the signal path so that if less than a certain fraction of the data is corrupted, the system can determine that this has occurred and possibly uncorrupt the data, or ask for the corrupted data to be resent. In a state-machine, the state transition logic can be designed to catch all unused states and trigger a reset sequence or other error recovery routine. For example, it is standard practice in embedded software design to fill unused programme memory with interrupt instructions that point to an error recovery routine, to help guard against a failure that corrupts the microcontroller's instruction pointer which could otherwise cause random code to be executed.

Construction

A digital circuit is often constructed from small electronic circuits called logic gates. Each logic gate represents a function of boolean logic. A logic gate is an arrangement of electrically controlled switches. The output is an electrical flow or voltage, that can, in turn, control more logic gates. Logic gates often use the fewest number of transistors in order to reduce their size, power consumption and cost, and increase their reliability. Manufactured as integrated circuits, they are the least expensive implementation when made in large volumes. They are usually designed by engineers using electronic design automation software. Another form of digital circuit is constructed from lookup tables, (many sold as "programmable logic devices", though other kinds of PLDs exist). Lookup tables can perform all the same functions as machines based on logic gates, but lookup tables can be easily reprogrammed without changing the wiring. This means that a designer can often repair errors without changing the arrangement of wires. Therefore, in small volume products, programmable logic devices are often the preferred solution. They are usually designed by engineers using electronic design automation software. When the volumes are medium to large, and the logic can be slow, or involves complex algorithms or sequences, often a small microcontroller is programmed to make an embedded system. These are usually programmed by software engineers. When only one digital circuit is needed, and its design is totally customized, as for a factory production line controller, the conventional solution is a programmable logic controller, or PLC. These are usually programmed by electricians, using ladder logic.

Structure of Digital Systems

Engineers use many methods to minimize logic functions, in order to reduce the complexity, and thus the number of errors and the expense of digital circuits. The most widely used method is the application of a minimization algorithm within a CAD system, although historically, truth tables, Karnaugh Maps, and Boolean algebra have also been used. Representations are crucial to an engineer's design of digital circuits. Some analysis methods only work with particular representations. The classical way to represent a digital circuit is with an equivalent set of logic gates. Another way, often with the least electronics, is to construct an equivalent system of electronic switches (usually transistors). One of the easiest ways is to simply have a memory containing a truth table. The inputs are fed into the address of the memory, and the data outputs of the memory become the outputs. For automated analysis, these representations have digital file formats that can be processed by computer programmes. Most digital engineers are very careful to select computer programmes ("tools") with compatible file formats. To choose representations, engineers consider types of digital systems. Most digital systems divide into "combinatorial systems" and "sequential systems". A combinatorial system always presents the same output when given the same inputs. It is basically a representation of a set of logic functions, as already discussed. A sequential system is a combinatorial system with some of the outputs fed back as inputs. This makes the digital machine perform a "sequence" of operations. The simplest sequential system is probably a flip flop, a mechanism that represents a binary digit or "bit". Sequential systems are often designed as state machines. In this way, engineers can design a system's gross behavior, and even test it in a simulation, without considering all the details of the logic functions.

Sequential systems divide into two further subcategories. "Synchronous" sequential systems change state all at once, when a "clock" signal changes state. "Asynchronous" sequential systems propagate changes whenever inputs change. Synchronous sequential systems are made of well-characterized asynchronous circuits such as flip-flops, that change only when the clock changes, and which have carefully designed timing margins. The usual way to implement a synchronous sequential state machine is divide it into a piece of combinatorial logic and a set of flip flops called a "state register." Each time a clock signal ticks, the state register captures the feedback generated from the previous state of the combinatorial logic, and feeds it back as an unchanging input to the combinatorial part of the state machine. The fastest rate of the clock is set by the most time-consuming logic calculation in the combinatorial logic. The state register is just a representation of a binary number. If the states in the state machine are numbered (easy to arrange), the logic function is just some logic that produces the number of the next state. In comparison, asynchronous systems are very hard to design because all possible states, in all possible timings must be considered. The usual method is to construct a table of the minimum and maximum time that each such state can exist, and then adjust the circuit to minimize the number of such states, and force the circuit to periodically wait for all of its parts to enter a compatible state. (This is called "self-resynchronization.") Without such careful design, it is easy to accidentally produce asynchronous logic that is "unstable", that is, real electronics will have unpredictable results because of the cumulative delays caused by small variations in the values of the electronic components. Certain circuits (such as the synchronizer flip-flops, switch debouncers, and the like which allow external unsynchronized signals to enter synchronous logic circuits) are inherently asynchronous in their design and must be analyzed as such. As of now (2005), almost all digital machines are synchronous designs because it is much easier to create and verify a synchronous design. However, asynchronous logic is thought to be superior, if it can be made to work, because its speed is not constrained by an arbitrary clock; instead, it simply runs at the maximum speed permitted by the propagation rates of the logic gates from which it is constructed. Building an asynchronous circuit using faster parts implicitly makes the circuit "go" faster. More generally, many digital systems are data flow machines. These are usually designed using synchronous register transfer logic, using hardware description languages such as VHDL or Verilog. In register transfer logic, binary numbers are stored in groups of flip flops called registers.

The outputs of each register are a bundle of wires called a "bus" that carries that number to other calculations. A calculation is simply a piece of combinatorial logic. Each calculation also has an output bus, and these may be connected to the inputs of several registers. Sometimes a register will have a multiplexer on its input, so that it can store a number from any one of several buses. Alternatively, the outputs of several items may be connected to a bus through buffers that can turn off the output of all of the devices except one. A sequential state machine controls when each register accepts new data from its input. In the 1980s, some researchers discovered that almost all synchronous register-transfer machines could be converted to asynchronous designs by using first-in-first-out synchronization logic. In this scheme, the digital machine is characterized as a set of data flows. In each step of the flow, an asynchronous "synchronization circuit" determines when the outputs of that step are valid, and presents a signal that says, "grab the data" to the stages that use that stage's inputs. It turns out that just a few relatively simple synchronization circuits are needed. The most general-purpose register-transfer logic machine is a computer.

This is basically an automatic binary abacus. The control unit of a computer is usually designed as a microprogramme run by a microsequencer. A microprogramme is much like a player-piano roll. Each table entry or "word" of the microprogramme commands the state of every bit that controls the computer. The sequencer then counts, and the count addresses the memory or combinatorial logic machine that contains the microprogramme. The bits from the microprogramme control the arithmetic logic unit, memory and other parts of the computer, including the microsequencer itself.

In this way, the complex task of designing the controls of a computer is reduced to a simpler task of programming a relatively independent collection of much simpler logic machines. Computer architecture is a specialized engineering activity that tries to arrange the registers, calculation logic, buses and other parts of the computer in the best way for some purpose. Computer architects have applied large amounts of ingenuity to computer design to reduce the cost and increase the speed and immunity to programming errors of computers. An increasingly common goal is to reduce the power used in a battery-powered computer system, such as a cell-phone. Many computer architects serve an extended apprenticeship as microprogramrs. “Specialized computers” are usually a conventional computer with a special-purpose microprogramme.

Design for Testability

A large logic machine (say, with more than a hundred logical variables) can have an astronomical number of possible states. Obviously, in the factory, testing every state is impractical if testing each state takes a microsecond, and there are more states than the number of microseconds since the universe began. Unfortunately, this ridiculous-sounding case is typical. Fortunately, large logic machines are almost always designed as assemblies of smaller logic machines. To save time, the smaller sub-machines are isolated by permanently-installed “design for test” circuitry, and are tested independently. One common test scheme known as “scan design” moves test bits serially (one after another) from external test equipment through one or more serial shift registers known as “scan chains”. Serial scans have only one or two wires to carry the data, and minimize the physical size and expense of the infrequently-used test logic. After all the test data bits are in place, the design is reconfigured to be in “normal mode” and one or more clock pulses are applied, to test for faults (e.g. stuck-at low or stuck-at high) and capture the test result into flip-flops and/or latches in the scan shift register(s). Finally, the result of the test is shifted out to the block boundary and compared against the predicted “good machine” result. In a board-test environment, serial to parallel testing has been formalized with a standard called “JTAG” (named after the “Joint Testing Acting Group” that proposed it). Another common testing scheme provides a test mode that forces some part of the logic machine to enter a “test cycle.” The test cycle usually exercises large independent parts of the machine.

Trade-offs

Several numbers determine the practicality of a system of digital logic. Engineers explored numerous electronic devices to get an ideal combination of speed, low cost and reliability. The cost of a logic gate is crucial. In the 1930s, the earliest digital logic systems were constructed from telephone relays because these were inexpensive and relatively reliable. After that, engineers always used the cheapest available electronic switches that could still fulfill the requirements. The earliest integrated circuits were a happy accident. They were constructed not to save money, but to save weight, and permit the Apollo Guidance Computer to control an inertial guidance system for a spacecraft. The first integrated circuit logic gates cost nearly $50 (in 1960 dollars, when an engineer earned $10,000/year). To everyone’s surprise, by the time the circuits were mass-produced, they had become the least-expensive method of constructing digital logic. Improvements in this technology have driven all subsequent improvements in cost. With the rise of integrated circuits, reducing the absolute number of chips used represented another way to save costs. The goal of a designer is not just to make the simplest circuit, but to keep the component count down. Sometimes this results in slightly more complicated designs with respect to the underlying digital logic but nevertheless reduces the number of components, board size, and even power consumption. For example, in some logic families, NAND gates are the simplest digital gate to build. All other logical operations can be implemented by NAND gates. If a circuit already required a single NAND gate, and a single chip normally carried four NAND gates, then the remaining gates could be used to implement other logical operations like logical and. This could eliminate the need for a separate chip containing those different types of gates. The "reliability" of a logic gate describes its mean time between failure (MTBF). Digital machines often have millions of logic gates. Also, most digital machines are "optimized" to reduce their cost. The result is that often, the failure of a single logic gate will cause a digital machine to stop working. Digital machines first became useful when the MTBF for a switch got above a few hundred hours. Even so, many of these machines had complex, well-rehearsed repair procedures, and would be nonfunctional for hours because a tube burned-out, or a moth got stuck in a relay. Modern transistorized integrated circuit logic gates have MTBFs of nearly a trillion (1x10^12) hours, and need them because they have so many logic gates. The "fan out" describes how many logic inputs can be controlled by a single logic output. The minimum practical fan out is about five. Modern electronic logic using CMOS transistors for switches have fanouts near fifty, and can sometimes go much higher. The "switching speed" describes how many times per second an inverter (an electronic representation of a "logical not" function) can change from true to false and back. Faster logic can accomplish more operations in less time. Digital logic first became useful when switching speeds got above fifty hertz, because that was faster than a team of humans operating mechanical calculators. Modern electronic digital logic routinely switches at five gigahertz ($5x10^9$ hertz), and some laboratory systems switch at more than a terahertz ($1x10^{12}$ hertz).

Automated Design Tools

To save costly engineering effort, much of the effort of designing large logic machines has been automated. The computer programmes are called "electronic design automation tools" or just "EDA." Simple truth table-style descriptions of logic are often optimized with EDA that automatically produces reduced systems of logic gates or smaller lookup tables that still produce the desired outputs. Most practical algorithms for optimizing large logic systems use algebraic manipulations or binary decision diagrams, and there are promising experiments with genetic algorithms and annealing optimizations. To automate costly engineering effort, some EDA can take state tables that describe state machines and automatically produce a truth table for the combinatorial part of a state machine. The state table is a piece of text that lists each state, and the conditions that can exit that state. It is common for the truth tables of such computer-generated state-machines to be optimized with logic-minimization software. This is a simple example of how complex logic machines are broken into simpler parts. Often, real logic systems are designed as a series of sub-projects, which are combined using a "tool flow". The tool flow is usually a "script", a simplified computer language that can invoke the software design tools in the right order. Tool flows for large logic systems such as microprocessors can be thousands of commands long, and combine the work of hundreds of engineers. Writing and debugging tool flows is an established engineering specialty in companies that produce complex logic machines. The tool flow usually terminates in a detailed computer file or set of files that describe how to physically construct the logic machine. Often it consists of instructions to draw the transistors and wires on an integrated circuit or a printed circuit board. Parts of tool flows are "debugged" by testing the outputs of simulated logic machines against expected inputs. The test tools take computer files with sets of inputs and outputs, and highlight discrepancies between the simulated behavior and the expected behavior. These test data are usually called "test vectors." Often, the test vectors are preserved and used in the factory to test that newly constructed logic machines work correctly.

Non-electronic Logic

It is possible to construct non-electronic digital mechanisms. In principle, any technology capable of representing discrete states and representing logic operations could be used to build mechanical logic. Danny Hillis, co-author of The Connection Machine, once built a working computer from Tinker Toys, string, a brick, and a sharpened pencil, which is supposed to be in the Houston Museum of Science. Hydraulic, pneumatic and mechanical versions of logic gates exist and are used in situations where electricity cannot be used. The first two types are considered under the heading of fluidics. One application of fluidic logic is in military hardware that is likely to be exposed to a nuclear electromagnetic pulse (nuclear EMP, or NEMP) that would destroy any electrical circuits. Mechanical logic is frequently used in inexpensive controllers, such as those in washing machines. Famously, the first computer design, by Charles Babbage, was designed to use mechanical logic. Mechanical logic might also be used in very small computers that could be built by nanotechnology. Another example is that if two particular enzymes are required to prevent the construction of a particular protein, this is the equivalent of a biological "NAND" gate.

Early Developments

The discovery of superconductivity has enabled the development of Rapid Single Flux Quantum (RSFQ) circuit technology, which uses Josephson junctions instead of transistors. Most recently, attempts are being made to construct purely optical computing systems capable of processing digital information using nonlinear optical elements.

Pre-electronic Computing Devices

The first high-speed electronic automatic computer, the ENIAC, was put into operation at Aberdeen Proving Ground in 1947 and introduced an era of possibilities never before available to the field of computation. It was one of the most significant developments of our time because it enabled us to expand out knowledge in almost every field through limitless quantities of accurate, inexpensive computation performed at high speeds. Prior to the advent of the ENIAC, however, were thousands of years of development to produce devices which could remove the drudgery of computation. The very first requirement was the invention of a means to record numbers. Various means were used in early times to do this. The Hebrews, Greeks, and Romans, for example, used the letters of their alphabets to represent numbers, but these systems did not lend themselves to easy computation of mathematical problems. Anyone familiar with the Roman numeral system can imagine the difficulty in multiplying CCXVII by XXIX to get MMMMMMCCXCIII. In spite of clumsy systems of recording numbers Egyptians, Greeks and Romans were nonetheless able to perform computations. A method of finger computation evolved and at some time prior to 600 B.C. an ingenious calculating device, the abacus, was developed and used by them. This calculating device employed a place system and was built around the base ten. Strangely enough it seems never to have occurred to those people to write numerals in this same system. That idea was to come many years later from India. The Roman-type abacus found its way to the Orient around the twelfth century A.D. and today it still remains the principal means of computing in China and Japan. It is a simple device and a skilled operator can add, subtract, multiply, and divide with amazing speed. In fact, the champion abacus operator of Japan some years ago defeated a man using an electric calculating machine. The achievement of such speed and accuracy on the abacus, however, requires considerable training, which is one disadvantage of the abacus. The modern abacus consists of a rectangular frame with a number of rods or wires. These rods are divided into two unequal portions by a transverse bar. On the upper, smaller portion of each rod are two beads and on the lower portion five beads. (The modern Japanese abacus has one bead above and four beads below the bar.) The whole acts as a numerical register, each rod representing a decimal order as in our familiar "arabic" notation. The chief disadvantage of the abacus is that the operator must perform his calculations mentally. The device merely stores his results step by step. It does not perform the actual calculations as does the modern desk calculator. As mentioned previously, in spite of the use of the abacus by the Greeks and Romans the Western peoples did not develop a convenient system of numeration. This was accomplished by Hindu scholars nearly two thousand years ago. They developed the symbols and the place system which enables us to express any number, no matter how large or small it may be. This system is easy to learn and simple to use. It is built around the base ten, although any number might have been used. It is possible that the base of ten was selected because man had always used his fingers for counting. The Hindu numerals with their place system were carried westward by merchants and scholars and finally reached Spain in the tenth century. However, it was not until the fifteenth century that they finally prevailed in the Western World and took their present form 0, 1, 2, 3, 4, 5, 6, 7, 8, and 9. This development opened the door to modern mathematics. Around 1600 John Napier, a Scottish mathematician, invented logarithms and also prepared a convenient multiplication table on pieces of wood or bone. "Napier's bones," as they were called, had no practical value but his logarithms did. Around 1632 William Oughtred in England made the first slide rule by inscribing logarithms on wood or ivory. The slide rule is an analog computer which is still widely used by scientists and engineers throughout the entire world. Shortly after Napier's achievements, around 1642, Blaise Pascal in France constructed an adding machine that resembled the modern desk calculator.

This machine consisted of a series of ratchet-driven wheels with the numbers 0 to 9 on them. Although it was a simple device and could only add and subtract it embodied one very important development which is an essential part of the digital computing technique, namely a means of making the "carry over" into an automatic process. It also indicated the possibility of multiplying numbers by successive addition. For the first time a machine was built that approached automatic computing because it removed a function from the operator to the machine. In 1671 Gottfried Leibnitz, in Germany, invented the stepped wheel, a cylindrical drum having nine teeth of increasing length along its surface. When the drum was rotated, a gear sliding on an axis parallel to that of the drum engaged some of the teeth, thereby undergoing a corresponding number of rotation steps. The Leibnitz wheel made it possible to multiply quickly by repeated additions. From then onwards a variety of improved calculating machines were devised, all based on the original idea of wheels moved around in steps, and by the nineteenth century commercial models began to appear. The Thomas machine (France) embodied this principle and, starting in 1822, was the first to be manufactured for widespread use. It was a dependable, crank- operated, four-process machine. In 1885 Burroughs, in the United states, produced an adding machine and in 1902 the first machine with completely automatic multiplication and division was built by Rechnitzer, also in the United states. Several machines were designed in various countries and by 1920, with the fully automatic Monroe machine, we reach the stage of desk calculators familiar to us in banks, offices, and laboratories. These are the machines that do most of the world's computation, the modern ones being electrically driven and assuming more and more of the operator's functions. These machines, however, are limited in scope and require the constant attention of a human operator to supply them with numbers and to record on paper the result of each stage of the calculation before proceeding to the next one. They do save time and mental effort but they are not fast enough where very large quantities of numerical data have to be handled.

It must also be noted that they are not true forerunners of the modern electronic computers. The principles of modern computers, albeit in mechanical form, were laid down by Charles Babbage in England. starting in 1812 he attempted to build an automatic mechanical calculator. He was familiar with Mullers idea for a difference engine (1786) and Jaques' idea for controlling a loom by means of punched holes (1775). He incorporated both ideas and actually made models of a difference engine which was card controlled. Technical problems of construction were too great for mechanical engineering of that period and the computer was never finished. Later, Babbage conceived an even more ambitious idea. He worked on the design of an analytical engine, which, had it been built, would have incorporated ideas familiar to the modern digital computer.

Babbage's new idea was to extend the capabilities of the difference engine so that it could not merely add and print, but also multiply, divide, and call for new data from its human operator. In order for the analytical engine to perform the tasks expected of it, it was necessary to express all the possible instructions to the machine in the form of stereotyped commands. Such a procedure is known as the logic or the logical design of a computer, and Babbage's engine was strikingly modern in regard to its logical design. Except for the need of a human attendant to read into the machine values from mathematical tables, this engine was logically parallel to most of the recent automatic computers. Naturally the speed of computation would have been far below that of the modern calculator (it could perform one addition per second), since Babbage had to use the purely mechanical techniques available in his day.

A significant part of his design for an analytical engine was the use of a "store" for holding the partial results of arithmetic operations performed in what he called the "mill." To feed numbers into the machine he proposed a system using patterns of holes punched in cards, while the results of calculations were to be presented by a mechanism which would set up the appropriate numerals in type ready for printing. Another proposal was that the engine should be capable of deciding on a course of action in the light of partial results obtained. He called this the "control." All these ideas have become features of the modern digital computer, and it is mainly because of them that our present-day machines are so fast in operation and so versatile in their range of calculations.

The next important development along this line was made by Hollerith and Powers during 1880 — 1890. Working for the United States Census Bureau they required some means of handling large masses of information. This led to the development of the first key punch, the first sorter, and the first tabulator, all using large punched cards. The patterns of round holes in the cards were formed by using a crude hand-punching device. The cards could be sorted into the series or order wanted, and then tabulated to reduce the census data to manageable form. Hollerith did not use the punched cards to control the course of computation, but simply used the holes in the cards to carry information. Hollerith and Powers also employed the electromagnetic techniques in their machine, that is, information on the card (hole or no hole) was converted into electric impulses, and the electric impulses actuated devices known as relays.

In 1925, at the Massachusetts Institute of Technology, Dr. Vannevar Bush and his associates began studying the problem of designing a machine to solve differential equations. In 1927, Dr. Bush started work on a mechanical differential analyzer. He experimented with mechanisms that would integrate, add, multiply, etc., and methods of connecting them together in a machine. Originally he made use of electrical currents flowing through watt-hour meters, which integrate the electrical power absorbed by circuits attached to them. Later he reverted to the mechanical integrators of the wheel and disc type. A major part of the success of the machine depended on a device whereby a very small turning force would do a rather large amount of work. By careful design of the discs and of the wheel mountings, Dr. Bush was able to make the integrators accurate, and, by introducing torque amplifiers to take the loads off the wheels so that they rotated very freely, he was able to reduce the slippage between the wheel and the disc. He combined a frame with the integrators, which contained movable shafts, changeable gears and couplings, input hand-wheels and output recording pens for producing a readable result. By 1930 the first differential analyzer was finished. It was entirely mechanical, having no electrical parts except the motors.

Its disadvantage was the great deal of work required in changing from one problem to another. This involved undoing old mechanical connections between shafts and setting up new ones. For this reason the design of a second analyzer was begun in 1935, on which all connections could be made electrically. As early as 1932 personnel of the Ballistic Section at Aberdeen Proving Ground had investigated the possible use of the Differential Analyzer for ballistic computations. The machine was used to compute numerous trajectories including a set sufficient for the preparation of a complete range table. It was also tested on interior ballistic problems. A careful study and evaluation of the results of this investigation led to the following conclusions:

1. Such a machine could be built at Aberdeen Proving Ground.
2. The machine could perform various kinds of ballistic computations with the necessary accuracy.
3. Operation and maintenance would require no unusual skill.
4. The speed of the machine was such that it would insure greatly increased output of work by the Ballistic Section in any emergency.
5. It could perform routine work at a smaller total expenditure of funds.
6. Its use in the preparation of range tables would replace numerous complicated and indirect methods by simple, uniform and direct process.
7. Its use would permit the investigation of various problems, the solution of which was necessary to any advance in ballistic theory or practice but which previously could not be studied because existing methods required a prohibitive amount of computing labor.

It was decided to use the Bush Differential Analyzer at Aberdeen Proving Ground and its installation was completed in 1935. After final adjustment and trials it was used in the computation of two firing tables. These were completed with gratifying results by mid 1936.

The Bush Differential Analyzer, an analog device, was installed under the direction of Major James Guion, who was in charge of the Ballistic Computing Section at Aberdeen Proving Ground at that time. Major Guion had been quick to realise the value of this continuous variable calculator to the computational needs of the Ordnance Department. The availability of this machine and the experience that was gained in its use were invaluable to the Ordnance Department during the crucial transition period prior to America's entry into World War II.

The analyzer installed at APG had ten integrating units and provisions for two input and two output tables. However, despite its value as an important mechanical aid to computation it had certain limitations. The torque amplifier, for example, although simple in mechanical design, frequently failed toward the end of a long trajectory run with the loss of the preceding computation and an appreciable delay associated with its repair. This type of failure and the interference that it caused with the carrying out of computations at the Ballistic Research Laboratory led to extensive study to overcome this problem.

At the outbreak of World War II in Europe the officer in charge of ballistic computations at APG was Lt. P. N. Gillon. He immediately recognized the immensity of the task that would fall upon the Ordnance Department in the event of United States participation in the war and this prompted him to seek both marked improvement in mechanical aids to computation and augmented facilities for its accomplishment. A number of very important things were undertaken to accomplish this purpose.

The Moore School of Electrical Engineering of the University of Pennsylvania had a Bush Differential Analyzer of somewhat larger capacity than the one at Aberdeen Proving Ground. It had fourteen integrating units instead of ten. Therefore the Ordnance Department awarded a contract to the University of Pennsylvania for the utilization of this device. Several additional contracts were later awarded to the University to carry out different phases of the increasingly important role which it was to play in the computation activities of the Ordnance Department during the war.

Lt. P. N. Gillon, in his capacity as officer in charge of ballistic computations, conferred frequently with Dean Pender, Professor Brainerd, and their associates at the Moore School in order to effect proper coordination of the computational work at the two localities, Philadelphia and Aberdeen. There was a very talented group at the Moore School under the direction of Professor Brainerd and as a result of Lt. Gillon's discussions with them Assistant Professor Weygand undertook to develop an electronic torque amplifier to replace the mechanical torque amplifiers on the Bush Differential Analyzers. This work was eminently successful and, in addition, photoelectric followers were developed by the Moore School group for both the input and output tables of the analyzer. As a result of these accomplishments the productive capacity of the analyzers at both the Moore School and Aberdeen Proving Ground were enhanced by at least an order of magnitude.

During World War II the Bush Differential Analyzer was used primarily to compute trajectories for firing tables and to prepare trajectory charts for use with VT fuzes. The machine could compute a 60-second trajectory in about 15 minutes, whereas a human operator using a desk calculator required about 20 hours to perform the same computation. Its value to the Ordnance Department during the war years was tremendous.

The next major development, prior to the advent of the high-speed electronic automatic computer, came in 1944 when Howard Aiken, in cooperation with some IBM engineers and some graduate students at Harvard University, completed the Mark I Relay Computer, also called the Automatic Sequence- Controlled Calculator.

This machine performed thousands of calculating steps, one after another, according to a scheme fixed ahead of time. Its individual operations were automatic, once the punched tape fixing the chain of operations had been put on the machine, and it was sequence-controlled, since control over the sequence of its operations was built into the machine.

The principle of operation of the Mark I Relay Computer was electro- mechanical. It combined the two applications of the concept of state, that is, the information for processing was represented by patterns of open and closed relays (like the patterns of holes and no holes which Babbage used).

Although the machine was efficient, fast, and capable of solving a variety of problems its speed could not approach that of the electronic computer, which is the next state in the development of computers and the subject of this monograph. Nevertheless, it holds a permanent place in the history of development of calculating machines, since it was the first automatic machine to be completed. Two IBM Relay Calculators were used for a short time but were not successful. Two Bell Relay Computers were used. They were accurate, but slow and required expert maintenance. Dust and humidity adversely affected their operation.

However, many useful results were obtained from the twin Bell Relay Computers during many years of successful operation. One good feature of the Bell Relay Machines was that they would run 16 hours overnight, unattended. A problem regularly would be placed on the computer at 4:00 PM. The next morning, arriving operating personnel would find the problem solved and the machine waiting, or the machine still feverishly running the problem to a successful conclusion. Many times, if it was felt that the machines would complete a problem during the night, a new problem was set before the machine for it to tackle until personnel arrived the next morning. This mode of operation increased the productivity of the computers with a minimum of personnel. Of course, once in a while a dirty relay would cause a stoppage, for the Bell A and the Bell B would either run without error or not run at all.)

Microelectronics

Microelectronics is a subfield of electronics. Microelectronics, as the name suggests, is related to the study and manufacture of electronic components which are very small. These devices are made from semiconductors using a process known as photolithography. Many components of normal electronic design are available in microelectronic equivalent: transistors, capacitors, inductors, resistors, diodes and of course insulators and conductors can all be found in microelectronic devices.

Digital integrated circuits consist mostly of transistors. Analog circuits commonly contain resistors and capacitors as well. Inductors are used in some high frequency analog circuits, but tend to occupy large chip area if used at low frequencies; gyrators can replace them.

As techniques improve, the size of microelectronic components continue to decrease. At smaller scales, the effects of minor circuit elements such as interconnections may become more important. These are called parasitic effects, and the goal of the microelectronics design engineer is to find ways to compensate for or to minimize these effects, while always delivering smaller, faster, and cheaper devices.

The Microelectronics Industry Structure

High-volume, low-cost electronic packaging technologies are critical for many of today's consumer electronics markets. Control of electronic packaging technologies provides companies with the competitive capabilities to design and manufacture smaller and more sophisticated consumer products like camcorders, cameras, and digital databooks. With innovative merging of semiconductor, packaging, and display technologies, also evolving are second- and third-generation technologies that will increasingly affect the design parameters of future products. Firms with capabilities in materials, equipment, design, and advanced manufacturing will be the future producers of low-cost electronic packages.

In Japan, unlike in the United States, most companies that are heavily invested in downstream electronics markets are also vertically integrated and heavily invested in upstream technologies. Six vertically integrated firms produced 85% of Japan's semiconductors, 80% of its computers, 80% of its telecommunications equipment, and 60% of its consumer electronics products. In the United States, approximately 80% of all semiconductors are manufactured by merchant firms that manufacture few or no other upstream materials and equipment or downstream products. The absence of upstream involvement can be readily seen. This U.S. electronic industry's depiction of the electronics technology chain shows a total neglect in identifying those products that need to be targeted (Gover and Gwyn 1992, 18). Instead, it describes the broad range of markets for which the technologies can be applied, without providing the roadmaps for technology and component development. While upstream electronics technology has a significant impact on downstream market development, the technology can be most effectively developed with a knowledge of specific product development requirements.

A firm's involvement in downstream products and markets provides the vision for setting priorities in developing future upstream technologies. Electronic packaging and other component technologies are becoming the critical technologies for advanced product designs and functions. Japanese firms have developed dominant positions in display technologies, in the miniaturization of low-cost, high-volume electronic packages, and in the development of advanced manufacturing equipment for ultrasmall component assembly. In order to introduce its "next-generation" products, Japanese firms have had to push the development of a number of technologies:

- fine-pitch devices

- advanced flex circuit designs
- cost-effective flip chip technology
- cost-effective high-density printed circuit boards
- cost-effective connector technology
- advanced flat panel display technology
- small passive components
- small, low-cost package assembly equipment
- high-speed pick and place equipment for ultrasmall components

These developments now provide Japanese firms with the ability to either design-in greater functionality and performance for any given size product, or to reduce the size or cost of products at any given level of functionality or performance. These "intermediate" packaging capabilities are expected to provide much of the value added for future electronic products from supercomputers to cameras. In fact, Sony argues that 65% of a product's value added comes from key component and device contributions, as compared to only 12% coming from final assembly operations. Therefore, some Japanese firms are reducing dependence on suppliers for key components as a strategy to improve financial performance. To focus development efforts in these high-value-added "intermediate" device markets, firms need a vision of new product concepts or next-generation product developments.

Sony's historical success is based on a strategy of developing key components to support new product developments such as the transistor radio in 1955, the Trinitron in 1968, the Betamax in 1975, the Walkman in 1979, the CD player in 1982, and the 8 mm camcorder in 1985. Sony's introduction of the Trinitron color television was dependent upon the development of its single electron gun with three electron beams and an aperture grill. After eight years of development, Sony's technological breakthrough was considered the next generation beyond the shadow mask developed by RCA. Its Trinitron technology continues to provide Sony with a basic technology for use in advanced high definition television applications. Sony also developed the charge-coupled device (CCD) as an image-sensing device. After two years of basic research, Sony took five years to produce the first small CCD camera for use in the industrial market; it took five more years to develop the mass production technology required to enter the consumer market. Miniaturization of the video camera gave Sony a dominant position in the 8 mm video camera market.

Sharp has used a similar key device development strategy. It introduced the first commercial application of a LCD in an electronic calculator in 1973. Since then, it has pioneered the application of LCDs in Japanese word processors and PCs in

1986, the development of the world's first 14-inch color thin-film-transfer (TFT) LCD panel in 1988, and the development of LCD video projectors in 1989. Sharp's Hi-8 LCD ViewCam, introduced in 1992, was the world's first camcorder with a 4-inch color TFT LCD monitor. In 1993, Sharp's ViewCam surpassed both Matsushita and JVC products to take second place in the video camera market. Sony now plans a similar LCD camcorder to respond to Sharp's innovation. Ability to take the lead in critical component technologies is vital to developing market leadership.

In support of next-generation product development and miniaturization goals, the Japanese electronics industry is investing in upstream technologies. In 1992 Lloyd Thorndyke, CEO of DataMax, found that electronic packaging technologies of Japan's supercomputer makers were highly advanced. He commented on this in his report—I was told that the Japanese super computer companies overtook U.S. companies in super computer packaging five years ago, and that now the lead is insurmountable. I tend to agree, but for a different reason. The newer technologies require increasingly greater capital and tooling funding to enter production. However, most U.S. super computer companies are relatively small, have low volumes, and limited capital money (1993, 31).

With their heavy commitment to consumer electronics products, Japanese firms have created a tremendous demand for upstream electronic technologies, including DRAM memory chips and many intermediate electronic component and parts technologies. Growing domination of these intermediate component and packaging technologies, including video display technology, provides competitive advantages for future product developments. For example, advanced display technology, integrating both display and packaging technologies, is expected to pull the development of other microelectronics technology into new consumer product applications ranging from hand-held computers to high definition television sets.

These conclusions are neither new nor surprising. The Council on Competitiveness reported (1991, 35) that the United States was losing badly or had already lost important electronic technologies in display materials, ceramics for electronics, electronic packaging materials, gallium arsenide materials, silicon materials, integrated circuit fabrication and test equipment, microelectronics memory chips, multichip packaging systems, printed circuit board technology, electroluminescent displays, plasma displays, vacuum fluorescent displays, and optical information storage. The Computer Systems Policy Project, composed of the major U.S. computer manufacturers, had come to a similar conclusion in 1990, determining that the United States was behind in displays, manufacturing technology, ultralarge-scale integrated (ULSI) circuit fabrication equipment and facilities, microelectronics, and electronics packaging. These studies identified six areas as needing special attention: optoelectronics, electronic packaging, electronics and semiconductor materials, display technology,

ULSI fabrication equipment, and memory chips. It was estimated that these six technologies would represent a world market worth of over $100 billion by the year 2000. What is more important, it is expected that whoever dominates these areas of technology will also dominate the world market for electronics products that is expected to exceed $2 trillion in revenues.

It was clearly evident to the JTEC panel that Japanese companies do not intend to give their competitive advantages away. Recently, Sony has limited the number of outsiders who visit its operations, for fear of losing proprietary information. In cases where outsiders are allowed to visit Sony, they are shown production technology that the company is already selling to outside customers. The same is true with Matsushita, the world leader in semiconductor insertion equipment, where advanced equipment developed in-house is used for several years before being made available on the open market. As product life cycles continue to shorten, six-month or one-year delays in product availability can mean the difference between substantial profits and significant losses over the short life of a product. The component requisition problems are not political issues but rather competitiveness issues. Pragmatic business executives are not likely to sell their advanced microelectronics technologies or equipment if doing so creates competitors in critical downstream markets. Even U.S. semiconductor firms stopped selling components to downstream calculator assemblers once they realised the potential for profit in producing calculators themselves. As Texas Instrument's chairman Patrick Haggerty reflected (1976), "TI's biggest mistake may have been in not integrating forward into portable radios in the early 1950s." It was the development of portable radios that gave Sony its first major consumer market success.

Microelectronics in Japan

The purpose of this JTEC study is to evaluate Japan's electronic manufacturing and packaging capabilities within the context of global economic competition. To carry out this study, the JTEC panel evaluated the framework of the Japanese consumer electronics industry and various technological and organisational factors that are likely to determine who will win and lose in the marketplace. This study begins with a brief overview of the electronics industry, especially as it operates in Japan today. Succeeding chapters examine the electronics infrastructure in Japan and take an in-depth look at the central issues of product development in order to identify those parameters that will determine future directions for electronic packaging technologies.

Our lives are being revolutionized by electronics. The ways we work, communicate, shop, bank, travel, and learn are changing radically. And whereas natural resources, labor, and capital once determined a nation's wealth, today technology — in aerospace, computers, telecommunications, and consumer electronics — significantly affects a nation's wealth and security. Communications, computers, and control technologies are merging to create new multimedia capabilities for use in business, education, and entertainment. Advanced technologies like superconductivity promise a whole new range of capabilities in another decade. Miniaturization of existing products will put libraries and supercomputers into our briefcases. The range of future opportunities is bounded only by the ability of our industries to utilize these new capabilities in developing next-generation products.

Production of high-quality, low-cost consumer electronics products is dependent on proficiency in electronic packaging technologies. Continuous improvement of packaging and related technologies has provided the impetus for development of new and improved consumer electronic products; likewise, consumer demand for new and improved electronic products at reasonable prices has provided the impetus for development of increasingly sophisticated electronic packaging. The most explosive improvements in low-cost, high-volume packaging for consumer products have been in Japan, precisely because Japan has been relentlessly pursuing the markets for consumer electronics. The United States is recognized for developing new technologies; Japan is recognized for continuously improving "old" technologies and pushing the technological limits of their applications in order to keep their costs down. In doing so, Japanese electronics firms have pushed electronic packaging into a whole new realm.

In the past, the term "electronic packaging" referred to a small number of formats for encasing electronic components, including integrated circuits, so they could readily and reliably be installed in electronic end-products. The principal packaging types were through hole, surface mount, tape automated bonding, single-chip, and multichip, and also packaging configurations like dual inline packages (DIP), small inline packages (SIP), and quad flat packages (QFP). Generally, the companies that specialized in manufacturing electronic packages did not participate in integrating them into the final products.

During several of the JTEC panel's site visits in Japan, it was evident that electronic packaging suppliers are integrating forward into both functional modules and integrated assemblies. TDK is making complex multichip modules with densities of 33 units per cubic centimeter. Murata is using its materials technology competence to develop and sell radio frequency (RF) components. Most suppliers now develop their own equipment and provide customers with the assembly equipment required to utilize their new components. At the same time, some of the major electronics companies are manufacturing more of their own electronic components based on in-house R&D. Sony, for example, manufactures about 65% of the key components for its compact disc player and 45% of the components for its 8 mm camcorder. In-house advances in liquid crystal display (LCD), charge-couple device (CCD), and electronic packaging technologies were all needed to realise these products. Consumer products that have been pulling the development of technological advances in electronic packaging include VCRs, cellular telephones, camcorders, personal digital assistants, and notebook computers. The goals that define the roadmaps for electronic packaging development for these products are miniaturization, portability, increased functionality, and cost reduction — in order to capture and retain consumer markets. These goals are being achieved through reduction of parts sizes and increased integration of technologies and functions. Electronic packaging technologies have seen increased pin counts, reduced pin pitch, and increased functional densities through the application of surface mounting techniques. Reduction in sizes of parts includes reductions in battery and display dimensions. For example, the reduction in the overall size of cellular phones from 500 cc in 1987 to 150 cc in 1991 was due to a variety of reductions in parts sizes that included the following:

- Power amp size was reduced by reducing part sizes and ICs.
- Filter size was reduced by reducing part sizes and using advanced designs.
- Controller size was reduced through development of special ASICs.
- Battery size was reduced after intermittent receiving methods cut power consumption.
- Board size was reduced by using smaller and thinner 0.5 mm pin pitch LSIs and 1.0 mm x 0.5 mm passive parts in new circuit design.

Electronic packages now are becoming hybrid assemblies. Displays are being integrated with electronic drivers, flex cards are being designed for the flexibility to be manipulated to fit into restricted areas, and the form factor of power supplies is being designed to conform to available spaces within products. The rapid integration of functions within electronic products is likely to continue: Japanese firms are all working on merging technologies like integrated circuits, electronic packaging, and flat panel displays. At some point an "electronic package" will likely consist of all the electronic and electrical components of a product, ultrasmall in size and custom-configured for the product. The technologies covered by the term "electronic packaging" are evolving rapidly. This report examines this process in terms of the goals, infrastructure, specific technological achievements, and dynamics of the electronics industry in Japan.

Electronics Industry in U.S.

The United States is losing technological and market leadership in the world as its electronics companies drop out of consumer product markets. Today's global competitive environment requires that companies be first to introduce attractive products of the highest quality at the lowest price. Although the United States has long been both a technology innovator and a market leader, in the last decade it has been losing strength in the marketplace. According to the National Advisory Committee on Semiconductors (1992, 2). At the beginning of a decade that promises unprecedented growth in global high-technology markets, the U.S. firms competing in these markets are experiencing disturbing weaknesses. Many high-volume electronics products, from low-cost goods to highly complex merchandise, are already manufactured overseas. In addition, concern is growing about the ability of U.S. firms to remain competitive in markets where they traditionally have been strong, such as low-cost segments of the computer and office equipment markets. Across the entire world electronics markets, the share produced by U.S.-owned firms has fallen by 14 percentage points since 1985. The market share loss translates to more than $100 billion in lost revenues, given the size of the current world electronics markets.

U.S. electronics manufacturers have lost market share to foreign-owned or foreign-based manufacturers in practically every electronics sector. This occurred while U.S. industry's R&D investment exceeded that of foreign competitors, and while U.S. government R&D dwarfed that of foreign governments. The Commerce Department was concerned that Japan could surpass the United States in production of electronic goods by 1994 and emphasized that since 1984 (except for software and medical equipment) the United States lost market share in 35 of 37 electronics categories. There are many who believe that the problem is the U.S. R&D structure's relative inattention to commercial applications, and that Americans must improve their focus on the basic problems of technology application and prototyping of new products. Bert Haskell of Kodak has stated the following the North America must develop a...low cost, high technology manufacturing infrastructure. This can only be accomplished through a commitment to manufacturing consumer products, and in particular consumer electronics. North American companies must identify emerging high volume consumer electronics products, and must be determined to participate broadly in the manufacture of these systems (MCC/Sandia 1993).

The United States also lags behind Japan in flexible automated manufacturing. Japan operates over 68% of all installed industrial robots in the world, compared to only 12.5% operated by the United States. Japan also has over 40% of the world's installed flexible manufacturing systems. Driven by the shortening of product life cycles and the growing segmentation of markets, Japanese companies are committed to improving manufacturing system flexibility. While this is costly, it has the associated advantages of making possible rapid response to new product introductions. Continuous improvements in manufacturing as well as component technologies resulted in Sharp successfully introducing three new models of its 8 mm ViewCam within one year of introducing the original product. In sophisticated, flexible electronic assembly equipment, Japanese companies are dominant. Proficiency in manufacturing high-technology consumer products is critical to maintenance of U.S. prosperity and leadership in a global marketplace; this is in turn dependent on electronic packaging proficiency. It is therefore likely that electronic packaging capabilities will play an increasingly important role in the future economic competitiveness of the United States. The MCC/Sandia report on electronic packaging (1993, 3-4) concluded the following:

- North American companies lead the world in several important segments of the Integrated Circuit [IC] market, but this lead is weakened by an ill-equipped low cost packaging infrastructure.
- Japanese IC packaging and assembling technology is significantly superior to North American capability in terms of miniaturization and cost effectiveness.
- The Japanese are the global leaders in manufacturing cost effective high density printed circuit boards [PCBs]. This leadership has resulted from a gradual improvement in high volume PCB fabrication processes for consumer electronics.
- Japanese manufacturers' experience in consumer electronics has given them a significant edge over their global competitors in fabricating and deploying miniaturized connectors and passive chip components.
- Japanese market share in consumer electronics has created the "product pull" required to justify large investments in manufacturing processes.
- While cost effective multichip modules [MCMs] are only beginning to emerge, Japanese manufacturers find themselves with a large share of the critical consumer electronics applications which will require MCMs. Japanese manufacturers' dominance of consumer video and PC memory card markets gives them a strategic advantage over North American manufacturers in amortizing the cost of new MCM processes.
- Japanese leadership in flat panel display fabrication is well known. The packaging of display modules, however, also provides Japanese manufacturers with a high volume application with which to distribute the cost of innovative packaging process developments.

The latest generation of consumer products is being integrated to provide new products for home and office: camcorders, electronic still cameras, mini-compact disc players, digital compact cassettes, hand-held televisions, and computers. Other consumer products include portable facsimile machines, copiers and printers, electronic data books, laptop computers, optical disk mass storage systems, smart cards, and portable telephones. Such products grew from 5% to more than 45% of Japanese electronics production between 1978 and 1988, an average growth rate of over 20%

per year, as compared to 10% for the electronics industry overall (Dataquest 1988, 4-7). Focusing on high-volume consumer electronics markets has been central to Japan's economic strategy. High-volume products have been estimated to account for at least one-third of global integrated chip consumption. U.S. companies have depended for 40-50% of the value added in their electronic products on foreign competitors, from whom they purchased large numbers of "upstream" electronic packages and components (IEEE 1989, 7). The majority of these imported products and technologies have come from Japan's electronics industry.

Japan's Electronics Industry

Of the $652 billion in global electronics production in 1991, Japan's production represented about 27%. Japan's electrical and electronics industry as a whole produced $176 billion in goods in 1991, second only to the United States' $232 billion. In consumer electronics, Japan produced 4.7 trillion yenin goods, a 48% share of world production, as compared to shares of 12% for the United States, 22% for Western Europe, and 18% for newly industrialized economies (NIEs). In industrial electronics, Japan produced 11.7 trillion yen in goods, a 22% share of world production, as compared to shares of 38% for the United States, 34% for Western Europe, and only 6% for the NIEs. In electronic components, Japan produced 8.8 trillion yen in goods, a 37% share of world production, compared to shares of 32% for the United States, 18% for Western Europe, and 13% for the NIEs. Japan's share of worldwide electronic component production was stable from the previous year, the United States' share showed a decline, and the NIE share showed an increase. In 1991, Japan exported over 45% of its electrical/electronics production (11 trillion yen of 25 trillion yen in production), which accounted for 27% of Japan's total exports. In that year, Japan's electrical and electronics industry provided jobs for over two million workers, or 18% of Japan's manufacturing work force (Dodwell 1993, 4-6).

Consumer Electronics in Recession

Of Japan's total 1991 electronic production, consumer electronics represented 19%, industrial electronic equipment represented 46%, and electronic components represented 35%. Both industrial electronics and components were expected to increase in 1993, to 47% and 37%, respectively; however, as a result of the 1992-1993 recession, consumer electronics' market share fell to 16%.

In 1991, Japan's 4.7 trillion yen in consumer electronics production consisted of 60% video equipment and 40% audio equipment. With Japan's burst bubble economy and ongoing recession, overall consumer sales were down 17% in 1992 and were projected to fall 3.5% in 1993 to below 3.7 trillion yen. Sales of audio and video equipment had provided the basis for strong growth in the past, but were in severe stagnation, as shown in Table 1.2. By 1993, audio equipment went from 40% of the total market to around 36%. Sony introduced its new MD (minidisc) Walkman in 1993 in hopes of stimulating future sales in this market.

Investments in the Electronics Industry

A MITI survey in 1992 of 1,667 companies found total plant and equipment investments in Japan valued at 20.8 trillion yen, as compared to 20.5 trillion yen in 1991 (Dodwell 1993). Of these totals, electronics equipment firms, including components firms, invested 1,399 billion yen in 1991 and 1,030 billion yen in 1992. That is, with the ongoing recession, investment fell 26% in 1992. Electrical appliance makers held their investment at 562 billion yen and 569 billion yen for 1991 and 1992, respectively. Production-related investment accounted for 45% of overall outlays for new and high-value-added products. R&D-related investment represented 24% of overall outlays, with a priority on supplying competitive products. Investment related to cost cutting and labor savings represented 13% of overall investments. The most significant product-focused investments were in LCD production. Notebook-type personal computers received significant increases in investment. Investment in 4M and 16M DRAM (dynamic random access memory) semiconductor capacity was significantly reduced in 1992. Investment in cordless and portable telephone capacity was heavy as demand continued to grow. Computer-related R&D investment was also high.

Moving Production Offshore

Japan's success in global competition has created new political problems for the country. Japan's aggressive export strategy has allowed it to dominate its trade relationships with all of its major trading partners but China. Continuing imbalance in trade and current accounts has generated surpluses in Japan for 31 straight months. For 1993, it was expected that Japan's account surplus would be $130 billion. This heavy imbalance continues to put a damper on the economies of its trading partners at a time of global recession. A 20% appreciation in the value of the yen in 1993 made it more difficult to maintain the low-cost requirement of Japanese consumer product strategy. This is part of the reason Japanese firms are moving operations, with the accompanying advanced production technologies, into countries where manufacturing costs are lower. The yen's appreciation has had a significant impact on consumer product exports. Color TVs and VCRs have been among Japan's major export items, as shown in Table 1.3. According to Japan's Ministry of Finance, camcorders surpassed VCRs as the number one export from Japan in 1992, with 47% of exports going to European markets and 40% to North American markets. Until the recession, camcorders had been Japan's number one growth product. Video discs and CD players were among the only products that continued to grow during the recession.

As a consequence of the recession, Japan has had to adjust to the yen's continuing appreciation in value. To stay competitive in world markets, Japanese electronics manufacturers have cut back on their labor forces, downsized plants and facilities, and reduced product lines and frequency of product model changes. Moreover, manufacturers are continuing to move their production facilities overseas. Of 400 overseas production bases owned by Japanese electronics makers, 60% are for consumer electronics plants and 40% for industrial products. The major shift in facilities began in 1985 with a move into Southeast Asia. The largest number of Japan's Asian plants are located in the Association of Southeast Asian Nations (ASEAN) nations of Malaysia, Singapore, Thailand, and most recently, Indonesia. Japan's move to ASEAN countries is a result of its need to restructure global operations in light of declining production advantages in Japan, the yen's appreciation, trade friction, and unification of regional markets. These plants provide low- and medium-priced electronics products and components. Of 136 billion yen in consumer electronics goods imported by Japan in 1991, 86% came from Asia, 8% from the United States, and 5% from Europe. A number of Japanese companies continued to expand plants in Southeast Asia during 1993; however, the investment priority was shifting to China. After having invested a total of nearly $30 billion in Malaysia, for example, Japanese firms invested only $1.5 billion in 1992. The number of Japanese investment applications fell from 46 to 35 for the January to April periods of 1992 and 1993, respectively. Japanese investments in Singapore remained high, with nearly $3.5 billion invested in 1993 (*Newsweek* 1993, 15). Japanese consumer electronics plants located offshore in 1992, 128 were located in Asia, 47 in Europe, 44 in North America, and 22 elsewhere in the world. Of 168 industrial electronics plants located offshore, 75 plants were in Asia, 38 in Europe, 48 in North America, and 7 elsewhere.

Shows the leading sources of Japan's electronics equipment and parts imports in 1992. Asia dominated Japan's consumer electronics imports with an 84% share. Asia also dominated Japan's import of passive devices and components and produced one-third of imported active devices. North America still dominated its industrial products imports and led in active devices, integrated circuits, and other parts and accessories. Only imports of U.S. microprocessors and memories continued to grow rapidly — up 23% from 1990-91. Japan's 1991 imports of components from ASEAN nations, China, and Hong Kong grew significantly, while those from Europe, North America, Korea, and Taiwan decreased.

Technological Relationships

Japan's manufacturing technology exports were 321 billion yen in 1990, and its imports were 364 billion yen. The electronics industry's technology exports accounted for 97 billion yen, or 29% of Japan's total technology exports. Other major exports included chemicals, 17% (58.2 billion yen) of total technology exports; industrial machinery, 4% (14.4 billion yen); and ceramics, 3% (11.9 billion yen). Thirty percent of technology exports went to the United States; Asia accounted for 45%, the major recipients being South Korea (14%), Thailand (7%), Taiwan (5%), Singapore (6%), and Indonesia (6%); Europe accounted for 18%, with the U.K. (6%) being the primary partner.

Electronics also accounted for the majority of Japan's technology imports — 43% (160 billion yen), compared to 14% for transportation (52 billion yen), 8% for industrial machinery (31 billion yen), and 3% for precision machinery (11.4 billion yen). The United States was the source for 70% of Japan's total technology imports. Outside of North America, these imports came primarily from European countries (29%), including Germany (7%), France (6%), and the Netherlands (5%).

Manufacturing industries accounted for over 90% of Japan's 9.3 trillion yen in R&D expenditures in 1990. While R&D expenditures had tripled since 1980, they were expected to double again by the mid-1990s. The Japanese government set a goal in 1992 of doubling Japan's R&D expenditures as a percent of GNP. Japan's electronics industry R&D expenditures (3.1 trillion yen) accounted for over 37% of total R&D expenditures (8.7 trillion yen), as shown in Table 1.6:

The growth rate of R&D in communication, electronics, and measuring equipment was the highest, having grown by a factor of four over the past decade. While the pharmaceutical industry showed the highest ratio of R&D to sales at 8%, communications, electronics, and measuring equipment R&D followed at 6.1% of sales. Electrical machinery R&D was 5.4% of sales, followed by chemicals (4%) and autos (3.7%).

Planning for Future Products

Japan's electronics industry is driven by expected growth in consumer products. The Electronics Industry Association of Japan forecasts growth by product category, which projects audiovisual production for the years 1995 and 2000. The most significant projected growth comes from the shift to high definition televisions and VCRs. Projected output growth of minidisc and digital compact cassette players was expected to triple during the latter half of this decade. Combination telephone/color TV sets were expected to become a new growth product by the end of the decade. This forecast shows very little that is totally new; most categories show development of next-generation models of products currently on the market. This type of industry projection provides the roadmaps for most Japanese companies as they develop plans for future products. Such roadmaps help to identify the technologies that will be needed to produce the coming generations of products.

Forecasts for growth in computer-related products to 1995. The highest volume of production is expected at the low-priced end of the product spectrum. High-volume desktop computers put few constraints on product size but are differentiated by advanced functions. In contrast, notebook computers and personal digital assistants will push the limits of product miniaturization. (Notebook computers have allowed new competition to enter the industry from outside Japan and the United States.)

Supporting Technologies

Japan's heavy emphasis on the electronics industry has lead it to become a major player in the production and export of electronic components. In 1992, 52% of electronics components were active components (electron tubes 8%, discrete semiconductors 9%, and integrated circuits 35%); 15% were passive components such as capacitors, resistors, and inductors; and 31% were other electronic parts (mechanical parts 14%, and audio parts 7%). Total production of electronic components was valued at 8.8 trillion yen in 1991, an increase of 6% over the previous year. The growth rate 1986 to 1991 was 10% per annum. Active components production totaled 4.6 trillion yen in 1991, up 6% over 1990.

Passive component production totaled 4.3 trillion yen, up over 5% from 1990. The highest growth areas were discrete semiconductors, passive devices and parts such as connectors, switches, relays, and PCBs, growing at over 7% in 1991. Japan was the largest semiconductor market in the world, accounting for 39% of 1991 sales, compared to 28% for the United States, 18% for Western Europe, and 15% for the rest of the world. As shown in Table 1.7, while electronic device sales were down in 1992, they were forecast to come back again in 1993.

Japan exported 57% of its electronic components production in 1991, totaling 5.1 trillion yen. Active components represented 33% of all exports, passive components 7%, electronics parts 6%, and audio parts 3%. With the increasing production of components in Asia, Japan's components imports grew 8% to 1.3 trillion yen in 1991, equivalent to one-quarter the value of Japan's exports.

Goals of the Study

This study of superconducting electronics (SCE) in Japan grew out of continuing U.S. interest in understanding Japan's strengths and progress in this field since a 1989 study of superconductivity (Dresselhaus 1989) was conducted by the Japanese (now the World) Technology Evaluation Center (JTEC/WTEC). WTEC assembled the present SCE panel in late 1996 under the sponsorship of the U.S. Department of Defense Advanced Research Projects Agency (DARPA) and the National Science Foundation (NSF). The primary objectives of this panel were to study R&D activities in Japan in the areas of radio frequency (rf) and microwave applications of passive devices, although an attempt was made to examine the full spectrum of superconducting electronics activity.

In addition, the SCE panel wished to gauge Japan's response to an almost frenetic U.S. push towards commercialization of rf applications. Four small U.S. companies (Conductus, ISC, SCT, and STI) have staked their future on the wireless communications market, and DARPA has emphasized this application by funding relevant research at some of those companies and at other laboratories. Progress in the two years prior to this study was dramatic: complete hybrid systems with HTS filters and low noise semiconductor amplifiers, integrated with a compact refrigerator, are now being used to carry cellular telephone calls in a number of base stations. However, markets have not fully materialized, and U.S. funding sources have limited time horizons, so Japan's relative ability to compete in these markets is of great consequence.

Finally, this panel has taken a particular interest in the styles and impacts of the various R&D consortia in Japan and the degree of collaboration between them, as they represent a large fraction of the activity in superconducting electronics.

REFERENCES

Agar A.W., Brown, P.D., Mulvey, T. & Smith K.C.A. The Curious History of the First SEM Produced Independently by AEI Manchester. The Electron, Proc. International Centennial Symposium on the Electron, Churchill College, Cambridge, (Ed. A.I. Kirkland and P.D. Brown) 266-269, (1997).

Arden, Lynie. Telecomputing: job training and placement for the homebound. Family and home office computing, v. 6, January 1988: 14, 16.

Berliss, Jane R., Peter A. Borden, and Gregg C. Vanderheiden, eds. Trace resourcebook: assistive technologies for communication, control, and computer access. 1989-90 ed. Madison, WI: Trace Research and Development Center, 1989. 797p. (University of Wisconsin, S-151 Waisman Center, 1500 Highland Avenue 53705).

Bowe, Frank. Making computers accessible to disabled people. Technology review, v. 90, January 1987: 52-59, 72.

Breton, B.C., Chand, G., Caldwell, N.H.M. & Holburn, D.M. Remote Microscopy in the Real World. Microscopy and Analysis, September 1997, pp19-21. (1997).

Broers A.N: Selective ion beam etching in the scanning electron microscope. PhD Dissertation, Cambridge University (1965)

Broers A. N. Combined electron and ion beam processes for microelectronics. Microelectron. Reliab. 4, 103-104. (1965).

Broers A.N. Micromachining by sputtering through a mask of contamination laid down by an electron beam. Int. Conf. Electron Ion Beam Sci. Technol. (R. A. Bakish ed) (Pap.) 1st, 1964 Toronto, pp. 191-204. (1965).

Oatley C.W, Nixon WC, Pease R.F.W: Scanning electron microscopy. Adv. Electronics Electron Phys 21, 181-247 (1965)

Pease R.F.W. The determination of the area of emission of reflected electrons in a scanning electron microscope. J. Sci. Instrum. 42, 158-159. (1965).

Pease R.F.W, Nixon W.C: High resolution scanning electron microscopy. J. Sci. Inst. 42, 81-85 (1965).

Pease R.F.W. and Nixon W.C. "Microformation of filaments," in First International Conference on Electron and Ion Beam Science and Technology, Toronto, May 1964, edited by R. A. Bakish (Wiley, New York) pp 22~230. (1965).

Stewart A.D.G. and Snelling M.A. A new scanning electron microscope, in Electron Microscopy: Proceedings of the Third European Regional Conference, Prague, Sept. 1964, edited by M. Titlebach (Czechoslovak Academy of Sciences, Prague), pp 55-56. (1965).

Brown, Carl, and others. Computer access in higher education for students with disabilities: a practical guide to the selection and use of adapted computer technology. 2d ed. Monterey, CA: Fund for the Improvement of Post-Secondary Education, 1989. 1 v. (various pagings). Free. (Available from High Tech Center for the Disabled, California Community College, 1109 Ninth Street, Sacramento, CA 95814).

Burkhead, E. Jane, James P. Sampson, Jr., and Brian T. McMahon. The liberation of disabled persons in a technological society: access to computer technology. Rehabilitation literature, v. 47, July-August 1986: 162-168.

Caldwell, N.H.M., Breton, B.C., & Holburn, D.M. "FIRST A.I.D: Using Remote Microscopy and Artificial Intelligence for SEM Fault Diagnosis" Scanning: The Journal of Scanning Microscopies,Vol 19, (3), pp204. (1997).

Caldwell, N.H.M., Breton, B.C., & Holburn, D.M. Towards the Intelligent SEM. Electron Microscopy and Analysis 1997, (Institute of Physics Conference Series Number 153), pp 53-56, Institute of Physics Publishing.(1997).

Caldwell, N.H.M., Breton, B.C., & Holburn, D.M. XpertEze: A Knowledge-Based Approach to Scanning Electron Microscopy. Applications and Innovations in Expert Systems V (pp 127-140), SGES Publications. (1997)

Cavalier, Al. The application of technology in the classroom and workplace: unvoiced premises and ethical issues. In Images of the disabled, disabling images. Edited by Alan Gartner and Tom Joe. New York: Praeger, 1987. p. 128-141.

Chand, G., Breton, B.C., Caldwell, N.H.M. & Holburn, D.M. World Wide Web Controlled SEM. Scanning: The Journal of Scanning Microscopies, Vol 19, 4, 292-296. (1997)

Edgcombe C.J., Roberts, D.E. & Smith K.C.A. Computer-Aided Teaching of Electron Optics. The Electron, Proc. International Centennial Symposium on the Electron, Churchill College, Cambridge, (Ed. A.I. Kirkland and P.D. Brown) 313-317, (1997)

Smith K.C.A. Charles Oatley: Pioneer of Scanning Electron Microscopy. Inst. Phys. Conf. Series No 153; 9-16 (1997).

Chong, Curtis, and Steve Jacobson. Access to personal computers for the blind: a review of speech and braille software and hardware systems designed to permit blind persons to access the video display of an IBM personal computer (PC). Baltimore, MD: Job Opportunities for the Blind, National Federation of the Blind, 1989. 45p. (National Federation of the Blind in Computer Science, 3530 Dupont Avenue North, Minneapolis, MN 55412).

Cook, Albert M., J. Douglas Leins, and Helen E. Woodall. Use of microcomputers by disabled persons: a rehabilitation engineering perspective. Rehabilitation counseling bulletin, v. 28, June 1985: 283-292.

Crimando, William, and Susan Harrington Godley. The computer's potential in enhancing employment opportunities of persons with disabilities. Rehabilitation counseling bulletin, v. 28, June 1985: 275-282.

Dixon, Judith M., and Jane B. Mandelbaum. Reading through technology: evolving methods and opportunities for print- handicapped individuals. Journal of visual impairment and blindness, v. 84, December 1990: 493-496.

Edwards, Sandra. Microcomputers and the visually impaired (low- vision to no-vision). OCLC micro, v. 5, December 1989: 20-21, 25-26, 28.

Enders, Alexandra, and Marian Hall, eds. Assistive technology sourcebook. Washington: RESNA Press, 1990. 576p. (1101 Connecticut Avenue NW, Suite 700, DC 20036).

Everhart T.E. Simple theory concerning the reflection of electrons from solids. J. Appl. Phys. 31, 1483-1490. (1960).

Everhart T.E., Thornley R.F.M: Wide-band detector for micro-microampere low-energy electron currents. J Sci Inst 37, 246-248 (1960).

Everhart T.E., Smith, K.C.A., Wells O.C. and Oatley C.W., (1960): Recent developments in scanning electron microscopy. in Proceedings of the Fourth International Conference on Electron Microscopy, Berlin, Sept. 1958, Physics, Vol. I, edited by W. Bargmann et al. (Springer Verlag, Berlin, (1958)) 269-273.

Sikorski J. Studies of fibrous structures. in Proceedings of the Fourth International Conference on Electron Microscopy, Berlin Sept. 1958, Physics, Vol. i, edited by W. Bargmann et. al. (Springer Verlag, Berlin (1960)) 686-707.

Thornley R.F.M. New applications of the scanning electron microscope. PhD Dissertation, Cambridge University (1960)

Wells O.C: Correction of errors in electron stereomicroscopy. Brit J Appl Phys 11, 119-201 (1960).

Graves, William H., and Bonita J. Maxson. Computer access technology: an ecological approach to meeting the information needs of people with visual disabilities. American rehabilitation, v. 15, summer 1990: 18-22, 31.

Green, Peter, and Alan J. Brightman. Independence day: designing computer solutions for individuals with disability. Allen, TX: DLM Teaching Resources, 1990. 137p.

Hall, Marian, Gregg Vanderheiden, and Christine Thompson. ABLEDATA and Hyper-ABLEDATA. Assistive technology, v. 1, 1989: 107-111.

Hinton, Daniel E. Research and technological aids for people who are deaf-blind. American rehabilitation, v. 15, summer 1989: 7-10.

Holburn, D.M., Robertson, R.P., Breton B.C., & Caldwell N.H.M. A Virtual Scanning Electron Microscope for Teaching and Training. Microscopy & Analysis, March 2000, pp5-7. (2000).

Holmes, Gary E., and Ronald H. Karst. Bringing computer technology to the VR system. American rehabilitation, v. 15, summer 1989: 11-14, 28.

Irons, Thomas R. Microcomputer usage for the person with a disability. Journal of rehabilitation, v. 51, Jan./Feb./Mar. 1985: 31-34.

Jernigan, Kenneth, ed. U.S.-Canada Conference on Technology for the Blind, September 19-21, 1991. Braille monitor, January 1992: 1-47 (entire issue).

Johns Hopkins National Search for Computing Applications to Assist Persons with Disabilities. Proceedings. Los Alamitos, CA: IEEE Computer Society Press, 1992. 221p.

K.C.A. Smith. A versatile scanning electron microscope. in Proceedings of the European Regional Conference on Electron Microscopy, Delft 1960, Vol. 1 edited by A. L. Houwink and B.J. Spit (De Nederlandse Vereniging Voor electronenmicroscopie, Delft, (1961)) pp 177-180.

Smith, K.C.A. Scanning. in "Encyclopedia of Microscopy" (G. L. Clark, ed.), pp.241-251. (Reinhold, New York), (1961).

Thornley, R.F.M. Recent developments in scanning electron microscopy. in Proceedings of the European Regional Conference on Electron Microscopy, Delft 1960, Vol. i, edited by A. L. Houwink and B. J. Spit, (De Nederlandse Vereniging Voor Electronenmicroscopie, Delft (1961) pp 173-176.

Lambert, Robert M. The challenge of rationality in computer access for the visually impaired. Behavior research methods, instruments, and computers, v. 19, 1987: 286-290.

Lavoie, Francis J. In offices, "disabled" doesn't mean "unable." Modern office technology, v. 33, June 1988: 92, 94, 96.

Lazzaro, Joseph J. Opening doors for the disabled: adaptive technology lets blind, deaf, and motor-disabled personal computer users lead more productive lives. Byte, v. 15, August 1990: 258, 260, 262-264, 266, 268.

Leventhal, Jay D. A national network of assistive technology and job information. Journal of visual impairment and blindness, v. 85, April 1991: 178-180.

Leventhal, Jay D., Mark M. Uslan, and Elliot M. Schreier. A review of technology-related publications. Journal of visual impairment and blindness, v. 84, March 1990: 127-130.

Luxton, Karen. Training students in adaptive computer technology. Journal of visual impairment and blindness, v. 84, December 1990: 523-525.

Margalit, Malka. Effective technology integration for disabled children: the family perspective. New York: Springer-Verlag, 1990. 226p.

Morrissey, Patricia A., and Robert Silverstein. The Technology- Related Assistance for Individuals with Disabilities Act of 1988. American rehabilitation, v. 15, summer 1989: 4-6, 28.

Regional Information Exchanges identify, then get the word out on exemplary programmes. NARIC quarterly, v. 3, winter 1990: 1, 4-7.

Rettig, Michael, Ela Shaklett, and Martha Wyrsch. Microcomputer applications with visually impaired preschool-aged children. Journal of visual impairment and blindness, v. 81, March 1987: 120-121.

Ruconich, Sandra K., S.C. Ashcroft, and Michael F. Young. Making microcomputers accessible to blind persons. Journal of special education technology, v. 8, summer 1986: 37-46.

Sampson, James P., Jr., Brian T. McMahon, and E. Jane Burkhead. Using computers for career exploration and decision making in vocational rehabilitation. Rehabilitation counseling bulletin, v. 28, June 1985: 242-261.

Schreier, Elliot M. The future of access technology for blind and visually impaired people. Journal of visual impairment and blindness, v. 84, December 1990: 520-523.

Smith K.C.A. The Origins and History of a Versatile Electron Optical Instrument Combining Facilities for SEM, TEM and X-ray Point Projection Microscopy. The Electron, Proc. International Centennial Symposium on the Electron, Churchill College, Cambridge, (Ed. A.I. Kirkland and P.D. Brown) 552-556. (1997).

St. P., Oliver W., and Crystal Ward Darby. Adaptive uses of microcomputers: a case study. Journal of visual impairment and blindness, v. 81, October 1987: 391.

U.S. General Services Administration. Information Resources Management Service. Clearinghouse on Computer Accommodation. Managing information resources for accessibility. Washington, 1991. 1 v. (various pagings). (Room 2022, KGDO, 18th and F Streets NW, DC 20405).

Velleman, Ruth A. New technology. In Velleman, Ruth A., Meeting the needs of people with disabilities: a guide for librarians, educators, and other service professionals. Phoenix, AZ: Oryx Press, 1990. p. 79-94.

4

Research Methodology in Ceramic Science

INTRODUCTION

Ceramic engineering is the technology of manufacturing and usage of ceramic materials. Approximately ten educational institutions in the United States offer degrees in this field, examples being Alfred University, and Rutgers University, and there are several in other countries. Some of these institutions are planning to change the names of their disciplines to "Materials science" or "Materials engineering." Clemson University recently merged Ceramic Engineering and Materials Science and Engineering into one major, Ceramic & Materials Engineering. Often the personnel working in these fields have been trained in Chemical engineering, Chemistry (for manufacturing), Mechanical engineering (for the study of strength, wear, etc.), or Electrical engineering and Physics (for optimization of Piezoelectric or Magnetic applications). Recently the field has come to include the studies of single crystals or glass fibers, in addition to traditional Polycrystalline materials, and the applications of these have been overlapping and changing rapidly. Ceramics, in addition to being a fine art, also requires a thorough working knowledge of certain materials. Whether you're helping to design a new office building, or a vase for your bedroom, you'll need to know what you're going to use to construct your next project, and that's where the engineering comes in. After you've nailed down the creative design part, someone has to figure out how to turn it into a reality. In walks the engineer. By joining together ceramics and engineering, this major will provide you with more than just a working knowledge of the material used by ceramicists. You'll be able to help create new and more interesting works with new materials of which only somebody with your knowledge could have ever dreamed. If you are interested in Ceramic Engineering, you might also like...

(i) Architectural Engineering
(ii) Architectural History
(iii) Architecture
(iv) Civil Engineering
(v) Engineering Design
(vi) Engineering Mechanics

A Case Study on Ceramic Engineers

What do astronauts, dentists, clumsy dishwashers, and astronomers have in common? Each depends on CERAMIC ENGINEERS to develop such varied products as protective tiles for space shuttles, ceramic fillings for teeth, unbreakable dinner plates, and sophisticated telescope lenses.

Ceramics have applications in virtually any industry which demands the use of heat-resistant materials. Ceramic Engineers are specialists in the study of these materials, their behavior, application, and use. They develop methods for processing nonmetallic inorganic materials into many ceramic products ranging from glassware, fiber optics products, cement, and bricks, to coatings for space vehicles, materials for microelectronics, components of nuclear fuel, and pollution control devices. Recent advances in physics and chemistry have expanded the applications of ceramic engineering from traditionally established industries to projects that encompass every area of technology. Ceramic Engineers often specialize in one or more products: whitewares (porcelain and china dinnerware or high voltage electrical insulators), structural materials (brick, tile, and turbine blades), electronic ceramics (magnetics, memory systems, and microwave devices), protective and refractory coatings for metals, glass products, abrasives, and fuel elements for nuclear energy. One of the top priority projects of Ceramic Engineers is the development of a ceramic engine which would replace the present diesel, gasoline and turbo engines.

The major functions of Ceramic Engineers are Research, product development, and production engineering. The engineer is frequently challenged to produce new ideas and to suggest solutions to difficult problems. Engineers may have extensive responsibilities such as preparing labor cost analyses or troubleshooting problems. Ceramic Engineers experienced in both scientific and production aspects of the profession may also work as administrators, project supervisors, sales engineers or technical consultants to firms using ceramic materials.

Working Conditions

The Ceramic Engineer's work world varies from job to job according to the specialty and place of employment. As a Research director, for example, the ceramic engineer may spend much of the day in the office evaluating and planning new projects or consulting with other engineers and company executives. By contrast, new engineers working in firms that manufacture ceramic products may work primarily in the laboratory where much of the time is spent running physical or chemical tests on raw materials or finished products and analyzing the results. Tension may be a part of the job when difficulty is encountered in meeting production schedules or project deadlines.

Employment Outlook

The following information is from the California Projections of Employment published by the Labor Market Information Division. These figures represent the broad occupational group Metallurgists, Related Engineers which includes Ceramic Engineers.

There is a shortage of Ceramic Engineers. Many Ceramic Engineers work in the nuclear field, as ceramic fuel materials make nuclear power generation possible. The electronics industry is a growth area for this technology, as ceramics are used as insulators for transistors and integrated circuits. Refractory ceramics are required in the refining of iron and aluminum, and this industry is especially in need of this type of worker. The exciting new field of fiber optics has had a dramatic effect on today's telecommunication and medical industries, and since ceramic components are used, Ceramic Engineers are playing a vital role in this new science. One of the top Research projects of Ceramic Engineers is the development of a ceramic engine which would replace the present diesel, gasoline, and turbo engines. This new engine would withstand extremely high temperatures, would be much lighter, would be more efficient, and would not wear out like metal engines. To maintain a competitive edge in the market, ceramic companies will often hire Ceramic Engineers to serve in vital business and management areas.

Wages, Hours, and Fringe Benefits

Firms hiring newly-graduated Ceramic Engineers with a bachelor's degree and no work experience usually offer starting salaries ranging from $19,000 to $29,000 annually. The range of pay for those holding master's degrees without work experience is between $28,000 and $36,000 a year. Engineers holding Ph.D.s who accept employment in private firms may expect starting wages of $40,000 to $55,000 a year. Top salaries vary widely according to the size of the firms, the type of work done, and the extent of the engineer's experience.Life, health, and accident insurance and retirement benefits are usually offered to Ceramic Engineers on a contributing or employer-paid basis. Some employers also offer stock options, profit-sharing plans or pay annual bonuses. The scheduled workweek for most engineers is 40 hours. However, if important project deadlines must be met or breakdowns in plants occur, engineers may be expected to work overtime as necessary.

Entrance Requirements and Training

A Bachelor of Science degree in ceramic engineering or materials science is virtually always required for entry-level jobs. Some firms, however, accept workers whose degrees are in materials engineering, physical chemistry, physics, or metallurgy if the undergraduate programme has included ceramics. Advanced training and degrees are required for an increasing number of jobs in the ceramic engineering field, particularly for those engineers who specialize in Research and development. Ceramic Engineers frequently work with people from many levels. They must be able to communicate their ideas to managers, technicians, craftworkers, production workers, and customers alike. They should be able to work as part of a team, be innovative, and have an analytical mind. They should also demonstrate initiative and a capacity for remembering details, plus have the ability to cut across various disciplines and systematically evaluate and solve problems. Success in this profession requires a solid background in mathematics, physical, and social sciences, as well as ceramic engineering analysis and design.

Advancement

Ceramic engineering graduates usually begin as junior or assistant engineers and, as they gain experience, may advance to positions of greater responsibility. Depending on the structure and product line of the firm, an engineer may advance to supervising engineer, chief engineer or plant manager. The Ceramic Engineer engaged in Research may be given increasingly responsible assignments with corresponding salary increases and may progress to such positions as supervisor, project engineer or director of Research. Most engineers who seek top industrial executive positions in administration or management will find it advantageous to obtain graduate or doctoral degrees in ceramic engineering, materials science or business administration.

Finding the Job

Ceramic Engineers can apply directly to firms which employ engineers in a particular specialty or reply to advertisements in newspapers and professional journals. Prospective workers should also check with their college placement centers, since recruiting employers often ask faculty members for recommendations. Personal contacts through professional organisations or societies are also common ways to find work. Federal and other governmental agencies employ Ceramic Engineers, and job seekers should take the appropriate civil service examinations. In addition, both engineers and employers use the offices of private employment agencies and the Job Service of the California Employment Development Department.

What is Ceramic?

The word ***ceramic*** is derived from the Greek word °µÁ±¼¹°ÌÂ (*keramikos*). The term covers inorganic non-metallic materials whose formation is due to the action of heat. Up until the 1950s or so, the most important of these were the traditional clays, made into pottery, bricks, tiles and are like, along with cements and glass. The traditional crafts are described in the article on pottery. A composite material of ceramic and metal is known as cermet. The word *ceramic* can be an adjective, and can also be used as a noun to refer to a ceramic material, or a product of ceramic manufacture. *Ceramics* is a singular noun referring to the art of making things out of ceramic materials. Many ceramic materials are hard, porous and brittle. The study and development of ceramics includes methods to mitigate problems associated with these characteristics, and to accentuate the strengths of the materials as well as to investigate novel applications. The American Society for Testing and Materials (ASTM) defines a ceramic article as *"an article having a glazed or unglazed body of crystalline or partly crystalline structure, or of glass, which body is produced from essentially inorganic, non-metallic substances and either is formed from a molten mass which solidifies on cooling, or is formed and simultaneously or subsequently matured by the action of the heat."*

Types of Ceramic Materials

For convenience ceramic products are usually divided into four sectors, and these are shown below with some examples:

- *Structural*, including bricks, pipes, floor and roof tiles
- *Refractories*, such as kiln linings, gas fire radiants, steel and glass making crucibles
- *Whitewares*, including tableware, wall tiles, decorative art objects and sanitaryware
- *Technical*, is also known as Engineering, Advanced, Special, and in Japan, Fine Ceramics. Such items include tiles used in the Space Shuttle programme, gas burner nozzles, ballistic protection, nuclear fuel uranium oxide pellets, bio-medical implants, jet engine turbine blades, and missile nose cones. Frequently the raw materials do not include clays.

Examples of Whiteware Ceramics

- Bone china
- Earthenware, which is often made from clay, quartz and feldspar.
- Porcelain, which usually contains the clay mineral kaolinite
- Stoneware

Classification of Technical Ceramics

Technical ceramics can also be classified into three distinct material categories:

- Oxides: Alumina, zirconia
- Non-oxides: Carbides, borides, nitrides, silicides
- Composites: Particulate reinforced, combinations of oxides and non-oxides.

Examples of technical ceramics

- Barium titanate (often mixed with strontium titanate) displays ferroelectricity, meaning that its mechanical, electrical, and thermal responses are coupled to one another and also history-dependent. It is widely used in electromechanical transducers, ceramic capacitors, and data storage elements. Grain boundary conditions can create PTC effects in heating elements.
- Bismuth strontium calcium copper oxide, a high-temperature superconductor
- Boron carbide (B_4C), which is used in ceramic plates in some personal, helicopter and tank armor.
- Boron nitride is structurally isoelectronic to carbon and takes on similar physical forms: a graphite-like one used as a lubricant, and a diamond-like one used as an abrasive.
- Ferrite (Fe_3O_4), which is ferrimagnetic and is used in the magnetic cores of electrical transformers and magnetic core memory.
- Lead zirconate titanate is another ferroelectric material.
- Magnesium diboride (MgB_2), which is an unconventional superconductor.
- Silicon carbide (SiC), which is used as a susceptor in microwave furnaces, a commonly used abrasive, and as a refractory material.
- Silicon nitride (Si_3N_4), which is used as an abrasive powder.
- Steatite is used as an electrical insulator.
- Uranium oxide (UO_2), used as fuel in nuclear reactors.
- Yttrium barium copper oxide ($YBa_2Cu_3O_{7-x}$), another high temperature superconductor.
- Zinc oxide (ZnO), which is a semiconductor, and used in the construction of varistors.
- Zirconium dioxide (zirconia), which in pure form undergoes many phase changes between room temperature and practical sintering temperatures,

can be chemically "stabilized" in several different forms. Its high oxygen ion conductivity recommends it for use in fuel cells. In another variant, metastable structures can impart transformation toughening for mechanical applications; most ceramic knife blades are made of this material.

Examples of Structural Ceramics

- Bricks (mostly aluminium silicates), used for construction.

Electrical Properties

Semiconductors

There are a number of ceramics that are semiconductors. Most of these are transition metal oxides that are II-VI semiconductors, such as zinc oxide. While there is talk of making blue LEDs from zinc oxide, ceramicists are most interested in the electrical properties that show grain boundary effects. One of the most widely used of these is the varistor. These are devices that exhibit the property that resistance drops sharply at a certain threshold voltage. Once the voltage across the device reaches the threshold, there is a breakdown of the electrical structure in the vicinity of the grain boundaries, which results in its electrical resistance dropping from several megaohms down to a few hundred ohms. The major advantage of these is that they can dissipate a lot of energy, and they self reset — after the voltage across the device drops below the threshold, its resistance returns to being high. This makes them ideal for surge-protection applications. As there is control over the threshold voltage and energy tolerance, they find use in all sorts of applications. The best demonstration of their ability can be found in electrical substations, where they are employed to protect the infrastructure from lightning strikes. They have rapid response, are low maintenance, and do not appreciably degrade from use, making them virtually ideal devices for this application. Semiconducting ceramics are also employed as gas sensors. When various gases are passed over a polycrystalline ceramic, its electrical resistance changes. With tuning to the possible gas mixtures, very inexpensive devices can be produced.

Superconductivity

Under some conditions, such as extremely low temperature, some ceramics exhibit superconductivity. The exact reason for this is not known, but there are two major families of superconducting ceramics.

Ferroelectricity and Supersets

Piezoelectricity, a link between electrical and mechanical response, is exhibited by a large number of ceramic materials, including the quartz used to measure time in watches and other electronics. Such devices use both properties of piezoelectrics, using electricity to produce a mechanical motion (powering the device) and then using this mechanical motion to produce electricity (generating a signal). The unit of time measured is the natural interval required for electricity to be converted into mechanical energy and back again. The piezoelectric effect is generally stronger in materials that also exhibit pyroelectricity, and all pyroelectric materials are also piezoelectric. These materials can be used to interconvert between thermal, mechanical, and/or electrical energy; for instance, after synthesis in a furnace, a pyroelectric crystal allowed to cool under no applied stress generally builds up a static charge of thousands of volts. Such materials are used in motion sensors, where the tiny rise in temperature from a warm body entering the room is enough to produce a measurable voltage in the crystal. In turn, pyroelectricity is seen most strongly in materials which also display the ferroelectric effect, in which a stable electric dipole can be oriented or reversed by applying an electrostatic field. Pyroelectricity is also a necessary consequence of ferroelectricity. This can be used to store information in ferroelectric capacitors, elements of ferroelectric RAM. The most common such materials are lead zirconate titanate and barium titanate. Aside from the uses mentioned above, their strong piezoelectric response is exploited in the design of high-frequency loudspeakers, transducers for sonar, and actuators for atomic force and scanning tunneling microscopes.

Mechanical Properties

Ceramic materials are usually ionic or covalently-bonded materials, and can be crystalline or amorphous. A material held together by either type of bond will tend to fracture before any plastic deformation takes place, which results in poor toughness in these materials. Additionally, because these materials tend to be porous, the pores and other microscopic imperfections act as stress concentrators, decreasing the toughness further, and reducing the tensile strength. These combine to give catastrophic failures, as opposed to the normally much more gentle failure modes of metals. These materials do show plastic deformation. However, due to the rigid structure of the crystalline materials, there are very few available slip systems for dislocations to move, and so they deform very slowly. With the non-crystalline (glassy) materials, viscous flow is the dominant source of plastic deformation, and is also very slow. It is therefore neglected in many applications of ceramic materials.

Positive Thermal Coefficient

Increases in temperature can cause grain boundaries to suddenly become insulating in some semiconducting ceramic materials, mostly mixtures of heavy metal titanates. The critical transition temperature can be adjusted over a wide range by variations in chemistry. In such materials, current will pass through the material until joule heating brings it to the transition temperature, at which point the circuit will be broken and current flow will cease. Such ceramics are used as self-controlled heating elements in, for example, the rear-window defrost circuits of automobiles. At the transition temperature, the material's dielectric response becomes theoretically infinite. While a lack of temperature control would rule out any practical use of the material near its critical temperature, the dielectric effect remains exceptionally strong even at much higher temperatures. Titanates with critical temperatures far below room temperature have become synonymous with "ceramic" in the context of ceramic capacitors for just this reason.

Classification of Ceramics

Non-crystalline ceramics: Non-crystalline ceramics, being glasses, tend to be formed from melts. The glass is shaped when either fully molten, by casting, or when in a state of toffee-like viscosity, by methods such as blowing to a mould. If later heat-treatments cause this class to become partly crystalline, the resulting material is known as a glass-ceramic. Crystalline ceramic materials are not amenable to a great range of processing. Methods for dealing with them tend to fall into one of two categories - either make the ceramic in the desired shape, by reaction in situ, or by "forming" powders into the desired shape, and then sintering to form a solid body. Ceramic forming techniques include shaping by hand (sometimes including a rotation process called "throwing"), slip casting, tape casting (used for making very thin ceramic capacitors, etc.), injection molding, dry pressing, and other variations. A few methods use a hybrid between the two approaches.

In Situ Manufacturing

The most common use of this method is in the production of cement and concrete. Here, the dehydrated powders are mixed with water. This starts hydration reactions, which result in long, interlocking crystals forming around the aggregates. Over time, these result in a solid ceramic. The biggest problem with this method is that most reactions are so fast that good mixing is not possible, which tends to prevent large-scale construction. However, small-scale systems can be made by deposition techniques, where the various materials are introduced above a substrate, and react and form the ceramic on the substrate. This borrows techniques from the semiconductor industry, such as chemical vapour deposition, and is very useful for coatings. These tend to produce very dense ceramics, but do so slowly.

Sintering-based Methods

The principles of sintering-based methods is simple. Once a roughly held together object (called a "green body") is made, it is baked in a kiln, where diffusion processes cause the green body to shrink. The pores in the object close up, resulting in a denser, stronger product. The firing is done at a temperature below the melting point of the ceramic. There is virtually always some porosity left, but the real advantage of this method is that the green body can be produced in any way imaginable, and still be sintered. This makes it a very versatile route. There are thousands of possible refinements of this process. Some of the most common involve pressing the green body to give the densification a head start and reduce the sintering time needed. Sometimes organic binders such as polyvinyl alcohol are added to hold the green body together; these burn out during the firing (at 200-350°C). Sometimes organic lubricants are added during pressing to increase densification. It is not uncommon to combine these, and add binders and lubricants to a powder, then press. (The formulation of these organic chemical additives is an art in itself. This is particularly important in the manufacture of high performance ceramics such as those used by the billions for electronics, in capacitors, inductors, sensors, etc. The specialized formulations most commonly used in electronics are detailed in the book "Tape Casting," by R.E. Mistler, et al., Amer. Ceramic Soc. [Westerville, Ohio], 2000.) A comprehensive book on the subject, for mechanical as well as electronics applications, is "Organic Additives and Ceramic Processing," by D. J. Shanefield, Kluwer Publishers [Boston], 1996. A slurry can be used in place of a powder, and then cast into a desired shape, dried and then sintered. Indeed, traditional pottery is done with this type of method, using a plastic mixture worked with the hands. If a mixture of different materials is used together in a ceramic, the sintering temperature is sometimes above the melting point of one minor component - a *liquid phase* sintering. This results in shorter sintering times compared to solid state sintering.

Other Applications of Ceramics

In the early 1980s, Toyota researched production of an adiabatic ceramic engine which can run at a temperature of over 6000 °F (3300 °C). Ceramic engines do not require a cooling system and hence allow a major weight reduction and therefore greater fuel efficiency. Fuel efficiency of the engine is also higher at high temperature, as show by Carnot's theorem. In a conventional metallic engine, much of the energy released from the fuel must be dissipated as waste heat in order to prevent a meltdown of the metallic parts. Despite all of these desirable properties, such engines are not in production because the manufacturing of ceramic parts in the requisite precision and durability is difficult. Imperfection in the ceramic leads to cracks, which can lead to potentially dangerous equipment failure. Such engines are possible in laboratory settings, but mass-production is unfeasible with current technology. Work is being done in developing ceramic parts for gas turbine engines. Currently, even blades made of advanced metal alloys used in the engines' hot section require cooling and careful limiting of operating temperatures. Turbine engines made with ceramics could operate more efficiently, giving aircraft greater range and payload for a set amount of fuel. Ceramics are used in the manufacture of knives. The blade of the ceramic knife will stay sharp for much longer than that of a steel knife, although it is more brittle and can be snapped by dropping it on a hard surface. Since the late 1990s, highly specialized ceramics, usually based on boron carbide, formed into plates and lined with Spectra, have been used in ballistic armored vests to repel large-caliber rifle fire.

Such plates are known commonly as small-arms protective inserts (SAPI). Very similar technology is used to protect cockpits of some military airplanes, because of the low weight of the material. Recently, there have been advances in ceramics which include bio-ceramics, such as dental implants and synthetic bones. Hydroxyapatite, the natural mineral component of bone, has been made synthetically from a number of biological and chemical sources and can be formed into ceramic materials.

Orthopedic implants made from these materials bond readily to bone and other tissues in the body without rejection or inflammatory reactions. Because of this, they are of great interest for gene delivery and tissue engineering scaffolds. Most hydroxyapatite ceramics are very porous and lack mechanical strength and are used to coat metal orthopedic devices to aid in forming a bond to bone or as bone fillers. They are also used as fillers for orthopedic plastic screws to aid in reducing the inflammation and increase absorption of these plastic materials. Work is being done to make strong-fully dense nano crystalline hydroxapatite ceramic materials for orthopedic weight bearing devices, replacing foreign metal and plastic orthopedic materials with a synthetic natural bone mineral. Ultimately these ceramic materials may be used as bone replacements or with the incorporation of protein collagens, synthetic bones.

REFERENCES

Armstrong, T. R., West, D. L., Montgomery, Fred C., "ORNL NOx Sensor Programme."

N.D. Evans, P.J. Maziasz, and J.J. Truhan, "Phase Transformations During Service Aging of Ni-based Superalloy Pyromet 31V," to be published in Solid-Solid Phase Transformations in Inorganic Materials 2005, TMS, May-June 2005, Warrendale, PA.

H. T. Lin, M. P. Brady, R. K. Richards, and D. M. Layton "Characterization of Erosion and Failure Processes of Spark Plugs After Field Service in Natural Gas Engines," Wear, Vol. 259/7-12 pp. 1063-1067 (2005).

P. J. Maziasz, J.P. Shingledecker and N.D. Evans, "Alloy Additions for Improved Creep-Rupture Properties of a Cast Austenitic Stainless Steel – CF8C-Plus with Cu, W," Symposium on Creep Deformation and Fracture, Design, and Life Extension, at MS&T'05, 25-28 September, 2005 Pittsburg, PA.

Maziasz, P. J., "Advanced Materials for Exhaust Components," ARES Programme Review.

R.K. Richards, T.J. Theiss, H.T. Lin, and M.P. Brady, "Characterization of Erosion Processes of Spark Plugs After Field Service in Natural Gas Engine Spark Plugs," presented at Internal Combustion Engine Division of ASME 2004 Fall Technical Conference, October 24-27, 2004, Long Beach, CA.

R. K. Roger, D. M. Layton, H. T. Lin, and M. P. Brady, "Characterization of Erosion Mechanisms for Natural Gas Engine Spark Plugs," ICEF2004-875 published at Proceedings of Internal Combustion Engine Division of ASME 2004 Fall Technical Conference, October 24-27, 2004, Long Beach, CA.

Properties of a Cast Austenitic Alloy," in Conf. Proc. Creep Deformation and Fracture, Design, and Life Extension, TMS, Warrendale, PA (2005), pp.129-138.

L. R. Walker, H. T. Lin, I. Levina, M. P. Brady,, and J. Lykowski, "SEM and EPMA Analysis of Spark Plug Electrode Erosion," pp. 1614-15 in Proceeding of Microscopy and Microanalysis 2005," July 31-August 4, 2005, Honolulu, Hawaii.

5

Research Methodology in Computer Science

INTRODUCTION

Computer science (or computing science) is the study and the science of the theoretical foundations of information and computation and their implementation and application in computer systems. Computer science has many sub-fields; some emphasize the computation of specific results (such as computer graphics), while others relate to properties of computational problems (such as computational complexity theory). Still others focus on the challenges in implementing computations. For example, programming language theory studies approaches to describing computations, while computer programming applies specific programming languages to solve specific computational problems. A further subfield, human-computer interaction, focuses on the challenges in making computers and computations useful, usable and universally accessible to people.

History

The early foundations of what would become computer science predate the invention of the modern digital computer. Machines for calculating fixed numerical tasks, such as the abacus, have existed since antiquity. Wilhelm Schickard built the first mechanical calculator in 1623. Charles Babbage designed a difference engine in Victorian times (between 1837 and 1901) helped by Ada Lovelace. Around 1900, the IBM corporation sold punch-card machines. However, all of these machines were constrained to perform a single task, or at best some subset of all possible tasks. During the 1940s, as newer and more powerful computing machines were developed, the term *computer* came to refer to the machines rather than their human predecessors. As it became clear that computers could be used for more than just mathematical calculations, the field of computer science broadened to study computation in general. Computer science began to be established as a distinct academic discipline in the 1960s, with the creation of the first computer science departments and degree programs. Since practical computers became available, many applications of computing have become distinct areas of study in their own right. Many initially believed it impossible that "computers themselves could actually be a scientific field of study" (Levy 1984, p. 11), though it was in the "late fifties" (Levy 1984, p.11) that it gradually became accepted among the greater academic population. It is the now well-known IBM brand that formed part of the computer science revolution during this time. IBM (short for International Business Machines) released the IBM 704 and later the IBM 709 computers, which were widely used during the exploration period of such devices. "Still, working with the IBM [computer] was frustrating...if you had misplaced as much as one letter in one instruction, the program would crash, and you would have to start the whole process over again" (Levy 1984, p.13). During the late 1950s, the computer science discipline was very much in its developmental stages, and such issues were commonplace. Time has seen significant improvements in the useability and effectiveness of computer science technology. Modern society has seen a significant shift from computers being used solely by experts or professionals to a more widespread user base. By the 1990s, computers became accepted as being the norm within everyday life. During this time data entry was a primary component of the use of computers, many preferring to streamline their business practices through the use of a computer. This also gave the additional benefit of removing the need of large amounts of documentation and file records which consumed much-needed physical space within offices.

Relationship with Other Fields

Despite its name, a significant amount of computer science does not involve the study of computers themselves. Because of this, several alternative names have been proposed. Danish scientist Peter Naur suggested the term *datalogy*, to reflect the fact that the scientific discipline revolves around data and data treatment, while not necessarily involving computers. The first scientific institution to use the term was the Department of Datalogy at the University of Copenhagen, founded in 1969, with Peter Naur being the first professor in datalogy. The term is used mainly in the Scandinavian countries. Also, in the early days of computing, a number of terms for the practitioners of the field of computing were suggested in the *Communications of the ACM—turingineer*, *turologist*, *flow-charts-man*, *applied meta-mathematician*, and *applied epistemologist*. Three months later in the same journal, *comptologist* was suggested, followed next year by *hypologist*. Recently the term *computics* has been suggested. *Informatik* was a term used in Europe with more frequency. The renowned computer scientist Edsger Dijkstra stated, "Computer science is no more about computers than astronomy is about telescopes." The design and deployment of computers and computer systems is generally considered the province of disciplines other than computer science. For example, the study of computer hardware is usually considered part of computer engineering, while the study of commercial computer systems and their deployment is often called information technology or information systems. Computer science is sometimes criticized as being insufficiently scientific, a view espoused in the statement "Science is to computer science as hydrodynamics is to plumbing", credited to Stan Kelly-Bootle and others. However, there has been much cross-fertilization of ideas between the various computer-related disciplines. Computer science research has also often crossed into other disciplines, such as cognitive science, economics, mathematics, physics (see quantum computing), and linguistics.

Computer science is considered by some to have a much closer relationship with mathematics than many scientific disciplines. Early computer science was strongly influenced by the work of mathematicians such as Kurt Gödel and Alan Turing, and there continues to be a useful interchange of ideas between the two fields in areas such as mathematical logic, category theory, domain theory, and algebra.

The relationship between computer science and software engineering is a contentious issue, which is further muddied by disputes over what the term "software engineering" means, and how computer science is defined. David Parnas, taking a cue from the relationship between other engineering and science disciplines, has claimed that the principal focus of computer science is studying the properties of computation in general, while the principal focus of software engineering is the design of specific computations to achieve practical goals, making the two separate but complementary disciplines. The academic, political, and funding aspects of computer science tend to have roots as to whether a department in the U.S. formed with either a mathematical emphasis or an engineering emphasis. In general, electrical engineering-based computer science departments have tended to succeed as computer science and/or engineering departments. Computer science departments with a mathematics emphasis and with a numerical orientation consider alignment computational science. Both types of departments tend to make efforts to bridge the field educationally if not across all research.

Education of Computer Science

Some universities teach computer science as a theoretical study of computation and algorithmic reasoning. These programs often feature the theory of computation, analysis of algorithms, formal methods, concurrency theory, databases, computer graphics and systems analysis, among others. They typically also teach computer programming, but treat it as a vessel for the support of other fields of computer science rather than a central focus of high-level study.

Other colleges and universities, as well as secondary schools and vocational programs that teach computer science, emphasize the practice of advanced computer programming rather than the theory of algorithms and computation in their computer science curricula. Such curricula tend to focus on those skills that are important to workers entering the software industry. The practical aspects of computer programming are often referred to as software engineering. However, there is a lot of disagreement over what the term "software engineering" actually means, and whether it is the same thing as programming.

Computer Software

Software, or programme, enables a computer to perform specific tasks, as opposed to the physical components of the system (*hardware*). This includes application software such as a word processor, which enables a user to perform a task, and system software such as an operating system, which enables other software to run properly, by interfacing with hardware and with other software or custom software made to user specifications.

Computer software is so called in contrast to computer hardware, which encompasses the physical interconnections and devices required to store and execute (or run) the software. In computers, software is loaded into RAM and executed in the central processing unit. At the lowest level, software consists of a machine language specific to an individual processor. A machine language consists of groups of binary values signifying processor instructions (object code), which change the state of the computer from its preceding state. Software is an ordered sequence of instructions for changing the state of the computer hardware in a particular sequence. It is usually written in high-level programming languages that are easier and more efficient for humans to use (closer to natural language) than machine language. High-level languages are compiled or interpreted into machine language object code. Software may also be written in an assembly language, essentially, a mnemonic representation of a machine language using a natural language alphabet. Assembly language must be assembled into object code via an assembler. The term "software" was first used in this sense by John W. Tukey in 1957. In computer science and software engineering, computer software is all computer programmes. The concept of reading different sequences of instructions into the memory of a device to control computations was invented by Charles Babbage as part of his difference engine. The theory that is the basis for most modern software was first proposed by Alan Turing in his 1935 essay *Computable numbers with an application to the Entscheidungsproblem*.

Types

Practical computer systems divide software into three major classes: system software, programming software and application software, although the distinction is arbitrary, and often blurred.

- System software helps run the computer hardware and computer system. It includes operating systems, device drivers, diagnostic tools, servers, windowing systems, utilities and more. The purpose of systems software is to insulate the applications programr as much as possible from the details of the particular computer complex being used, especially memory and other hardware features, and such accessory devices as communications, printers, readers, displays, keyboards, etc.
- Programming software usually provides tools to assist a programr in writing computer programmes and software using different programming languages in a more convenient way. The tools include text editors, compilers, interpreters, linkers, debuggers, and so on. An Integrated development environment (IDE) merges those tools into a software bundle, and a programr may not need to type multiple commands for compiling, interpreter, debugging, tracing, and etc., because the IDE usually has an advanced *graphical user interface,* or GUI.
- Application software allows end users to accomplish one or more specific (non-computer related) tasks. Typical applications include industrial automation, business software, educational software, medical software, databases, and computer games. Businesses are probably the biggest users of application software, but almost every field of human activity now uses some form of application software. It is used to automate all sorts of functions.

Programme and Library

A programme may not be sufficiently complete for execution by a computer. In particular, it may require additional software from a software library in order to be complete. Such a library may include software components used by stand-alone programmes, but which cannot work on their own. Thus, programmes may include standard routines that are common to many programmes, extracted from these libraries. Libraries may also *include* 'stand-alone' programmes which are activated by some computer event and/or perform some function (e.g., of computer 'housekeeping') but do not return data to their calling programme. Programmes may be called by one to many other programmes; programmes may call zero to many other programmes.

Three Layers

Users often see things differently than programrs. People who use modern general purpose computers (as opposed to embedded systems, analog computers, supercomputers, etc.) usually see three layers of software performing a variety of tasks: platform, application, and user software.

Platform Software

Platform includes the basic input-output system (often described as *firmware* rather than *software*), device drivers, an operating system, and typically a graphical user interface which, in total, allow a user to interact with the computer and its peripherals (associated equipment). Platform software often comes bundled with the computer, and users may not realise that it exists or that they have a choice to use different platform software.

Application Software

Application software or Applications are what most people think of when they think of software. Typical examples include office suites and video games. Application software is often purchased separately from computer hardware. Sometimes applications are bundled with the computer, but that does not change the fact that they run as independent applications. Applications are almost always independent programmes from the operating system, though they are often tailored for specific platforms. Most users think of compilers, databases, and other "system software" as applications.

User-written Software

User software tailors systems to meet the users specific needs. User software include spreadsheet templates, word processor macros, scientific simulations, graphics and animation scripts. Even email filters are a kind of user software. Users create this software themselves and often overlook how important it is. Depending on how competently the user-written software has been integrated into purchased application packages, many users may not be aware of the distinction between the purchased packages, and what has been added by fellow co-workers.

Creation

Creation (Computer programming) (often shortened to programming or coding) is the process of writing, testing, and maintaining the source code of computer programmes. The source code is written in a programming language. This code may be a modification of existing source or something completely new. The process of writing source code requires expertise in many different subjects, including knowledge of the application domain and algorithms to implement the desired behavior. Within software engineering, programming (the *implementation*) is regarded as one phase in a software development process.

In some specialist applications or extreme situations a programme may be written or modified (known as patching) by directly storing the numeric values of the machine code instructions to be executed into memory.

There is an ongoing debate on the extent to which the writing of programmes is an art or an engineering discipline.

Another ongoing debate is the extent to which the programming language used in writing programmes affects the form that the final programme takes. This debate is analogous to that surrounding the Sapir Whorf hypothesis in linguistics.

Programmers

Computer programrs are those who write computer software. Their job usually involves:

- Requirements analysis
- Specification
- Software architecture
- Coding
- Compilation
- Software testing
- Documentation
- Integration
- Maintenance

Programming Languages

Different programming languages support different styles of programming (called *programming paradigms*). The choice of language used may be an individual's choice or may be dictated by company policy. Ideally the programming language best suited for the task at hand will be selected. Trade-offs from this ideal involve finding enough programrs, who know the language, to build a team, the availability of compilers for that language, and the efficiency with which programmes written in a given language execute.

History of Programming

The earliest programmable machine (that is, a machine that can adjust its capabilities based upon changing its "program") can be said to be the Jacquard Loom, which was developed in 1801. The machine used a series of pasteboard cards with holes punched in them. The hole pattern represented the pattern that the loom had to follow in weaving cloth. The loom could produce entirely different weaves using different sets of cards. This innovation was later refined by Herman Hollerith of IBM in the development of the famous IBM punch card. These were used with a variety of machines called unit record equipment to perform data processing tasks. The unit record equipment were programmed by changing the wiring of plug-boards. Early computers used similar programming methods.

The invention of the Von Neumann architecture allowed programmes to be stored in computer memory. Early programmes had to be painstakingly crafted using the instructions of the particular machine, often in binary notation. Every model of computer would be likely to need different instructions to do the same task. Later assembly languages were developed that let the programer specify each instruction in a text format, entering abbreviations for each operation code instead of a number and specifying addresses in symbolic form (e.g. ADD X, TOTAL). In 1954 Fortran, the first higher level programming language, was invented. This allowed programmers to specify calculations by entering a formula directly (e.g. Y = X*2 + 5*X + 9). The programme text, or *source*, was converted into machine instructions using a special programme called a compiler. Many other languages were developed, including ones for commercial programming, such as COBOL. Programmes were mostly still entered using punch cards or paper tape. In the mid-1970s, mass storage devices and computer terminals became inexpensive enough so programmes could be created by typing directly into the computers. Text editors were developed that allowed changes and corrections to be made much more easily than with punch cards.

As time has progressed computers have made giant leaps in the area of processing power. This has brought about newer programing languages that are more abstracted from the underlying hardware. Although these more abstracted languages require additional overhead, in most cases the huge increase in speed of modern computers has brought about little performance decrease compared to earlier counterparts. The benefits of these more abstracted languages is that they allow both an easier learning curve for people less familiar with the older lower-level programming languages, and they also allow a more experienced programmer to develop simple applications quickly. Despite these benefits, large complicated programmes, and programmes that are more dependent on speed still require the faster and relatively lower-level languages with todays hardware. (The same concerns were raised about the original Fortran language.)

Throughout the second half of the twentieth century, programming was an attractive career in most developed countries. Some forms of programming have been increasingly subject to offshore outsourcing (importing software and services from other countries, usually at a lower wage), making programming career decisions in developed countries more complicated, while increasing economic opportunities in less developed areas. It is unclear how far this trend will continue and how deeply it will impact programmer wages and opportunities. Despite the "outsourcing trend" it can be argued that some of the richest persons on the globe are programmers by profession. Examples: Bill Gates (Microsoft), Larry Ellison (Oracle), Larry Page (Google), Hasso Plattner (SAP) and so on. Programming is clearly a leading-edge craftsmanship that continues to reward its professionals both in countries such as India and developed countries like the USA or Germany.

Modern Programming

Methodologies: The first step in every software development project should be requirements analysis, followed by modeling, implementation and failure elimination (debugging). There exist a lot of differing approaches for each of those tasks; with the most popular modeling technique being Object-Oriented Analysis and Design (OOAD) and Model-Driven Architecture (MDA). The Unified Modeling language (UML) is a notation used for OOAD. A similar technique used for database design is Entity-Relationship Modeling (ER Modeling). Implementation techniques include imperative languages (object-oriented or procedural), functional languages and logic languages. Debugging is most often done with IDEs like Visual Studio, Eclipse or gdb.

Modern Languages: The most popular programming languages in the 21st century are C++, Cobol, Fortran, Java and PHP. Java is popular because it avoids a lot of failure modes of lower-level languages such as C++ or Assembler. Still, most PC desktop applications such as word processors or image manipulation programmes are written in more (runtime- and memory-)efficient languages like C++, Delphi or even Assembler. Scientific applications are often implemented in Fortran because very efficient optimization (using optimizing Compilers) is possible in this language. Cobol is still very strong in the corporate data center, mainly on big Mainframe computers. PHP and Java excel in database-oriented applications which are often delivered over the internet or corporate intranets.

Debugging: Debugging is a very important task for every programmer, because an erroneous programme is often useless. Languages like C++ and Assembler are very challenging even to expert programmers because of failure modes like Buffer overruns, bad pointers or uninitialized memory. A buffer overrun can damage adjacent memory regions and cause a failure in a totally different programme line. Because of those memory issues tools like Valgrind, Purify or Boundschecker are virtually a necessity for modern software development in the C++ language. Languages such as Java and PHP protect the programmer from most of these runtime failure modes, but this comes at the price of a dramatically lower execution speed of the resulting programme. This is acceptable for a large class of enterprise applications, which spend most of their execution time on database access.

Operation

Computer software has to be "loaded" into the computer's storage (such as a *hard drive*, *memory*, or *RAM*). Once the software is loaded, the computer is able to execute the software. Computers operate by *executing* the computer programme. This involves passing instructions from the application software, through the system software, to the hardware which ultimately receives the instruction as machine code. Each instruction causes the computer to carry out an operation — moving data, carrying out a computation, or altering the control flow of instructions. Data movement is typically from one place in memory to another. Sometimes it involves moving data between memory and registers which enable high-speed data access in the CPU. Moving data, especially large amounts of it, can be costly. So, this is sometimes avoided by using "pointers" to data instead. Computations include simple operations such as incrementing the value of a variable data element. More complex computations may involve many operations and data elements together. Instructions may be performed sequentially, conditionally, or iteratively. Sequential instructions are those operations that are performed one after another. Conditional instructions are performed such that different sets of instructions execute depending on the value(s) of some data. In some languages this is known as an "if" statement. Iterative instructions are performed repetitively and may depend on some data value.

This is sometimes called a "loop." Often, one instruction may "call" another set of instructions that are defined in some other programme or module. When more than one computer processor is used, instructions may be executed simultaneously. A simple example of the way software operates is what happens when a user selects an entry such as "Copy" from a menu. In this case, a conditional instruction is executed to copy text from data in a 'document' area residing in memory, perhaps to an intermediate storage area known as a 'clipboard' data area. If a different menu entry such as "Paste" is chosen, the software may execute the instructions to copy the text from the clipboard data area to a specific location in the same or another document in memory. Depending on the application, even the example above could become complicated. The field of software engineering endeavors to manage the complexity of how software operates. This is especially true for software that operates in the context of a large or powerful computer system. Currently, almost the only limitations on the use of computer software in applications is the ingenuity of the designer/programr.

Consequently, large areas of activities (such as playing grand master level chess) formerly assumed to be incapable of software simulation are now routinely programmed. The only area that has so far proved reasonably secure from software simulation is the realm of human art— especially, pleasing music and literature.

Kinds of software by operation: computer programme as executable, source code or script, configuration.

License

Software license gives the user the right to use the software in the licensed environment, some software comes with the license when purchased off the shelf, or OEM license when bundled with hardware. Software can also be in the form of freeware or shareware. See also License Management

Quality and Reliability

Software reliability considers the errors, faults, and failures related to the creation and operation of software. See Software auditing, Software quality, Software testing, and Software reliability.

Patents

The issue of software patents is controversial. Some believe that they hinder software development. See Hacker ethic and software patent debate.

Computing Technology

Computing is a very broad topic that has become pandemic to modern uses of technology. If includes the following:

- Computer hardware
  - Computer
  - Home computer
  - Mini computer
  - Mainframe computer
  - Routing
- Software or computer programme
  - Firmware
  - Operating systems
  - Application Software
  - Databases
  - Geographic information system
  - Spreadsheet
  - Word processor
  - Programming languages

    - Interpreters
    - Compilers
    - Speech recognition
- Collaborative Ether
- Collaborative workspace
- Computer network
- Handheld computing technologies
    - Abacus
    - Calculators
    - Pencil (Stylus, chalk, etc.)
    - Personal digital assistants
    - Tablet PCs
- Internet
- Industrial data processing
- Programmable logic controller or PLC
- Network Management
- Utility Computing
- Network
    - Wide Area Network
    - Metropolitan Area Network
    - City Area Network
    - Town Area Network
    - Village Area Network
    - Rural Area Network
    - Local Area Network
    - Wireless Local Area Network

Computer Hardware

Computer hardware is the physical part of a computer, including the digital circuitry, as distinguished from the computer software that executes within the hardware. The hardware of a computer is infrequently changed, in comparison with software and data, which are "soft" in the sense that they are readily created, modified or erased on the computer. Firmware is a special type of software that rarely, if ever, needs to be changed and so is stored on hardware devices such as read-only memory (ROM) where it is not readily changed (and is therefore "firm" rather than just "soft"). Most computer hardware is not seen by normal users. It is in embedded systems in automobiles, microwave ovens, electrocardiograph machines, compact disc players, and other devices. Personal computers, the computer hardware familiar to most people, form only a small minority of computers (about 0.2% of all new computers produced in 2003). See Market statistics.

Personal Computer Hardware

A typical personal computer consists of a case or chassis in desktop or tower shape and the following parts:

- Motherboard or system board with slots for expansion cards and holding parts including:
  - o Central processing unit (CPU)
  - o Computer fan — used to cool down the CPU
  - o Random Access Memory (RAM) — for programme execution and short term data storage, so the computer does not have to take the time to access the hard drive to find the file(s) it requires. More RAM will normally contribute to a faster PC. RAM is almost always removable as it sits in slots in the motherboard, attached with small clips. The RAM slots are normally located next to the CPU socket.
  - o Basic Input-Output System (BIOS) or Extensible Firmware Interface (EFI) in some newer computers
  - o Buses
  - PCI
  - PCI-E
  - USB
  - HyperTransport
  - CSI (expected in 2008)
  - AGP (being phased out)
  - VLB (outdated)
  - ISA (outdated)
  - EISA (outdated)

- Power supply — a case that holds a transformer, voltage control, and (usually) a cooling fan
- Storage controllers of IDE, SATA, SCSI or other type, that control hard disk, floppy disk, CD-ROM and other drives; the controllers sit directly on the motherboard (on-board) or on expansion cards
- Video display controller that produces the output for the computer display. This will either be built into the motherboard or attached in it's own separate slot (PCI, PCI-E or AGP), requiring a Graphics Card.
- Computer bus controllers (parallel, serial, USB, FireWire) to connect the computer to external peripheral devices such as printers or scanners
- Some type of a removable media writer:
    - o CD — the most common type of removable media, cheap but fragile.
        - CD-ROM Drive
        - CD Writer
    - o Floppy disk
    - o Zip drive
    - o USB flash drive AKA a Pen Drive
    - o Tape drive — mainly for backup and long-term storage
- Internal storage — keeps data inside the computer for later use.
    - o Hard disk — for medium-term storage of data.
    - o Disk array controller
- Sound card — translates signals from the system board into analog voltage levels, and has terminals to plug in speakers.
- Networking — to connect the computer to the Internet and/or other computers
    - o Modem — for dial-up connections
    - o Network card — for DSL/Cable internet, and/or connecting to other computers.
- Other peripherals

In addition, hardware can include external components of a computer system. The following are either standard or very common.

- Input or Input devices

- o Text input devices
  - Keyboard
- o Pointing devices
  - Mouse
  - Trackball
- o Gaming devices
  - Joystick
  - Gamepad
  - Game controller
- o Image, Video input devices
  - Image scanner
  - Webcam
  - Audio input devices
  - Microphone
  - Output or Output devices
- o Image, Video output devices
  - Printer Peripheral device that produces a hard copy. (Inkjet, Laser)
  - Monitor Device that takes signals and displays them. (CRT, LCD)
- o Audio output devices
  - Speakers A device that converts analog audio signals into the equivalent air vibrations in order to make audible sound.
  - Headset A device similar in functionality to that of a regular telephone handset but is worn on the head to keep the hands free.

Computer Network

A computer network is two or more computers connected together using a telecommunication system for the purpose of communicating and sharing resources. Experts in the field of networking debate whether *two* computers that are connected together using some form of communications medium constitute a network. Therefore, some sources will state that a network requires *three* connected computers. A computer connected to a non-computing device (e.g., networked to a printer via an Ethernet link) may also represent a computer network, although this article does not currently address this configuration. For example, states that "the term network describes two or more connected computers" while states that a computer network is "A network of data processing nodes that are interconnected for the purpose of data communication", the term "network" being defined in the same document as "An interconnection of three or more communicating entities" (author's emphasis).

This article uses the definition which requires two or more computers to be connected together to form a network. The same basic functions are generally present in this case as with larger numbers of connected computers.

Basic Computer Network Building Blocks

Computers

Many of the components of an average network are individual computers, which are generally either workstations (including personal computers) or servers.

Types of Workstations

There are many types of workstations that may be incorporated into a particular network, some of which have high-end displays, multiple CPUs, large amounts of RAM, large amounts of hard drive storage space, or other enhancements required for special data processing tasks, graphics, or other resource intensive applications.

Types of Servers

The following lists some common types of servers and their purpose.

(i) *File Server:* Stores various types of files and distributes them to other clients on the network.

(i) *Print Server:* Controls and manages one or more printers and accepts print jobs from other network clients, spooling the print jobs, and performing most or all of the other functions that a workstation would perform to accomplish a printing task if the printer were connected directly to the workstation's printer port.

(iii) *Mail Server:* Stores, sends, receives, routes, and performs other email related operations for other clients on the network.

(iv) *Fax Server:* Stores, sends, receives, routes, and performs other functions necessary for the proper transmission, reception, and distribution of faxes.

(v) *Telephony Server:* Performs telephony related functions such as answering calls automatically, performing the functions of an interactive voice response system, storing and serving voice mail, routing calls between the Public Switched Telephone Network (PSTN) and the network or the Internet (e.g., voice over IP (VoIP) gateway), etc.

(vi) *Proxy Server:* Performs some type of function on behalf of other clients on the network to increase the performance of certain operations (e.g., prefetching and caching documents or other data that is requested very frequently) or as a security precaution to isolate network clients from external threats.

(vii) *Remote Access Server (RAS):* Monitors modem lines or other network communications channels for requests to connect to the network from a remote location, answers the incoming telephone call or acknowledges the network request, and performs the necessary security checks and other procedures necessary to log a user onto the network.

(viii) *Application Server:* Performs the data processing or business logic portion of a client application, accepting instructions for operations to perform from a workstation and serving the results back to the workstation, while the workstation performs the user interface or GUI portion of the processing (i.e., the presentation logic) that is required for the application to work properly.

(ix) *Web Server:* Stores HTML documents, images, text files, scripts, and other Web related data (collectively known as *content*), and distributes this content to other clients on the network on request.

(x) *Backup Server:* Has network backup software installed and has large amounts of hard drive storage or other forms of storage (tape, etc.) available to it to be used for the purpose of ensuring that data loss does not occur in the network.

Printers

Many printers are capable of acting as part of a computer network without any other device, such as a print server, to act as an intermediary between the printer and the device that is requesting a print job to be completed.

Dumb Terminals

Many networks use dumb terminals instead of workstations either for data entry and display purposes or in some cases where the application runs entirely on the server.

Other Devices

There are many other types of devices that may be used to build a network, many of which require an understanding of more advanced computer networking concepts before they are able to be easily understood (e.g., hubs, routers, bridges, switches, hardware firewalls, etc.). On home and mobile networks, connecting consumer electronics devices such as video game consoles is becoming increasingly common.

Dumb Terminals

Many networks use dumb terminals instead of workstations either for data entry and display purposes or in some cases where the application runs entirely on the server.

Building a Computer Network

Practical Networks

Practical networks generally consist of more than two interconnected computers and generally require special devices addition to the Network Interface Controller that each computer needs to be equipped with. Examples of some of these special devices are listed above under Basic Computer Network Building Blocks / Other devices.

A Simple Network

A simple computer network may be constructed from two computers by adding a network adapter (Network Interface Controller (NIC)) to each computer and then connecting them together with a special cable called a crossover cable. This type of network is useful for transferring information between two computers that are not normally connected to each other by a permanent network connection or for basic home networking applications.

Network Types

Here, is a list of the most common types of computer networks.

Local Area Network (LAN)

A network that is limited to a relatively small spatial area such as a room, a single building, a ship,or an aircraft,local area network is colled of singen location network. Note: For administrative purposes, large LANs are generally divided into smaller logical segments called *workgroups*. A workgroup is a group of computers that share a common set of resources within a LAN.

Campus Area Network (CAN)

A network that connects two or more LANs but that is limited to a specific (possibly private) geographical area such as a college campus, industrial complex, or a military base. Note: A CAN is generally limited to an area that is smaller than a Metropolitan Area Network (MAN).

Metropolitan Area Network (MAN)

A network that connects two or more LANs or CANs together but that does not extend beyond the boundaries of the immediate town, city, metropolitan area, and multipal router's, swetch & hups or connacted to call MAN asheesh sharma.

Wide Area Network (WAN)

A network that covers a broad geographical area (i.e., any network whose communications links cross metropolitan, regional, or national boundaries) or, less formally, a network that uses routers and public communications links.

Types of WANs

(i) *Centralized:* A centralized WAN consists of a central computer that is connected to dumb terminals and / or other types of terminal devices.

(ii) *Distributed:* A distributed WAN consists of two or more computers in different locations and may also include connections to dumb terminals and other types of terminal devices.

Internetwork:

Two or more networks or network segments connected using devices that operate at layer 3 (the 'network' layer) of the OSI Basic Reference Model, such as a router. Note: Any interconnection among or between public, private, commercial, industrial, or governmental networks may also be defined as an internetwork.

Intranet

A network or internetwork that is limited in scope to a single organisation or entity or, also, a network or internetwork that is limited in scope to a single organisation or entity and which uses the TCP/IP protocol suite, HTTP, FTP, and other network protocols and software commonly used on the Internet. Intranets may also be categorized as a LAN, CAN, MAN, WAN, or other type of network.

Extranet

A network or internetwork that is limited in scope to a single organisation or entity but which also has limited connections to the networks of one or more other usually, but not necessarily, trusted organisations or entities (e.g., a company's customers may be provided access to some part of its intranet thusly creating an extranet while at the same time the customers may not be considered 'trusted' from a security standpoint). Note: Technically, an extranet may also be categorized as a CAN, MAN, WAN, or other type of network, although, by definition, an extranet cannot consist of a single LAN, because an extranet must have at least one connection with an outside network. Intranets and extranets may or may not have connections to the Internet. If connected to the Internet, the intranet or extranet is normally protected from being accessed from the Internet without proper authorization. The Internet itself is not considered to be a part of the intranet or extranet, although the Internet may serve as a portal for access to portions of an extranet.

Computer Network Classifications

By Scale

Computer networks may be classified according to the scale or extent of reach of the network, for example as a Personal area network (PAN), Local area network (LAN), Wireless local area network (WLAN), Campus area network (CAN), Metropolitan area network (MAN), or Wide area network (WAN).

By Connection Method

Computer networks may be classified according to the technology that is used to connect the individual devices in the network such as HomePNA, Power line communication, Ethernet, or WiFi.

By Network Layer

Computer networks may be classified according to the network layer at which they operate according to some basic reference models that are considered to be standards in the industry such as the seven layer OSI reference model and the five layer TCP/IP model.

By Functional Relationship

Computer networks may be classified according to the functional relationships which exist between the elements of the network, for example Active Networking, Client-server and Peer-to-peer (workgroup) architectures.

By Protocol

Computer networks may be classified according to the communications protocol that is being used on the network. See the articles on List of network protocol stacks and List of network protocols for more information.

By Network Topology

Computer networks may be classified according to the network topology upon which the network is based, such as Bus network, Star network, Ring network, Mesh network, Star-bus network, Tree or Hierarchical topology network, etc. Topology can be arranged in a *Geometric Arragement*

By Services Provided

Computer networks may be classified according to the services which they provide, such as Storage area networks, Server farms, Process control networks, Value-added network, SOHO network, Wireless community network, XML appliance, Jungle Networks, khadar network, etc.

Local Area Network

A local area network (LAN) is a computer network covering a local area, like a home, office, or group of buildings. Current LANs are most likely to be based on switched IEEE 802.3 Ethernet technology, running at 10, 100 or 1,000 Mbit/s, or on Wi-Fi technology. Each node or computer in the LAN has its own computing power but it can also access other devices on the LAN subject to the permissions it has been allowed. These could include data, the more expensive devices / less used resources that it would be impractical to have multiple copies of, and the ability to communicate or chat with other users in the network. The defining characteristics of LANs, in contrast to WANs (wide area networks), are: their much higher data rates, smaller geographic range, and that they do not require leased telecommunication lines.

Technical Aspects

Although switched Ethernet is now the most common data link layer protocol (OSI 7-Layer Model), and IP as a network layer protocol, many different options have been used, and some continue to be popular in niche areas. Smaller LANs consist of a few switches typically connected to each other and with one connected to a router, cable modem, or DSL modem. A traditional model of access, distribution, and core switches was popularized by Cisco Systems and has been in use for many years. Larger LANs are characterized by distributing Ethernet traffic roles within the network. Each layer aggregates traffic of the layer below it and will typically maintain redundant links with switches capable of quality of service and spanning tree protocol to prevent loops and the recovery of failed uplinks. While initially used for basic data or programme sharing functionality the humble LAN has served as a catalyst for the indispensible role the intranet has come to play in modern government departments and businesses. The LAN based intranet has been a large contributor to the productivity increases in western economies during the early part of the 21st century. Initial implementations of LANs tended to revolve around the type of computers and devices attached to the LAN, and to the permissions they would be granted. Modern considerations include a carefully planned intranet strategy — to comply with legislative and other responsibilities — content management software, accessibility, scalability, audit requirements, document and information control and integration with telephone systems.

LANs may have connections to other LANs via routers and leased lines. Traditionally, the network connecting two or more LANs is referred to as the WAN (Wide Area Network). Recently, service providers have begun to offer additional services to link LANs together. These technologies, such as Metropolitan Area Networks (MANs), and MPLS/VPN services have diversified the standard model of interconnecting sites. There are also methods of connecting LANs together through the use of Internet connections, VPN software or hardware, and 'tunneling' across the Internet using VPN technologies. Topology, protocols and media (The cables, like CAT5, or radio waves that connect devices in the LAN) are the characteristics that differentiate LANs.

Home Networks

With the proliferation of computers and IT devices in the modern home has come the frequent use of LANs to connect them together. Many of these home LANs are wireless and use the 802.11g/b wireless networking standard which transmits data at 2.4 GHz.

History

In the days before personal computers, a site might have just one central computer, with users accessing this via computer terminals over simple low-speed cabling. Networks such as IBM's SNA (Systems Network Architecture) were aimed at linking terminals or other mainframes at remote sites over leased lines—hence these were wide area networks. The first LANs were created in the late 1970s and used to create high-speed links between several large central computers at one site. Of many competing systems created at this time, Ethernet and ARCNET were the most popular. The development and proliferation of CP/M- and then DOS-based personal computers meant that a single site began to have dozens or even hundreds of computers. The initial attraction of networking these was generally to share disk space and laser printers, which were both very expensive at the time. There was much enthusiasm for the concept and for several years, from about 1983 onward, computer industry pundits would regularly declare the coming year to be "the year of the LAN". In reality, the concept was marred by proliferation of incompatible physical layer and network protocol implementations, and confusion over how best to share resources. Typically, each vendor would have their own type of network card, cabling, protocol, and network operating system. A solution appeared with the advent of Novell NetWare which gave: (a) even-handed support for the 40 or so competing card/cable types, and (b) a much more sophisticated operating system than most of its competitors. Netware dominated the personal computer LAN business from early after its introduction in 1983 until the mid 1990s when Microsoft introduced Windows NT Advanced Server and Windows for Workgroups. Of the competitors to NetWare, only Banyan Vines had comparable technical strengths, but Banyan never gained a secure base. Microsoft and 3Com worked together to create a simple network operating system which formed the base of 3Com's 3+Share, Microsoft's LAN Manager and IBM's LAN Server. None of these were particularly successful. In this same timeframe, Unix computer workstations from vendors such as Sun

Microsystems, Hewlett-Packard, Silicon Graphics, Intergraph, NeXT and Apollo were using TCP/IP based networking. Although this market segment is now much reduced, the technologies developed in this area continue to be influential on the Internet and in both Linux and Apple Mac OS X networking, and the TCP/IP protocol has now almost completely replaced IPX, AppleTalk, NETBEUI and other protocols used by the early PC LANs.

Internet

The Internet is the worldwide, publicly accessible network of interconnected computer networks that transmit data by packet switching using the standard Internet Protocol (IP). It is a "network of networks" that consists of millions of smaller domestic, academic, business, and government networks, which together carry various information and services, such as electronic mail, online chat, file transfer, and the interlinked Web pages and other documents of the World Wide Web. Internet, computer-based worldwide information network. The Internet is composed of a large number of smaller interconnected networks called internets. These internets may connect tens, hundreds, or thousands of computers, enabling them to share information with each other and to share various resources, such as powerful supercomputers and databases of information. The Internet has made it possible for people all over the world to effectively and inexpensively communicate with each other. Unlike traditional broadcasting media, such as radio and television, the Internet is a decentralised system. Each connected individual can communicate with anyone else on the Internet, can publish ideas, and can sell products with a minimum overhead cost. In the future, the Internet may have a dramatic impact on higher education and business as more universities offer courses and more companies offer goods and services online. The internets from which the Internet is composed are usually public access networks, meaning that the resources of the network can be shared with anyone logging on to, or accessing, idle network. Other types of internets, called intranets, are closed to public use. Intranets are the most common type of computer network used in companies and organisations where it is important to restrict access to the information contained on the newwork. *See also* Local Area Network; Wide Area Network. During the 1990s the Internet has grown tremendously in the number of people using it and the amount of information contained on it. According to the Internet Society, a non-profit society that studies and promotes the use of the Internet, 134 countries had full internet connection and an additional 52 countries had limited access (for example, e-mail only) in 1996. Surveys performed by International Data Corporation and Matrix Information and Directory Services found that as of September 1997 there were between 53 and 57 million users of the Internet worldwide.

History

The Internet is an extension of a computer network originally formed in the United States during the 1960s by the Advanced Research Projects Agency (ARPA). Working under contract to the U.S. Department of Defense, ARPA initially connected computers at the Stanford Research Institute in California, the University of California at Los Angeles (UCLA), the University of California at Santa Barbara (UCSB), and the University of Utah. This original network, the very first computer network, was called ARPANET (ARPA NETwork). Scientists built ARPANET with the intention of creating a network that would still be able to function efficiently if part of the network was damaged. This concept was important to military organisations, which were studying ways to maintain a working communications network in the event of nuclear war.

As ARPANET grew in the 1970s, with more and more universities and institutions connecting to it, users found it necessary to establish standards for the way that data was transmitted over the network. To meet the needs of data transmission standards, computer scientists developed the Transmission Control Protocol (TCP) and the Internet Protocol (IP). During the 1970s various government, scientific, and academic groups developed their own networks. Examples include the Department of Energy's (DoE) Magnetic Fusion Energy Network (MFENet), the High Energy Physics NETwork (HEPNET), and the National Science Foundation NETwork.

In 1989 English computer scientist Timothy Berners-Lee introduced the World Wide Web. Berners-Lee initially designed the WWW to aid communication between physicists who were working indifferent parts of the world for the European Laboratory for Particle Physics (CERN). As it grew, however, the WWW revolutionised the use of the Internet. During the early 1990s increasingly large numbers of users who were not part of the scientific or academic communities began to use the Internet, due in large part to the ability of the WWW to easily handle multimedia documents.

Terminology: Internet vs. Web

The Internet and the World Wide Web are not synonymous: the Internet is a collection of interconnected *computer networks*, linked by copper wires, fiber-optic cables, wireless connections, etc.; the Web is a collection of interconnected documents and other *resources*, linked by hyperlinks and URLs. The World Wide Web is accessible via the Internet, as are many other services including e-mail, file sharing, and others described below.

The best way to define and distinguish between these terms is with reference to the Internet protocol suite. This collection of standards and protocols is organised into layers such that each layer provides the foundation and the services required by the layer above. In this conception, the term Internet refers to computers and networks that communicate using IP (Internet protocol) and TCP (transfer control protocol). Once this networking structure is established, then other protocols can run "on top." These other protocols are sometimes called services or applications. Hypertext transfer protocol, or HTTP, is the application layer protocol that links and provides access to the files, documents and other resources of the World Wide Web.

Creation of the Internet

The USSR's launch of Sputnik spurred the United States to create the Advanced Research Projects Agency (ARPA, later known as the Defense Advanced Research Projects Agency, or DARPA) in February 1958 to regain a technological lead. ARPA created the Information Processing Technology Office (IPTO) to further the research of the Semi Automatic Ground Environment (SAGE) programme, which had networked country-wide radar systems together for the first time. J. C. R. Licklider was selected to head the IPTO, and saw universal networking as a potential unifying human revolution.

In 1950, Licklider moved from the Psycho-Acoustic Laboratory at Harvard University to MIT where he served on a committee that established MIT Lincoln Laboratory. He worked on the SAGE project. In 1957 he became a Vice President at BBN, where he bought the first production PDP-1 computer and conducted the first public demonstration of time-sharing.

Licklider recruited Lawrence Roberts to head a project to implement a network, and Roberts based the technology on the work of Paul Baran who had written an exhaustive study for the U.S. Air Force that recommended packet switching (as opposed to Circuit switching) to make a network highly robust and survivable. After much work, the first node went live at UCLA on October 29, 1969 on what would be called the ARPANET, one of the "eve" networks of today's Internet. Following on from this, the British Post Office, Western Union International and Tymnet collaborated to create the first international packet switched network, referred to as the International Packet Switched Service (IPSS), in 1978. This network grew from Europe and the US to cover Canada, Hong Kong and Australia by 1981.

The first TCP/IP wide area network was operational by 1 January 1983, when the United States' National Science Foundation (NSF) constructed a university network backbone that would later become the NSFNet. (This date is held by some to be technically that of the birth of the Internet.) It was then followed by the opening of the network to commercial interests in 1985. Important, separate networks that offered gateways into, then later merged with, the NSFNet include Usenet, Bitnet and the various commercial and educational X.25 Compuserve and JANET. Telenet (later called Sprintnet), was a large privately-funded national computer network with free dialup access in cities throughout the U.S. that had been in operation since the 1970s. This network eventually merged with the others in the 1990s as the TCP/IP protocol became increasingly popular. The ability of TCP/IP to work over these pre-existing communication networks, especially the international X.25 IPSS network, allowed for a great ease of growth. Use of the term "Internet" to describe a single global TCP/IP network originated around this time.

The network gained a public face in the 1990s. On August 6th, 1991 CERN, which straddles the border between France and Switzerland publicized the new World Wide Web project, two years after Tim Berners-Lee had begun creating HTML, HTTP and the first few Web pages at CERN.

An early popular Web browser was *ViolaWWW* based upon HyperCard. It was eventually replaced in popularity by the Mosaic Web Browser. In 1993 the National Center for Supercomputing Applications at the University of Illinois at Urbana-Champaign released version 1.0 of *Mosaic* and by late 1994 there was growing public interest in the previously academic/technical Internet. By 1996 the word "Internet" was coming into common daily usage, frequently misused to refer to the World Wide Web.

Meanwhile, over the course of the decade, the Internet successfully accommodated the majority of previously existing public computer networks (although some networks such as FidoNet have remained separate). This growth is often attributed to the lack of central administration, which allows organic growth of the network, as well as the non-proprietary open nature of the Internet protocols, which encourages vendor interoperability and prevents any one company from exerting too much control over the network.

Today's Internet

Aside from the complex physical connections that make up its infrastructure, the Internet is facilitated by bi- or multi-lateral commercial contracts (e.g., peering agreements), and by technical specifications or protocols that describe how to exchange data over the network. Indeed, the Internet is essentially defined by its interconnections and routing policies. As of September 18, 2006, 1.09 billion people use the Internet according to Internet World Stats.

Internet Protocols

In this context, there are three layers of protocols:

- At the lowest level is IP (Internet Protocol), which defines the datagrams or packets that carry blocks of data from one node to another. The vast majority of today's Internet uses version four of the IP protocol (i.e. IPv4), and although IPv6 is standardized, it exists only as "islands" of connectivity, and there are many ISPs who don't have any IPv6 connectivity at all.

- Next come TCP (Transmission Control Protocol) and UDP (User Datagram Protocol) — the protocols by which one host sends data to another. The former makes a virtual 'connection', which gives some level of guarantee of reliability. The latter is a best-effort, connectionless transport, in which data packets that are lost in transit will not be re-sent.
- On top comes the application protocol. This defines the specific messages and data formats sent and understood by the applications running at each end of the communication.

Internet Structure

There have been many analyses of the Internet and its structure. For example, it has been determined that the Internet IP routing structure and hypertext links of the World Wide Web are examples of scale-free networks. Similar to the way the commercial Internet providers connect via Internet exchange points, research networks tend to interconnect into large subnetworks such as:

(i) GEANT
(ii) GLORIAD
(iii) Abilene Network
(iv) JANET (the UK's Joint Academic Network aka UKERNA)

These in turn are built around relatively smaller networks. See also the list of academic computer network organisations

In network schematic diagrams, the Internet is often represented by a cloud symbol, into and out of which network communications can pass.

Future of Internet

A major challenge facing the continued growth of the Internet is the difficulty of providing enough bandwidth to sustain the network. As Internet applications become more sophisticated, and as more people around the world use the Internet, the amount of information transmitted across the Internet will demand very high bandwidth connections. While many communications companies are attempting to develop higher bandwidth technologies, it is not known whether the technology will be able to satisfactorily keep up with demand. In order to accommodate the increasing number of users, the non-profit organisation University Corporation for Advanced Internet Development (UCAID) is working on the construction of Internet 2. Internet 2 will add more bandwidth, or available communication lines, to the current information superhighway in order to accommodate larger packets of data. UCAID members include representatives from universities, the government, and the computer industry. Another important question facing Internet growth is the issue of censorship. Because the Internet has grown so rapidly, governments have been slow to regulate its use and to pass laws regarding what content is acceptable. Many Internet users also see such laws as an infringement on their right to free speech. In 1996 the Congress of the United States passed the Communications Decency Act, which made it a crime to transmit indecent material over the Internet. This decision resulted in an immediate outcry from users, industry experts, and civil liberties groups opposed to such censorship. In 1997 the United States Supreme Court declared the act to be unconstitutional because it violated 1st Amendment rights to free speech. Commercial use of the Internet is sure to grow dramatically as more individuals gain access to it.

It may be possible in the future to order nearly any goods from internet sites and have them delivered using the postal service. Many companies are worried about security issues and the possibility of losing money through Internet commerce. They are therefore being very cautious about doing business on the Internet. Other businesses, however, are embracing the Internet, hoping to be first in what may be a rapidly expanding market.

The issue of business being conducted over the Internet raises important security issues. Companies doing business over the Internet must have very sophisticated security measures in place so that information such as credit card, bank account, and social security numbers cannot be accessed by unauthorised users. Similarly, government facilities, universities, and institutions must ensure that access to their computers over the Internet is strictly regulated.

ICANN

The Internet Corporation for Assigned Names and Numbers (ICANN) is the authority that coordinates the assignment of unique identifiers on the Internet, including domain names, Internet protocol addresses, and protocol port and parameter numbers. A globally unified namespace (i.e., a system of names in which there is one and only one holder of each name) is essential for the Internet to function. ICANN is headquartered in Marina del Rey, California, but is overseen by an international board of directors drawn from across the Internet technical, business, academic, and non-commercial communities. The US government continues to have the primary role in approving changes to the root zone file that lies at the heart of the domain name system. Because the Internet is a distributed network comprising many voluntarily interconnected networks, the Internet, as such, has no governing body. ICANN's role in coordinating the assignment of unique identifiers distinguishes it as perhaps the only central coordinating body on the global Internet, but the scope of its authority extends only to the Internet's systems of domain names, Internet protocol addresses, and protocol port and parameter numbers.

On Nov. 16, 2005, the World Summit on the Information Society, held in Tunis, established the Internet Governance Forum (IGF) to discuss Internet-related issues.

Language

The most prevalent language for communication on the Internet is English. This may be a result of the Internet's origins, as well as English's role as the lingua franca. It may also be related to the poor capability of early computers to handle characters other than those in the basic Latin alphabet.

After English (30% of Web visitors) the most-requested languages on the World Wide Web are Chinese 14%, Japanese 8%, Spanish 8%, German 6%, and French 4% (from Internet World Stats, updated June 30, 2006).

By continent, 37% of the world's Internet users are based in Asia, 28% in Europe, and 22% in North America.

The Internet's technologies have developed enough in recent years that good facilities are available for development and communication in most widely used languages. However, some glitches such as *mojibake* (incorrect display of foreign language characters, also known as *krakozyabry*) still remain.

Internet and the workplace

The Internet is allowing greater flexibility in working hours and location, especially with the spread of unmetered high-speed connections and Web applications.

The Mobile Internet

The Internet can now be accessed virtually anywhere by numerous means. Mobile phones, datacards, and cellular routers allow users to connect to the Internet from anywhere there is a cellular network supporting that device's technology.

Common uses of the Internet

E-mail

The concept of sending electronic text messages between parties in a way analogous to mailing letters or memos predates the creation of the Internet. Even today it can be important to distinguish between Internet and internal e-mail systems. Internet e-mail may travel and be stored unencrypted on many other machines and networks out of both the sender's and the recipient's control. During this time it is quite possible for the content to be read and even tampered with by third parties, if anyone considers it important enough. Purely internal or intranet mail systems, where the information never leaves the corporate or organisation's network and servers, is much more secure, although in any organisation there will be IT and other personnel whose job may involve monitoring, or at least occasionally accessing, the email of other employees not addressed to them. Web-based email (webmail) between parties on the same webmail system may not actually 'go' anywhere—it merely sits on the one server and is tagged in various ways so as to appear in one person's 'sent items' list and in one or more others' 'in boxes' or other 'folders' when viewed.

E-mail attachments have greatly increased the usefulness of e-mail in many ways. When a file is attached to an email, a text representation of the attached data (which may itself be binary data) is actually appended to the e-mail text, later to be reconstituted into a 'file' on the recipient's machine for their use. See MIME (Multipurpose Internet Mail Extensions) for details of how the problems involved in doing this have been overcome.

The World Wide Web

Through keyword-driven Internet research using search engines, like Google, millions worldwide have easy, instant access to a vast and diverse amount of online information. Compared to encyclopedias and traditional libraries, the World Wide Web has enabled a sudden and extreme decentralization of information and data.

Many individuals and some companies and groups have adopted the use of "Web logs" or blogs, which are largely used as easily-updatable online diaries. Some commercial organisations encourage staff to fill them with advice on their areas of specialization in the hope that visitors will be impressed by the expert knowledge and free information, and be attracted to the corporation as a result. One example of this practice is Microsoft, whose product developers publish their personal blogs in order to pique the public's interest in their work.

For more information on the distinction between the World Wide Web and the Internet itself — as in everyday use the two are sometimes confused — see Dark internet where this is discussed in more detail.

Remote Access

The Internet allows computer users to connect to other computers and information stores easily, wherever they may be across the world. They may do this with or without the use of security, authentication and encryption technologies, depending on the requirements.

This is encouraging new ways of working from home, collaboration and information sharing in many industries. An accountant sitting at home can audit the books of a company based in another country, on a server situated in a third country that is remotely maintained by IT specialists in a fourth. These accounts could have been created by home-working book-keepers, in other remote locations, based on information e-mailed to them from offices all over the world. Some of these things were possible before the widespread use of the Internet, but the cost of private, leased lines would have made many of them infeasible in practice.

An office worker away from his desk, perhaps the other side of the world on a business trip or a holiday, can open a remote desktop session into his normal office PC using a secure Virtual Private Network (VPN) connection via the Internet. This gives him complete access to all his normal files and data, including e-mail and other applications, while he is away.

This concept is also referred to by some network security people as the Virtual Private Nightmare, because it extends the secure perimeter of a corporate network into its employees' homes; this has been the source of some notable security breaches, but also provides security for the workers.

Collaboration

The low-cost and nearly instantaneous sharing of ideas, knowledge, and skills has made collaborative work dramatically easier. Not only can a group cheaply communicate and test, but the wide reach of the Internet allows such groups to easily form in the first place, even among niche interests. An example of this is the Free/Libre/Open-Source Software (FLOSS) movement in software development, such as Linux, Mozilla, and OpenOffice.org. Cooperation has been greatly eased in other fields, as well. Internet 'chat', whether in the form of IRC 'chat rooms' or channels, or via instant messaging systems allow colleagues to stay in touch in a very convenient way when working at their computers during the day. Messages can be sent and viewed even more quickly and conveniently than via e-mail. Extension to these systems may allow files to be exchanged, 'whiteboard' drawings to be shared as well as voice and video contact between team members. Version control systems allow collaborating teams to work on shared sets of documents without either accidentally overwriting each other's work or having members wait until they get 'sent' documents to be able to add their thoughts and changes.

File Sharing

A computer file can be e-mailed to customers, colleagues and friends as an attachment. It can be uploaded to a Web site or FTP server for easy download by others. It can be put into a "shared location" or onto a file server for instant use by colleagues. The load of bulk downloads to many users can be eased by the use of "mirror" servers or peer-to-peer networks. In any of these cases, access to the file may be controlled by user authentication; the transit of the file over the Internet may be obscured by encryption and money may change hands before or after access to the file is given. The price can be paid by the remote charging of funds from, for example a credit card whose details are also passed — hopefully fully encrypted — across the Internet. The origin and authenticity of the file received may be checked by digital signatures or by MD5 or other message digests. These simple features of the Internet, over a world-wide basis, are changing the basis for the production, sale, and distribution of anything that can be reduced to a computer file for transmission. This includes all manner of office documents, publications, software products, music, photography, video, animations, graphics and the other arts. This in turn is causing seismic shifts in each of the existing industry associations, such as the RIAA and MPAA in the United States, that previously controlled the production and distribution of these products in that country.

Streaming Media

Many existing radio and television broadcasters provide Internet 'feeds' of their live audio and video streams (for example, the BBC). They may also allow time-shift viewing or listening such as Preview, Classic Clips and Listen Again features. These providers have been joined by a range of pure Internet 'broadcasters' who never had on-air licenses. This means that an Internet-connected device, such as a computer or something more specific, can be used to access on-line media in much the same way as was previously possible only with a TV or radio receiver. The range of material is much wider, from pornography to highly specialized technical Web-casts. Podcasting is a variation on this theme, where—usually audio—material is first downloaded in full and then may be played back on a computer or shifted to a digital audio player to be listened to on the move. These techniques using simple equipment allow anybody, with little censorship or licensing control, to broadcast audio-visual material on a worldwide basis. Webcams can be seen as an even lower-budget extension of this phenomenon. While some webcams can give full frame rate video, the picture is usually either small or updates slowly. Internet users can watch animals around an African waterhole, ships in the Panama Canal, the traffic at a local roundabout or their own premises, live and in real time. Video chat rooms, video conferencing, and remote controllable webcams are also popular. Many uses can be found for personal webcams in and around the home, with and without two-way sound.

Voice Telephony (VoIP)

VoIP stands for Voice over IP, where IP refers to the Internet Protocol that underlies all Internet communication. This phenomenon began as an optional two-way voice extension to some of the Instant Messaging systems that took off around the year 2000. In recent years many VoIP systems have become as easy to use and as convenient as a normal telephone. The benefit is that, as the Internet carries the actual voice traffic, VoIP can be free or cost much less than a normal telephone call, especially over long distances and especially for those with always-on ADSL or DSL Internet connections.

Thus VoIP is maturing into a viable alternative to traditional telephones. Interoperability between different providers has improved and the ability to call or receive a call from a traditional telephone is available. Simple inexpensive VoIP modems are now available that eliminate the need for a PC.

Voice quality can still vary from call to call but is often equal to and can even exceed that of traditional calls.

Remaining problems for VoIP include emergency telephone number dialing and reliability. Currently a few VoIP providers provide some 911 dialing but it is not universally available. Traditional phones are line powered and operate during a power failure, VoIP does not do so without a backup power source for the electronics.

Most VoIP providers offer unlimited national calling but the direction in VoIP is clearly toward global coverage with unlimited minutes for a low monthly fee.

VoIP has also become increasingly popular within the gaming world, as a form of communication between players. Popular gaming VoIP clients include Ventrilo and Teamspeak, and there are others available also.

Censorship

Some governments, such as those of Iran and the People's Republic of China restrict what people in their countries can access on the Internet, especially political and religious content. This is accomplished through software that filters domains and content so that they may not be easily accessed or obtained without elaborate circumvention.

In Finland, major Internet service providers have voluntarily (possibly to avoid such an arrangement being turned into law) agreed to restrict access to sites listed by police. While this list of forbidden URL's is only supposed to contain addresses of known child pornography sites, content of the list is secret.

Many countries have enacted laws making the possession or distribution of certain material, such as child pornography, illegal, but do not use filtering software.

There are many free and commercially available software programmes with which a user can choose to block offensive Web sites on individual computers or networks, such as to limit a child's access to pornography or violence. See *Content-control software*.

Internet Access

Common methods of home access include dial-up, landline broadband (over coaxial cable, fibre optic or copper wires), Wi-Fi, satellite and cell phones.

Public places to use the Internet include libraries and Internet cafes, where computers with Internet connections are available. There are also Internet access points in many public places such as airport halls and coffee shops, in some cases just for brief use while standing. Various terms are used, such as "public Internet kiosk", "public access terminal", and "Web payphone". Many hotels now also have public terminals, though these are usually fee based.

Wi-Fi provides wireless access to computer networks, and therefore can do so to the Internet itself. Hotspots providing such access include Wi-Fi-cafes, where a would-be user needs to bring their own wireless-enabled devices such as a laptop or PDA. These services may be free to all, free to customers only, or fee-based. A hotspot need not be limited to a confined location. The whole campus or park, or even the entire city can be enabled. Grassroots efforts have led to wireless community networks. Commercial WiFi services covering large city areas are in place in London, Vienna, San Francisco, Philadelphia, Chicago, Pittsburgh and other cities, including Toronto by the end of 2006. The Internet can then be accessed from such places as a park bench.

Apart from Wi-Fi, there have been experiments with proprietary mobile wireless networks like Ricochet, various high-speed data services over cellular phone networks, and fixed wireless services.

High-end mobile phones such as smartphones generally come with Internet access through the phone network. Web browsers such as Opera are available on these advanced handsets, which can also run a wide variety of other Internet software. More mobile phones have Internet access than PCs, though this is not as widely used. An internet access provider and protocol matrix differentiates the methods used to get online.

Leisure

The Internet has been a major source of leisure since before the World Wide Web, with entertaining social experiments such as MUDs and MOOs being conducted on university servers, and humor-related Usenet groups receiving much of the main traffic. Today, many Internet forums have sections devoted to games and funny videos; short cartoons in the form of Flash movies are also popular. Over 6 million people use blogs or message boards as a means of communication and for the sharing of ideas.

The pornography and gambling industries have both taken full advantage of the World Wide Web, and often provide a significant source of advertising revenue for other Web sites. Although many governments have attempted to put restrictions on both industries' use of the Internet, this has generally failed to stop their widespread popularity. A song in the Broadway musical show Avenue Q is titled "The Internet is for Porn" and refers to the popularity of this aspect of the internet.

One main area of leisure on the Internet is multiplayer gaming. This form of leisure creates communities, bringing people of all ages and origins to enjoy the fast-paced world of multiplayer games. These range from MMORPG to first-person shooters, from role-playing games to online gambling. This has revolutionized the way many people interact and spend their free time on the Internet.

While online gaming has been around since the 1970s, modern modes of online gaming began with services such as GameSpy and MPlayer, which players of games would typically subscribe to. Non-subscribers were limited to certain types of gameplay or certain games.

Many use the Internet to access and download music, movies and other works for their enjoyment and relaxation. As discussed above, there are paid and unpaid sources for all of these, using centralized servers and distributed peer-to-peer technologies. Discretion is needed as some of these sources take more care over the original artists' rights and over copyright laws than others.

Many use the World Wide Web to access news, weather and sports reports, to plan and book holidays and to find out more about their random ideas and casual interests.

People use chat, messaging and email to make and stay in touch with friends worldwide, sometimes in the same way as some previously had pen pals. Social networking Web sites like Friends Reunited and many others like them also put and keep people in contact for their enjoyment.

Cyberslacking has become a serious drain on corporate resources; the average UK employee spends 57 minutes a day surfing the Web at work, according to a study by Peninsula Business Services.

Complex Architecture

Many computer scientists see the Internet as a "prime example of a large-scale, highly engineered, yet highly complex system". The Internet is extremely heterogeneous.

(For instance, data transfer rates and physical characteristics of connections vary widely.) The Internet exhibits "emergent phenomena" that depend on its large-scale organisation. For example, data transfer rates exhibit temporal self-similarity.

Marketing

The Internet has also become a large market for companies; some of the biggest companies today have grown by taking advantage of the efficient nature of low-cost advertising and commerce through the Internet; also known as e-commerce. It is the fastest way to spread information to a vast amount of people simultaneously. The Internet has also subsequently revolutionized shopping—for example; a person can order a CD online and receive it in the mail within a couple of days, or download it directly in some cases. The Internet has also greatly facilitated personalized marketing which allows a company to market a product to a specific person or a specific group of people more so than any other advertising medium.

Examples of personalized marketing include online communities such as Myspace, Friendster, and others which thousands of Internet users join to advertise themselves and make friends online. Many of these users are young teens and adolescents ranging from 13 to 25 years old. In turn, when they advertise themselves they advertise interests and hobbies, which online marketing companies can use as information as to what those users will purchase online, and advertise their own companies' products to those users.

A very ineffective way of advertising on the internet is through spamming an email with advertisements. This is ineffective because, now, most email providers offer protection against email spam. Most spam messages are sent automatically to everybody in the email database of the company/person that is spamming. This way of advertising is almost like using adware.

Adware is another ineffective way of advertising because most people simply close a popup window when it shows up, not bothering to read it.

The Name Internet

Internet is traditionally written with a capital first letter, as it is a proper noun. The Internet Society, the Internet Engineering Task Force, the Internet Corporation for Assigned Names and Numbers, the World Wide Web Consortium, and several other Internet-related organisations use this convention in their publications.

Many newspapers, newswires, periodicals, and technical journals capitalize the term. Examples include the *New York Times*, the *Associated Press*, *Time*, *The Times of India*, *Hindustan Times*, and *Communications of the ACM*.

Others assert that the first letter should be written in lower case (*internet*). A significant number of publications use this form, including *The Economist*, the Canadian Broadcasting Corporation, the *Financial Times*, *The Guardian*, *The Times*, and *The Sydney Morning Herald*. As of 2005, many publications using *internet* appear to be located outside of North America—although one U.S. news source, *Wired News*, has adopted the lower case spelling.

Historically, *Internet* and *internet* have had different meanings, with *internet* being a contraction of *internetwork* or *internetworking* and *Internet* referring to the International Network. Under this distinction, the Internet is a particular internet, but the reverse does not apply. The distinction was evident in many RFCs, books, and articles from the 1980s and early 1990s (some of which, such as RFC 1918, refer to "internets" in the plural), but has recently fallen into disuse. Instead, the term intranet is generally used for private networks.

Wireless LAN

A wireless LAN or WLAN is a wireless local area network, which is the linking of two or more computers without using wires. WLAN utilizes spread-spectrum technology based on radio waves to enable communication between devices in a limited area, also known as the basic service set. This gives users the mobility to move around within a broad coverage area and still be connected to the network. However this technology is getting increasingly unpopular and may fade away soon in aid of new technologies such as 4G and 5G. It is certain as some point that GARV inc. leading manufacturers of wireless routers will quit investing in wireless devices. For the home user, wireless has become popular due to ease of installation, and location freedom with the gaining popularity of laptops. For the business, public businesses such as coffee shops or malls have begun to offer wireless access to their customers; some are even provided as a free service. Large wireless network projects are being put up in many major cities. Google is providing a free service to Mountain View, California and has entered a bid to do the same for San Francisco.[2] New York City has also begun a pilot programme to cover all five boroughs of the city with wireless Internet access.

In 1971, researchers at the University of Hawaii developed the world's first WLAN, or wireless local area network, named ALOHAnet. The bi-directional star topology of the system included seven computers deployed over four islands to communicate with the central computer on the Oahu Island without using phone lines.

Originally WLAN hardware was so expensive that it was only used as an alternative to cabled LAN in places where cabling was difficult or impossible. Early development included industry-specific solutions and proprietary protocols, but at the end of the 1990s these were replaced by standards, primarily the various versions of IEEE 802.11 (Wi-Fi). An alternative ATM-like 5 GHz standardized technology, HIPERLAN, has so far not succeeded in the market, and with the release of the faster 54 Mbit/s 802.11a (5 GHz) and 802.11g (2.4 GHz) standards, almost certainly never will.

The Australian Commonwealth Scientific and Industrial Research Organisation (CSIRO) claims to have first developed wireless networking, and as of 2006 they are engaged in a controversial battle with software and hardware giants looking for royalties on the alleged patents held by CSIRO regarding these technologies.[4]

Benefits

The popularity of wireless LANs is a testament primarily to their convenience, cost efficiency, and ease of integration with other networks and network components. The majority of computers sold to consumers today come pre-equipped with all necessary wireless LAN technology.

The benefits wireless LANs include:

- *Convenience*: The wireless nature of such networks allows users to access network resources from nearly any convenient location within their primary networking environment (a home or office). With the increasing saturation of laptop-style computers, this is particularly relevant.
- *Mobility*: With the emergence of public wireless networks, users can access the internet even outside their normal work environment. Most chain coffee shops, for example, offer their customers a wireless connection to the internet at little or no cost.
- *Productivity*: Users connected to a wireless network can maintain a nearly constant affiliation with their desired network as they move from place to place. For a business, this implies that an employee can potentially be more productive as his or her work can be accomplished from any convenient location.
- *Deployment*: Initial setup of an infrastructure-based wireless network requires little more than a single access point. Wired networks, on the other hand, have the additional cost and complexity of actual physical cables being run to numerous locations (which can even be impossible for hard-to-reach locations within a building).
- *Expandability*: Wireless networks can serve a suddenly-increased number of clients with the existing equipment. In a wired network, additional clients would require additional wiring.

- *Cost*: Wireless networking hardware is at worst a modest increase from wired counterparts. This potentially increased cost is almost always more than outweighed by the savings in cost and labor associated to running physical cables.

Disadvantages

Wireless LAN technology, while replete with the conveniences and advantages described above, has its share of downfalls. For a given networking situation, wireless LANs may not be desirable for a number of reasons. Most of these have to do with the inherent limitations of the technology.

- *Security*: Wireless LAN transceivers are designed to serve computers throughout a structure with uninterrupted service using radio frequencies. Furthermore, because of space and cost, the "antennas" typically present on wireless networking cards in the end computers are generally nothing more than the most naive of reception devices. In order to properly receive signals using such limited antennas throughout even a modest area, the wireless LAN transceiver utilizes a fairly considerable amount of power. What this means is that not only can the wireless packets be intercepted by a nearby adversary's poorly-equipped computer, but more importantly, a user willing to spend a small amount of money on a good quality antenna can pick up packets at a remarkable distance; perhaps hundreds of times the radius as the typical user. In fact, there are even computer users dedicated to locating and sometimes even hacking into wireless networks, known as wardrivers. On a wired network, any adversary would first have to overcome the physical limitation of tapping into the actual wires, but this is not an issue with wireless packets. To combat this consideration, wireless networks may choose to utilize some of the various encryption technologies available. Some of the more commonly utilized encryption methods, however, are known to have weaknesses that a dedicated adversary can compromise.
- *Range*: The typical range of a common 802.11g network with standard equipment is on the order of tens of meters. While sufficient for a typical home, it will be insufficient in a larger structure. To obtain additional range, repeaters or additional access points will have to be purchased. Costs for these items can add up quickly. Other technologies are in the development phase, however, which feature increased range, hoping to render this disadvantage irrelevant.
- *Reliability*: Like any radio frequency transmission, wireless networking

signals are subject to a wide variety of interference, as well as complex propagation effects (such as multipath, or especially in this case Rician fading) that are beyond the control of the network administrator. In the case of typical networks, modulation is achieved by complicated forms of phase-shift keying (PSK) or quadrature amplitude modulation (QAM), making interference and propagation effects all the more disturbing. As a result, important network resources such as servers are rarely connected wirelessly.

- *Speed*: The speed on most wireless networks (typically 1-54 Mbps) is far slower than even the slowest common wired networks (100Mbps up to several Gbps). There are also performance issues caused by TCP and its built-in congestion avoidance. For most users, however, this observation is irrelevant since the speed bottleneck is not in the wireless routing but rather in the outside network connectivity itself. For example, the maximum ADSL throughput (usually 8Mbps or less) offered by telecommunications companies to general-purpose customers is already far slower than the slowest wireless network to which it is typically connected. That is to say, in most environments, a wireless network running at its slowest speed is still faster than the internet connection serving it in the first place. However, in specialized environments, the throughput of a wired network might be necessary.

Architecture

Stations

http://en.wikipedia.org/wiki/Wireless_LAN#History All components that can connect into a wireless medium in a network are referred to as stations. All stations are equipped with wireless network interface cards (WNICs). Wireless stations fall into one of two categories: access points and clients.

Access Points

Access points (APs) are base stations for the wireless network. They transmit and receive radio frequencies for wireless enabled devices to communicate with.

Clients

Wireless clients can be mobile devices such as laptops, personal digital assistants, IP phones, or fixed devices such as desktops and workstations that are equipped with a wireless network interface card.

Basic Service Set

The basic service set (BSS) is a set of all stations that can communicate with each other. There are two types of BSS: independent BSS and infrastructure BSS. Every BSS has an identification (ID) called the BSSID, which is the MAC address of the access point servicing the BSS.

Independent Basic Service Set

An independent BSS is an ad-hoc network that contains no access points, which means they can not connect to any other basic service set.

Infrastructure Basic Service Set

An infrastructure BSS can communicate with other stations not in the same basic service set by communicating through access points.

Extended Service Set

An extended service set (ESS) is a set of connected BSSes. Access points in an ESS are connected by a distribution system. Each ESS has an ID called the SSID which is a 32-byte (maximum) character string. For example, "linksys" is the default SSID for Linksys routers.

Distribution System

A distribution system connects access points in an extended service set. A distribution system is usually a wired LAN but can be a wireless LAN.

Types of wireless LANs

Peer-to-peer

A peer-to-peer (P2P) allows wireless devices to directly communicate with each other. Wireless devices within range of each other can discover and communicate directly without involving central access points. This method is typically used by two computers so that they can connect to each other to form a network. If a signal strength meter is used in this situation, it may not read the strength accurately and can be misleading, because it registers the strength of the strongest signal, which may be the closest computer.

Wireless Distribution System

When it is difficult to connect all of the access points in a network by wires, it is also possible to put up access points as repeaters.

Hypertext

When Vannevar Bush, in his *1945* article *As We May think,* presented his vision of the *Memex,* the proposed information retrieval system that later served as an inspiration for Ted Nelson's *Hypertext* concept, this vision was clearly and necessarily rooted in *modernity* as it appeared, unchallenged, at the end of World Warn. Bush held the view that science, having been in the service of destructive forces for the duration of the war, now was able to return to its main objective — to secure progress of mankind. It was to this end that he proposed the *Memex* system: Presumably man's spirit should be elevated if he can better review his shady past and analyse more completely and objectively his present problems. He has built a civilisation so complex that he needs to mechanise his records more fully if he is to push his experiment to its logical conclusion and not merely become bogged down part way there by overtaxing his limited memory (Bush 1945:108). This Utopian modem optimism elicited by Bush, was considerably tempered by the time Ted Nelson's *Computer Lib* appeared in 1974, a book that clearly places Nelson within the social critical tradition of the American intellectual left in the 1960s. His critical stance was augmented by the ecological awareness of the 1970s expressed through journals like *Co-Evolution Quarterly* and *The Whole Earth Catalogue,* and it is no coincidence that the editor of these two publications, Stewart Brand, wrote the introduction to the 1987 edition of *Computer Lib.*

This dramatic conclusion to the 1974 text belies the prevalent enthusiasm of *Computer Lib,* and may be viewed as a "politically correct" afterthought. The rest of Nelson's book presents a firmly consistent belief in modern man's capability to control and influence his destiny with the help of computers ("You can and must understand computers NOW"), and the 1974/87 "companion" book, *Dream Machines,* prophesies a pivotal role for hyper-textual computer design in this respect. 1984 has come and gone and a good many of Nelson's predictions in *Computer Lib* and *Dream Machines* have come true, especially those pertaining to technological development Another striking aspect of this book today is a consistent argumentation that clearly places Nelson on one side of an ongoing debate between modernism and postmodernism. Critical modernism has during the last decade been challenged by various versions *of postmodern* theory, from writers, artists, and theoreticians who all express either doubts about or outright rejection of the central pillars of modernity. In this critical discourse the distinction between modernism and modernity has become increasingly important in order to avoid confusion with the old modemist/ antimodernist debates, *modernity* being identified with the general direction of philosophical and social thought of the Enlightenment.

MTV, a media phenomenon universally proclaimed as "postmodernist," announces a daily series of new music videos under the heading *Postmodern,* lending further credibility to the view that "postmodern" in today's everyday language has taken over many of the meanings "modern" contained in the everyday usage yesterday, with the music video as a major metaphor. The word now connotes the transitory, the ephemeral, the fragmented, the multifaceted, as well as leaning strongly to a hedonist philosophy. As for the word "postmodernism" itself, it is, as Fredric Jameson has pointed out, with its multitude of meanings and uses symptomatic for postmodern thought — "the sheer enumeration of changes and modifications." (Jameson, 1991). Jameson comments on his 1984 article on postmodernism, *The Cultural Logic of Late Capitalism,* by pointing out that the main change in the general view on postmodernism as a phenomenon in 1984 and 1989 was that in the latter year it was nearly impossible, on principle grounds, to *avoid* using the word "postmodern."

Postmodern Traits of Hypertext Example

In 1990 The BBC produced a television programme that presented and demonstrated the potentiality of hypertext as a harbinger of *nonlinear television.* In the programme, Douglas Adams (author of *The Hitchhiker's Guide to the Galaxy)* is transported into the near future where he is confronted with a "fully customizable," on-line, humanoid guide through the world of non-linearity. Adams is presented with a control panel of *micons,* or icons containing small loops of digitised video. These micons represent hypertext nodes, and pointing at a micon, or a part of it, will take him to that hypertext node.

The *Live Feed* micon then takes the user to a concurrent video image from the weather satellite MarSat West in orbit over the Southern Atlantic. Over this image then two more micons representing submersible observation stations in the Atlantic, and a touch on one of these takes the astounded Adams to a live video of dolphins curiously looking at the camera. From here, a touch on the "Return" icon on the screen, again brings up the five micons of the *Atlantic* menu. The *Literature* micon brings up the images and names of Melville, Coleridge, Conrad, C.S. Forrester, and Hemingway, the appearance of each micon accompanied by selected lines from the works of these authors read aloud on the soundtrack. By touching *Coleridge,* a micon representing *The Rime of the Ancient Mariner* appears over a portrait of Coleridge, accompanied by further micons related to this author. Another touch, this time on *More works,* brings up a new series of choices, among those *Kubla Khan.* After choosing this poem, it is read while the text scrolls in "Star Wars" fashion over the screen. Pointing at any word in the text will stop the text and lead to an explanation of some sorts. Moving our fingers over the phrase "widening chasm," we are informed that this may be viewed as a "metaphor for the female sexual organ," a touch on the word "dulcimer" opens up for a discourse on mediaeval music, as well as a treatise on rhombic shapes, and in the middle of all this, up pops the micon with Ted Nelson's continually shaking head. Why? Because the on-line hypertext system for organising literature that Nelson has been working on for almost two decades is called — "had to be called," as Nelson puts it — *XANADU.* I will use this example to illustrate how the hypertext idea is marked by a series of contradictions typical of the modern/postmodern controversy. Although it may be contended that the chosen example is a hypothetical one, and an example of dubious hypertextual design at that, there is no doubt that it represents a very real simulation, based on the current state of the art in the field of hypermedia. Furthermore, the obvious design "faults" in the programme are very helpful in illustrating inherent problems in the hyper-textual presentation.

Hypertext in the Modern / Postmodern Controversy

In his article *Concepts of Postmodernism,* Ihab Hassan (Hassan, 1987) has compiled a "postmodern checklist" consisting of a dual listing of "modem" phenomena presented with their postmodern counterparts. In this list we find four pairs of contrasting concepts with a definite relevance to the situation experienced by the watcher of *Hyperland:*

Modernism	*Postmodernism*
Purpose	Play
Design	Chance
Centering	Dispersal
Hierarchy	Anarchy

This set of contradictions can easily be found to be contained within the practice of hypertextual structures. Although the idea behind hypertext is based on a very strong sense of *purpose,* the *Hyperland* film ends up with a strong emphasis on the *playfulness* of the medium, with a tour-de-force presentation of virtual reality "goggles." In the sequence referred to, the user clearly falls prey to playful curiosity as the beckoning micons pop up, one after another.

Play and games are central components of the computer culture as such, as a visit to any computer store and a look at any BBS files list should bear witness to. The counterpart to the purpose-oriented "computer programmer" is the play-oriented "hacker." This contradiction, between purpose and play, spills over into the next pair of concepts. In authoring languages and systems for interactive multimedia, an area of application where hypertext holds a central position, purposeful *design* is what textbooks and courses propagate. Although the interface with the user should appear as "friendly" as possible, presenting the user with what seems to be a wide choice of options, the programme in the background is specifically designed in order to fulfil a stated purpose behind the programme, usually didactically defined. At every hypertext node this design is challenged by *chance* in the form of possible "wrong" choices of links or paths. A critical part of multimedia design is therefore to minimise chances of "wrong" decisions, at the same time keeping up the appearance of presenting "real" choices. A first glance at a design chart for a hypertext programme can thus easily give the false impression of an information flow that lead in all directions, seemingly at random. This impression of information *dispersal* is in turn contrasted with the previously mentioned *centering* represented by the many pointers imbedded in the programme design aimed at leading the user through a presumed meaningful discourse. The implied *hierarchy* of instructional design is made as a defense against the playful *anarchy* that is the didactic lure of computer-assisted learning programmes. These four major contradictions within the concept of hypertext-based learning programmes all point to the contested ground of *space* in the ongoing debate on modernity and post-modernity, and lead to a detour to the field of architecture and urban geography.

Getting Lost in Postmodern Hyperspace

The case for the modern conception of orientation in space is perhaps best made by Kevin Lynch in his classic study from 1960, *The Image of the City*. This book is especially interesting in our context because some of Lynch's key concepts for city geography bear close resemblance to important principles of hypertext Lynch defines five types of elements pertaining to the physical form of the city: *paths, nodes, landmarks, districts, and edges.*

These elements are crucial in our perception of the city, as they help us define the *legibility* of the urban environment *Paths* are the routes of frequent travel, and are invariably related to the concept of *nodes* defined as strategic junction points and, according to Lynch, a dominant feature in the individual's image of the city. *Landmarks* are reference points, usually in some form of physical shape, like monuments of buildings that facilitates navigation in the city landscape. *Districts* are areas with a common identity, and *edges* are linear structures representing the boundaries between areas (Lynch, 1960: 46-49).

All of these five elements can and have been transferred to hypertext, where concepts like nodes and paths (links) are part of any definition of the concept, like the one made by McKnight, Dillon, and Richardson in their book *Hypertext in Context:* "Simply stated, hypertext consists of *nodes* (or "chunks") of information and *links* between them" (McKnight, Dillon, Richardson, 1991: 2). Further on in that book, the authors make extensive use of the geography analogy in order to cast light over the problem of *navigation* in hypertext. Referring to several empirical studies of learning efficiency in hypertext programmes as compared to line text presentation of the same subject matter, the authors conclude that hypertextual presentation is no guarantee of better performance, and emphasise the problem of navigation. Interestingly, these studies seem to suggest that the hypertext structure places an extra burden on the reader in terms of navigation and consequently leads to poorer performance. And: With the advent of hypertext it has become widely accepted that the departure from the so-called "linear" structure of paper increases the likelihood of readers or users of getting lost. This danger of getting lost is underscored by the authors of *Hypertext in Context,* who devote an entire chapter to the problem of navigation in hypertextual space, based on the (surprisingly scant, according to the authors) research done in the psychology of navigation with an emphasis on the development of *cognitive mapping.*

Loss of Place-identity

One obvious effect of this is what Harvey terms as a "loss of place-identity" — the inability of the individual to identify his or her world geographically — and there seem to be two distinct reactions to this in contemporary thinking. One reaction, emanating from what could be termed "postmodern ideology," is to view this as a positive phenomenon, where the individual ought to take advantage of this new cultural pluralism, freed from the shackles of the old hierarchic, moralistic, place-bound, and static culture. An early manifestation of this view is to be found in one of the seminal texts of postmodern theory, *Learning from Las Vegas,* by Robert Venturi, Denise Scott Brown, and Steven Izenour. This book on architecture was published in 1972 and proposed an architecture of the "ugly and ordinary" by using popular and commercial building styles as examples for an architecture in opposition to the dominating modern and functionalist architecture. The authors suggested that by drawing lessons from the way urban architecture in America had developed on its own, outside the world of systemised and institutionalised modern architecture, an alternative position to modernist architecture could be developed. The geographical expression of this is *the urban sprawl,* as it has grown organically in the automobile oriented culture of the United States. The counterpart and identified enemy to this expression of popular, "low culture" and commercial city non-planning in *Learning from Las Vegas,* is the planned, elitist, "high culture," modern city planning tradition identified as *megastructure.* Using a contrasting table very much like Hassan's modern/postmodern "checklist," the authors go through a list of how urban sprawl and megastructure differ fundamentally: ugly and ordinary vs. heroic and original, mixed media vs. pure architecture, popular life-style, vs. "correct" life-style, vital mess vs. "Total Design," building for men (markets) vs. building for Man, to name a few of the 30 pairs in question. (Venturi, Brown, and Izenour. 1972: 84). The aim is clearly to "rehabilitate" the "vital mess" of urban sprawl, pointing to Los Angeles and Las Vegas as the Rome and Florence for future generations of architects. For the postmodern architects, loss of place-identity is no great loss. For the other view, we can return to Kevin Lynch and his description of the urban sprawl of Jersey City as it appeared through interviews with inhabitants: "In studying the individual sketches and interviews, it became apparent that none of the respondents had anything like a comprehensive view of the city they had lived in for many years. The maps were often fragmented, with large, blank areas" (Lynch, 1960:29). Jersey City is made into a negative example by Lynch by the very lack of place-identity that it elicits, and Lynch is absolutely clear on the alternative to this in his conclusion: "By appearing as a remarkable and well-knit *place.* the city could provide a ground for the clustering and organisation of... meanings and associations. Such a sense of place in itself enhances every human activity that occurs there." Harvey points out that the apparently liberating function of antiauthoritar-ian, anti-structural "organic" growth has some sinister overtones. The accelerating speed of time-space compression is not matched by a similar speedily reorientation of our mental maps and this loss of place-awareness may have serious political implications. One such implication that Harvey suggests, the retreat into geopolitical fragmentation, has been strongly emphasised by recent developments (winter of 1992) in the former Soviet Union and Yugoslavia. Another negative aspect to this loss of space pertains to the experience of *space as a reality.* During the Gulf War of 1991, the television audience of the world was bombarded by high-tech images from the war, to an extent that it was referred to as *the Nintendo effect.* This metaphor very revealingly points to a loss of reality in perception — reality extended to the level where the borders between play and physical reality becomes obscure, the realm of postmodern *hyperreality.*

Going Off on an Ice-lolly: The Digression as Master

In *Hyperland* an exasperated Douglas Adams finally asks his "guide": "Where were we before we went off on this — what do you call it?" Guide: "You can call it anything you like." "What if I call it an ice-lolly?" "Very good!" "So what happened when we went off on this ice-lolly?" And since the field of hypertext is an uncharted one, with numerous ' nameless concepts yet to be mapped and named, let us appropriate Douglas Adams' new word into the hyperspeak vocabulary and look closer at the ice-lolly" as a hypertext phenomenon. In ordinary conversation the ice-lolly is known as a *digression,* the situation where two partners engage in a conversation on one topic and end up on a completely different topic. The digression in turn, has relevance to the *coherence* of the text. Coherence, recent work in text linguistics suggests (for example, Agar and Hobbs, 1982), comes in three versions that act together. *Thematic coherence* refers to our ability to relate a proposition to an explicit theme. It is the quality that enables us to recognise what a certain text "is about" Closely connected to this, is *local coherence* where one sentence is obviously linked to the next, virtually "pointing" at it, without necessarily referring to the thematic coherence. The footnote is a typical example of local coherence Thematic coherence and local coherence are participating in building a third kind of encompassing coherence that enables us to perceive series of isolated propositions as a whole — a *global coherence*. What happens in the *Hyperland* example is that local coherence becomes dominant at the cost of thematic and global coherence and we feel the need to retrace the path to find our bearings. Local coherence is the stuff that di-gressions are made of. The rapidly expanding field of hypertext theory take diverging views on the dangers of digression, and these views fall roughly along the separating lines of the followers and adversaries of postmodern ideology referred to above. One clear contradiction seems to follow the purpose/play dichotomy set forth by Hassan, with George P. Landow as a stern defender of purpose and global coherence.

Landow treats hypertext as the modern learning-efficient tool that Bush and Nelson expected it to be, and his set of rules contributes to this. His 19 rules construct a useful set of concepts for those wanting to map and structure the seemingly chaotic field of hypertext In fact, what Landow does is provide the hypertext authors with rules that help them create maps for the users to navigate by in the "urban sprawl" of multi-linear hypertext. Another and different stance on the question of digression and lack of coherence in hypertext is taken by Terence Harpold, who puts the phenomenon of digression into a psychoanalytic context (Harpold, 1991). Turning to the French psychoanalytic tradition from Lacan, Harpold delivers a "defense" for the digression in hypertext that is strongly reminiscent of psychoanalytically oriented film theory.

The common concept here is what Jacques-Alain Millar named *suture* literally the "sewing together" of the "cut" or "gap" in the signifying chain, representing the death of the subject. In Lacanian and Althusserian inspired film theory, *suture* is used to explain how the "seamless" narrative techniques of the Hollywood film is able to elicit pleasure in the viewer by representing a "whole" subject, a world where all the uncomfortable gaps have been "sewn together." Thus digression becomes a revealing agent in the process of de-centering the subject, and hypertext appears to be an ideal medium for making this more visible. Instead of being an anarchic detour into meaninglessness and nothingness, the digression actually allows for greater insight. Stewart Moulthorpe takes this view even further, when he suggests hypertext as an answer to Jameson's scepticism about the possibility of a politically relevant postmodern art (Aarseth, 1991: 81).

Knowing Where You are, or Getting Lost and Enjoying it

In this study we have pointed out how some of the crucial aspects of hypertext and hypermedia de in with the continuing controversy around postmodern thought Popularly it can be stated as a controversy between upholding the modernist vision of "knowing where you are" or succumbing to the temptation of the postmodern position of "getting lost and enjoying it." From the debate in architecture between modern and postmodern, represented by the views of Lynch and Venturi et al., this contradiction can be said to crystallise between the "imaginable city" of Lynch and the "urban sprawl" of Venturi, with the first emphasising the need for *knowledge and control* and the latter pointing to the *enjoyment* aspect of popular culture. These two stances can be viewed as representing the same dialectics conveyed by the selected pairs from Hassan's postmodern "checklist" — purpose/play, design/chance, centering/dispersal, and hierarchy/anarchy, where special consideration should be given to the first pair, that of purpose *versus* play.

When we look to hypertextual practices in the present and in the near future, it is quite obvious that this debate does not easily resolve into an either/or. In the established field of interactive hypermedia (mainly interactive video learning programmes), the question of "correct" navigation and securely structured pathways is and will definitely be the main concern, clearly signalling a bias toward "purpose." "Interactive design" has for several years existed as an academic discipline at American universities, adjusting and im-proving the purpose-related hypertext tools of interactive authoring systems. On the other hand, development in hypertextual literary systems seems to have developed a duality. In addition to normative work on the rhetoric of hypertext, such as Landow's, there is also a marked emphasis on the "playful," in theory as well as in practice, as the examples cited from Harpold and Moulthorpe suggest In certain areas of hypertextual practices, the "play" side seems to be totally dominating. In a recent master's thesis, Espen Aarseth focuses on the practices of *MUDs* — multi-user dungeons — which has developed into a sub-culture within the on-line community. Admittedly, the practices of online role-playing in a constantly changing cybernetic environment stretches the hypertext concept to its outer limit, but Aarseth maintains that "if we can study the games within a text, then why not study the texts within a game?" (Aarseth, 1991: 84-85). This raises the question where to place the latest technological innovation related with hypertext — *virtual reality* where the postmodern simulacrae described by Baudrillard and others is taken to the extreme. With the help of a pair of "goggles" connected to a powerful three-dimensional graphic computer, the "reader" can enter the text pseudo-physically, seemingly without having to resort to representing devices like film. TV, or a book. At the bottom of this experience (or really pseudo-experience) Des a hypertext design with links and nodes that only differ from "ordinary" hypertext in its computational complexity.

According to recent rumors, commercial versions of virtual reality programmes are expected to be available as the next generation of video games in the near future. We will then have an extraordinary example illustrating the paradox of "the postmodern condition" in the fact that large, centralised entertainment corporations, with the help of tightly, hierarchically designed virtual reality programmes, will provide the public with pseudo-realities invoking playful multiplicity and chance.

Cognitive Mapping: A Counter Strategy to Hyperspace

The question of cognitive mapping is also prominent in the work of Fredric Jameson on postmodernism. In his 1991 book on the subject, he elaborates on the points of view set forth in his 1984 article, where he places the postmodern phenomenon in a wider social and cultural context. Unlike other theoreticians with a Marxist background who have rejected the postmodern argumentation (for example, Callinicos, 1989), Jameson has set out to "historise" a concept that appears to be ahistorical. Postmodernism, Jameson contends, is the cultural logic of late capitalism, representative for an epoch where capital expands truly *multinationally,* not only imperialistically. It is the period when the last pre-capitalist enclaves in modem time — nature and the unconscious — are invaded by omnipresent multinational capital. Instead of viewing postmodernism as something that transcends the ideology of capitalism, Jameson sees postmodernism as the cultural logic of "late capitalism" as defined by the Marxist economist Ernest Mandel.

Jameson turns to architecture to illustrate his point and uses John Portman's Westin Bonaventure Hotel in Los Angeles as an analysis example. This building, prominent among its large number of siblings all over the industrialised world, sticks out in the city landscape with its rejective glass facade (Jameson uses the word "repulsive"), signaling itself as a self-contained world. Which it in a way is, with its combination of habitation (hotel) and consumption (restaurants and shopping arcades).

It is interesting to note that Jameson uses the word "alarming" in this context, thus echoing the horror of getting lost expressed by Kevin Lynch, and he has followed this up in his 1988 article *Cognitive Mapping* (Jameson, 1988) by suggesting a counter strategy of cognitive mapping based on acceptance of the idea of a *social totality.* This is where Jameson departs from other theoreticians of the postmodern (like Lyotard and Baudrillard) for whom the rejection of any social totality is one of the very hallmarks of the postmodern condition. A similar strategy, underscoring the historical importance of mapping, is proposed by David Harvey in his book. *The Condition of Postmodernity.* Harvey points out how the accessibility, appropriation, domination, and production of space has been crucial in the development of modem society from the first, primitive stages of capitalism and up to today's "flexible accumulation," which is his more precise definition of Jameson's "late capitalism." Linking the growth of capitalism with the concept of spatial control, Harvey shows that, historically, the fragmentation and pulverisation of space was a major factor in achieving this, and that the development of accurate maps was one of the tools facilitating this. ("Space can be conquered only through the production of space.") During the last hundred years, this development has, quite literally, been "speeded up," mainly as a result of the development in communication, represented by the now so-trite metaphor about "the shrinking world" or, as Harvey put it, the annihilation of space through time. This time-space compression has resulted in the "great global multinational and decentered communicational network" that Jameson points to, which has given rise to a cultural homogenisation that Harvey describes this way: "Extraordinary decentralisation and proliferation of industrial production ends up putting Bennetton or Laura Ashley in almost every serially produced shopping mall in the advanced capitalist world" (Harvey, 1989: 296).

Industrial Data Processing

Industrial data processing is a branch of applied computer science that covers the area of design and programming of computerized systems which are not computers as such — often referred to as embedded systems (PLCs, automated systems, intelligent instruments, etc). The products concerned contain at least one microprocessor or microcontroller, as well as couplers (for I/O). Another current definition of industrial data processing is that it concerns those computer programmes whose variables in some way represent physical quantities; for example the temperature and pressure of a tank, the position of a robot arm, etc.

Quantum Computer

A quantum computer is any device for computation that makes direct use of distinctively quantum mechanical phenomena, such as superposition and entanglement, to perform operations on data. In a classical (or conventional) computer, the amount of data is measured by bits; in a quantum computer, the data is measured by qubits. The basic principle of quantum computation is that the quantum properties of particles can be used to represent and structure data, and that quantum mechanisms can be devised and built to perform operations with these data. Though quantum computing is still in its infancy, experiments have been carried out in which quantum computational operations were executed on a very small number of qubits. Research in both theoretical and practical areas continues at a frantic pace, and many national government and military funding agencies support quantum computing research to develop quantum computers for both civilian and national security purposes, such as cryptanalysis. It is widely believed that if large-scale quantum computers can be built, they will be able to solve certain problems asymptotically faster than any classical computer. Quantum computers are different from other computers such as DNA computers and computers based on transistors, even though these may ultimately use some kind of quantum mechanical effect (for example covalent bonds). Some computing architectures such as optical computers may use classical superposition of electromagnetic waves, but without some specifically quantum mechanical resource such as entanglement, they do not share the potential for computational speed-up of quantum computers.

The Basis of Quantum Computing

In quantum mechanics, the state of a physical system (such as an electron or a photon) is described by a vector in a mathematical object called a Hilbert space. The realisation of the Hilbert space depends on the particular system. For instance, in the case of a single particle system in three dimensions, the state can be described by a complex-valued function defined on R^3 (three-dimensional space) called a wave function. As described in the article on quantum mechanics, this function has a probabilistic interpretation; of particular significance is that quantum states can be in a superposition of the basis states. The time evolution of the system state vector is assumed to be unitary, meaning that it is reversible.

A classical computer has a memory made up of bits, where each bit holds either a one or a zero. The device computes by manipulating those bits, i.e. by transporting these bits from memory to (possibly a suite of) logic gates and back. A quantum computer maintains a vector of qubits. A qubit can hold a one, or a zero, or a superposition of these. A quantum computer operates by manipulating those qubits, i.e. by transporting these bits from memory to (possibly a suite of) quantum logic gates and back.

Qubits for a quantum computer can be implemented using particles with two spin states: "up" and "down" (typically written in fact, any system possessing an observable quantity A which is *conserved* under time evolution and such that A has at least two discrete and sufficiently spaced consecutive eigenvalues, is a suitable candidate for implementing a qubit, since any such system can be mapped onto an effective spin-1/2.

For discussion of foundational aspects of quantum computing, see the article on quantum circuits.

Bits vs Qubits

Consider first a classical computer that operates on a 3 bit register. At any given time, the bits in the register are in a definite state, such as 101. In a quantum computer, however, the qubits can be in a superposition of all the classically allowed states. In fact, the register is described by a wavefunction: where the coefficients á, â, ã,... are complex numbers whose amplitudes squared are the probabilities to measure the qubits in each state. Consequently, $|\,ã\,|^2$ is the probability to measure the register in the state 010. It is important that these numbers are complex, due to the fact that the phases of the numbers can constructively and destructively interfere with one another; this is an important feature for quantum algorithms.

For an n qubit quantum register, recording the state of the register requires 2^n complex numbers (the 3-qubit register requires $2^3 = 8$ numbers). Consequently, the number of classical states encoded in a quantum register grows exponentially with the number of qubits. For n=300, this is roughly $10^{90.308998699195}$, more states than there are atoms in the known universe. Note that the coefficients are not all independent, since the probabilities must sum to 1. The representation is also (for most practical cases) non-unique, since there is no way to physically distinguish between a particular quantum register and a similar one where all of the amplitudes have been multiplied by the same phase such as -1, i, or in general any number on the complex unit circle. One can show the dimension of the set of states of an n qubit register is $2^{n+1} - 2$. See Bloch sphere.

Initialization, Execution and Termination

In our example, the contents of the qubit registers can be thought of as an 8-dimensional complex vector. An algorithm for a quantum computer must initialize this vector in some specified form (dependent on the design of the quantum computer). In each step of the algorithm, that vector is modified by multiplying it by a unitary matrix. The matrix is determined by the physics of the device. The unitary character of the matrix ensures the matrix is invertible (so each step is reversible).

Upon termination of the algorithm, the 8-dimensional complex vector stored in the register must be somehow read off from the qubit register by a quantum measurement. However, by the laws of quantum mechanics, that measurement will yield a random 3 bit string (and it will destroy the stored state as well). This random string can be used in computing the value of a function because (by design) the probability distribution of the measured output bitstring is skewed in favor of the correct value of the function. By repeated runs of the quantum computer and measurement of the output, the correct value can be determined, to a high probability, by majority polling of the outputs. In brief, quantum computations are probabilistic, see quantum circuit for a more precise formulation.

A quantum algorithm is implemented by an appropriate sequence of unitary operations. Note that for a given algorithm, the operations will always be done in exactly the same order. There is no "IF THEN" statement to vary the order, since there is no way to read the state of a qubit before the final measurement. There are, however, conditional gate operations such as the controlled NOT gate, or CNOT.

For more details on the sequences of operations used for various algorithms, see universal quantum computer, Shor's algorithm, Grover's algorithm, Deutsch-Jozsa algorithm, quantum Fourier transform, quantum gate, quantum adiabatic algorithm and quantum error correction. Also refer to the growing field of quantum programming.

The Power of Quantum Computers

Integer factorization is believed to be computationally infeasible with an ordinary computer for large numbers that are the product of two prime numbers of roughly equal size (e.g., products of two 300-digit primes). By comparison, a quantum computer could solve this problem relatively easily. If a number has n bits (is n digits long when written in the binary numeral system), then a quantum computer with just over $2n$ qubits can use Shor's algorithm to find its factors. It can also solve a related problem called the discrete logarithm problem. This ability would allow a quantum computer to "break" many of the cryptographic systems in use today, in the sense that there would be a relatively fast (polynomial time in n) algorithm for solving the problem. In particular, most of the popular public key ciphers could be much more quickly broken, including forms of RSA and ElGamal. These are used to protect secure Web pages, encrypted email, and many other types of data. Breaking these would have significant ramifications for electronic privacy and security. The only way to increase the security of an algorithm like RSA would be to increase the key size and hope that an adversary does not have the resources to build and use a powerful enough quantum computer. It seems plausible that it will always be possible to build classical computers that have more bits than the number of qubits in the largest quantum computer. If that's true, then algorithms like RSA could be made secure by ensuring that keylengths exceed the storage capacities of quantum computers, but at the cost of an extreme penalty in computational time.

There are some digital signature schemes that are believed to be secure against quantum computers. See for instance Lamport signatures. Perhaps not as surprisingly, quantum computers could also be useful for running simulations of quantum mechanics. This idea goes back to Richard Feynman (1982) who observed that there is no known algorithm for simulating quantum systems on a classical computer and suggested to study the use of quantum computer for this purpose. The speedup achieved by quantum computers could be just as large as for factoring. This could be a great boon to physics, chemistry, materials science, nanotechnology, biology and medicine, all of which are limited today by the slow speed of quantum mechanical simulations. For example, some modern simulations that are taking IBM's Blue Gene supercomputer years, would take a quantum computer only a matter of seconds.

This dramatic advantage of quantum computers is currently known to exist for only those three problems: factoring, discrete logarithm, and quantum physics simulations. However, there is no proof that the advantage is real: an equally fast classical algorithm may still be discovered (though some consider this unlikely). There is one other problem where quantum computers have a smaller, though significant (quadratic) advantage. It is *quantum database search*, and can be solved by Grover's algorithm. In this case the advantage is provable. This establishes beyond doubt that (ideal) quantum computers are superior to classical computers for at least one problem.

Consider a problem that has these four properties:

- The only way to solve it is to guess answers repeatedly and check them,
- There are n possible answers to check,
- Every possible answer takes the same amount of time to check, and
- There are no clues about which answers might be better: generating possibilities randomly is just as good as checking them in some special order.

An example of this is a password cracker that attempts to guess the password for an encrypted file (assuming that the password has a maximum possible length).

For problems with all four properties, it will take an average of $(n + 1)/2$ guesses to find the answer using a classical computer. The time for a quantum computer to solve this will be proportional to the square root of n. That can be a very large speedup, reducing some problems from years to seconds. It can be used to attack symmetric ciphers such as Triple DES and AES by attempting to guess the secret key. But it is also easy to defend against, by doubling the size of this key. There are also more complicated methods for secure communication, such as using quantum cryptography.

Regardless of whether any of these problems can be shown to have an advantage on a quantum computer, they nonetheless will always have the advantage of being an excellent tool for studying quantum mechanical interactions, which of itself is an enormous value to the scientific community.

There are currently no other practical problems known where quantum computers give a large speedup over classical computers. Research is continuing, and more problems may yet be found.

Problems and Practicality Issues

There are a number of practical difficulties in building a quantum computer, and thus far quantum computers have only solved trivial problems. David DiVincenzo, of IBM, listed the following requirements for a practical quantum computer:

- scalable physically to increase the number of qubits
- qubits can be initialized to arbitrary values
- quantum gates faster than decoherence time
- Turing-complete gate set
- qubits can be read easily

To summarize the problem from the perspective of an engineer, one needs to solve the challenge of building a system which is isolated from everything *except* the measurement and manipulation mechanism. Furthermore, one needs to be able to turn off the coupling of the qubits to the measurement so as to not decohere the qubits while performing operations on them.

Quantum Decoherence

One major problem is keeping the components of the computer in a coherent state, as the slightest interaction with the external world would cause the system to decohere. This effect causes the unitary character (and more specifically, the invertibility) of quantum computational steps to be violated. Decoherence times for candidate systems, in particular the transverse relaxation time T_2 (terminology used in NMR and MRI technology, also called the *dephasing time*), typically range between nanoseconds and seconds at low temperature. The issue for optical approaches are more difficult as these timescales are orders of magnitude lower and an often cited approach to overcome it uses optical pulse shaping approach. Error rates are typically proportional to the ratio of operating time to decoherence time, hence any operation must be completed much quicker than the decoherence time. If the error rate is small enough, it is possible to use quantum error correction, which corrects errors due to decoherence, thereby allowing the total calculation time to be longer than the decoherence time. An often cited (but rather arbitrary) figure for required error rate in each gate is 10^{-4}. This implies that each gate must be able to perform its task 10,000 times faster than the decoherence time of the system.

Meeting this scalability condition is possible for a wide range of systems. However the use of error correction brings with it the cost of a greatly increased number of required qubits. The number required to factor integers using Shor's algorithm is still polynomial, and thought to be between L^4 and L^6, where L is the number of bits in the number to be factored. For a 1000 bit number, this implies a need for 10^{12} to 10^{18} qubits. Fabrication and control of this large number of qubits is non-trivial for any of the proposed designs.

One approach to the stability-decoherence problem is to create a topological quantum computer with anyons, quasi-particles used as threads and relying on knot theory to form stable logic gates.

Candidates

There are a number of quantum computing candidates, among those:

1. Superconductor-based quantum computers (including SQUID-based quantum computers)

2. Trapped ion quantum computer
3. Electrons on helium quantum computers
4. "Nuclear magnetic resonance on molecules in solution"-based
5. "Quantum dot on surface"-based (e.g. the Loss-DiVincenzo quantum computer)
6. "Cavity quantum electrodynamics" (CQED)-based
7. "Molecular magnet"-based
8. Fullerene-based ESR quantum computer
9. Solid state NMR Kane quantum computers
10. Optic-based quantum computers (Quantum optics)
11. Topological quantum computer

In 2005, researchers at the University of Michigan built a semiconductor chip which functioned as an ion trap. Such devices, produced by standard lithography techniques, may point the way to scalable quantum computing tools. An improved version was made in 2006.

Quantum Computing in Computational Complexity Theory

This section surveys what is currently known mathematically about the power of quantum computers. It describes the known results from computational complexity theory and the theory of computation dealing with quantum computers.

The class of problems that can be efficiently solved by quantum computers is called BQP, for "bounded error, quantum, polynomial time". Quantum computers only run randomized algorithms, so BQP on quantum computers is the counterpart of BPP on classical computers. It is defined as the set of problems solvable with a polynomial-time algorithm, whose probability of error is bounded away from one quarter (Nielsen & Chuang 2000). A quantum computer is said to "solve" a problem if, for every instance, its answer will be right with high probability. If that solution runs in polynomial time, then that problem is in BQP.

BQP is suspected to be disjoint from NP-complete and a strict superset of P, but that is not known. Both integer factorization and discrete log are in BQP. Both of these problems are NP problems suspected to be outside BPP, and hence outside P. Both are suspected to not be NP-complete. There is a common misconception that quantum computers can solve NP-complete problems in polynomial time. That is not known to be true, and is generally suspected to be false.

An operator for a quantum computer can be thought of as changing a vector by multiplying it with a particular matrix. Multiplication by a matrix is a linear operation. It has been shown that if a quantum computer could be designed with *nonlinear* operators, then it could solve NP-complete problems in polynomial time. It could even do so for #P-complete problems. It is not yet known whether such a machine is possible.

Although quantum computers are sometimes faster than classical computers, ones of the types described above can't solve any problems that classical computers can't solve, given enough time and memory (albeit possibly an amount that could never practically be brought to bear). A Turing machine can simulate these quantum computers, so such a quantum computer could never solve an undecidable problem like the halting problem. The existence of "standard" quantum computers does not disprove the Church-Turing thesis (Nielsen and Chuang 2000).

Very recently, many researchers have begun to investigate the possibility of using quantum mechanics for hypercomputation — that is, solving undecidable problems. Such claims have been met with considerable skepticism as to whether it is even theoretically possible; see the hypercomputation article for more details.

Behold your computer. Your computer represents the culmination of years of technological advancements beginning with the early ideas of Charles Babbage (1791-1871) and eventual creation of the first computer by German engineer Konrad Zuse in 1941. Surprisingly however, the high speed modern computer sitting in front of you is fundamentally no different from its gargantuan 30 ton ancestors, which were equipped with some 18000 vacuum tubes and 500 miles of wiring! Although computers have become more compact and considerably faster in performing their task, the task remains the same: to manipulate and interpret an encoding of binary bits into a useful computational result. A bit is a fundamental unit of information, classically represented as a 0 or 1 in your digital computer. Each classical bit is physically realised through a macroscopic physical system, such as the magnetization on a hard disk or the charge on a capacitor. A document, for example, comprised of n-characters stored on the hard drive of a typical computer is accordingly described by a string of $8n$ zeros and ones. Herein lies a key difference between your classical computer and a quantum computer. Where a classical computer obeys the well understood laws of classical physics, a quantum computer is a device that harnesses physical phenomenon unique to quantum mechanics (especially quantum interference) to realise a fundamentally new mode of information processing.

In a quantum computer, the fundamental unit of information (called a quantum bit or *qubit*), is not binary but rather more quaternary in nature. This qubit property arises as a direct consequence of its adherence to the laws of quantum mechanics which differ radically from the laws of classical physics. A qubit can exist not only in a state corresponding to the logical state 0 or 1 as in a classical bit, but also in states corresponding to a blend or *superposition* of these classical states. In other words, a qubit can exist as a zero, a one, or simultaneously as both 0 and 1, with a numerical coefficient representing the probability for each state. This may seem counterintuitive because everyday phenomenon are governed by classical physics, not quantum mechanics — which takes over at the atomic level. This rather difficult concept is perhaps best explained through an experiment.:

Here a light source emits a photon along a path towards a half-silvered mirror. This mirror splits the light, reflecting half vertically toward detector A and transmiting half toward detector B. A photon, however, is a single quantized packet of light and cannot be split, so it is detected with equal probability at either A or B. Intuition would say that the photon randomly leaves the mirror in either the vertical *or* horizontal direction. However, quantum mechanics predicts that the photon actually travels *both* paths simultaneously!.

In an experiment like that in figure a, where a photon is fired at a half-silvered mirror, it can be shown that the photon does not actually split by verifying that if one detector registers a signal, then no other detector does. With this piece of information, one might think that any given photon travels either vertically or horizontally, randomly choosing between the two paths. However, quantum mechanics predicts that the photon actually travels both paths simultaneously, collapsing down to one path only upon measurement.

In this experiment, the photon first encounters a half-silvered mirror, then a fully silvered mirror, and finally another half-silvered mirror before reaching a detector, where each half-silvered mirror introduces the probability of the photon traveling down one path or the other. Once a photon strikes the mirror along either of the two paths after the first beam splitter, the arrangement is identical to that and so one might hypothesize that the photon will reach either detector A or detector B with equal probability. However, experiment shows that in reality this arrangement causes detector A to register *100%* of the time, and *never* at detector B! How can this be?

depicts an interesting experiment that demonstrates the phenomenon of single-particle interference. In this case, experiment shows that the photon *always* reaches detector A, *never* detector B! If a single photon travels vertically and strikes the mirror, then, by comparison to the experiment in there should be an equal probability that the photon will strike either detector A *or* detector B. The same goes for a photon traveling down the horizontal path. However, the actual result is drastically different. The only conceivable conclusion is therefore that the photon somehow traveled both paths simultaneously, creating an interference at the point of intersection that destroyed the possibility of the signal reaching B. This is known as *quantum interference* and results from the *superposition* of the possible photon *states*, or potential paths. So although only a single photon is emitted, it appears as though an identical photon exists and travels the 'path not taken,' only detectable by the interference it causes with the original photon when their paths come together again. If, for example, either of the paths are blocked with an absorbing screen, then detector B begins registering hits again just as in the first experiment! This unique characteristic, among others, makes the current research in quantum computing not merely a continuation of today's idea of a computer, but rather an entirely new branch of thought. And it is because quantum computers harness these special characteristics that gives them the potential to be incredibly powerful computational devices.

The Potential and Power of Quantum Computing

In a traditional computer, information is encoded in a *series* of bits, and these bits are manipulated via Boolean logic gates arranged in succession to produce an end result. Similarly, a quantum computer manipulates qubits by executing a series of quantum gates, each a unitary transformation acting on a single qubit or pair of qubits. In applying these gates in succession, a quantum computer can perform a complicated unitary transformation to a set of qubits in some initial state. The qubits can then be measured, with this measurement serving as the final computational result. This similarity in calculation between a classical and quantum computer affords that in theory, a classical computer can accurately simulate a quantum computer. In other words, a classical computer would be able to do anything a quantum computer can. So why bother with quantum computers? Although a classical computer can theoretically simulate a quantum computer, it is incredibly inefficient, so much so that a classical computer is effectively incapable of performing many tasks that a quantum computer could perform with ease. The simulation of a quantum computer on a classical one is a computationally hard problem because the correlations among quantum bits are qualitatively different from correlations among classical bits, as first explained by John Bell. Take for example a system of only a few hundred qubits, this exists in a Hilbert space of dimension $\sim 10^{90}$ that in simulation would require a classical computer to work with exponentially large matrices (to perform calculations on each individual state, which is also represented as a matrix), meaning it would take an exponentially longer time than even a primitive quantum computer.

Richard Feynman was among the first to recognize the potential in quantum superposition for solving such problems much much faster. For example, a system of 500 qubits, which is impossible to simulate classically, represents a quantum superposition of as many as 2^{500} states. Each state would be classically equivalent to a single list of 500 1's and 0's. Any quantum operation on that system —a particular pulse of radio waves, for instance, whose action might be to execute a controlled-NOT operation on the 100th and 101st qubits— would simultaneously operate on all 2^{500} states. Hence with one fell swoop, one tick of the computer clock, a quantum operation could compute not just on one machine state, as serial computers do, but on 2^{500} machine states at once! Eventually, however, observing the system would cause it to collapse into a single quantum state corresponding to a single answer, a single list of 500 1's and 0's, as dictated by the measurement axiom of quantum mechanics. The reason this is an exciting result is because this answer, derived from the massive quantum parallelism achieved through superposition, is the equivalent of performing the same operation on a classical super computer with $\sim 10^{150}$ separate processors (which is of course impossible)!!

Early investigators in this field were naturally excited by the potential of such immense computing power, and soon after realising its potential, the hunt was on to find something interesting for a quantum computer to do. Peter Shor, a research and computer scientist at AT&T's Bell Laboratories in New Jersey, provided such an application by devising the first quantum computer algorithm. Shor's algorithm harnesses the power of quantum superposition to rapidly factor very large numbers (on the order $\sim 10^{200}$ digits and greater) in a matter of seconds. The premier application of a quantum computer capable of implementing this algorithm lies in the field of encryption, where one common (and best) encryption code, known as RSA, relies heavily on the difficulty of factoring very large composite numbers into their primes. A computer which can do this easily is naturally of great interest to numerous government agencies that use RSA — previously considered to be "uncrackable" — and anyone interested in electronic and financial privacy.

Encryption, however, is only one application of a quantum computer. In addition, Shor has put together a toolbox of mathematical operations that can only be performed on a quantum computer, many of which he used in his factorization algorithm. Furthermore, Feynman asserted that a quantum computer could function as a kind of simulator for quantum physics, potentially opening the doors to many discoveries in the field. Currently the power and capability of a quantum computer is primarily theoretical speculation; the advent of the first fully functional quantum computer will undoubtedly bring many new and exciting applications.

A Brief History of Quantum Computing

The idea of a computational device based on quantum mechanics was first explored in the 1970's and early 1980's by physicists and computer scientists such as Charles H. Bennett of the IBM Thomas J. Watson Research Center, Paul A.

Benioff of Argonne National Laboratory in Illinois, David Deutsch of the University of Oxford, and the late Richard P. Feynman of the California Institute of Technology (Caltech). The idea emerged when scientists were pondering the fundamental limits of computation. They understood that if technology continued to abide by Moore's Law, then the continually shrinking size of circuitry packed onto silicon chips would eventually reach a point where individual elements would be no larger than a few atoms. Here a problem arose because at the atomic scale the physical laws that govern the behavior and properties of the circuit are inherently quantum mechanical in nature, not classical. This then raised the question of whether a new kind of computer could be devised based on the principles of quantum physics.

Feynman was among the first to attempt to provide an answer to this question by producing an abstract model in 1982 that showed how a quantum system could be used to do computations. He also explained how such a machine would be able to act as a simulator for quantum physics. In other words, a physicist would have the ability to carry out experiments in quantum physics inside a quantum mechanical computer.

Later, in 1985, Deutsch realised that Feynman's assertion could eventually lead to a general purpose quantum computer and published a crucial theoretical paper showing that *any* physical process, in principle, could be modeled perfectly by a quantum computer. Thus, a quantum computer would have capabilities far beyond those of any traditional classical computer. After Deutsch published this paper, the search began to find interesting applications for such a machine.

Unfortunately, all that could be found were a few rather contrived mathematical problems, until Shor circulated in 1994 a preprint of a paper in which he set out a method for using quantum computers to crack an important problem in number theory, namely factorization. He showed how an ensemble of mathematical operations, designed specifically for a quantum computer, could be organised to enable a such a machine to factor huge numbers extremely rapidly, much faster than is possible on conventional computers. With this breakthrough, quantum computing transformed from a mere academic curiosity directly into a national and world interest.

Obstacles and Research

The field of quantum information processing has made numerous promising advancements since its conception, including the building of two- and three-qubit quantum computers capable of some simple arithmetic and data sorting. However, a few potentially large obstacles still remain that prevent us from "just building one," or more precisely, building a quantum computer that can rival today's modern digital computer. Among these difficulties, error correction, decoherence, and hardware architecture are probably the most formidable. Error correction is rather self explanatory, but what errors need correction? The answer is primarily those errors that arise as a direct result of decoherence, or the tendency of a quantum computer to decay from a given quantum state into an incoherent state as it interacts, or entangles, with the state of the environment. These interactions between the environment and qubits are unavoidable, and induce the breakdown of information stored in the quantum computer, and thus errors in computation. Before any quantum computer will be capable of solving hard problems, research must devise a way to maintain decoherence and other potential sources of error at an acceptable level. Thanks to the theory (and now reality) of quantum error correction, first proposed in 1995 and continually developed since, small scale quantum computers have been built and the prospects of large quantum computers are looking up. Probably the most important idea in this field is the application of error correction in phase coherence as a means to extract information and reduce error in a quantum system without actually measuring that system. In 1998, researches at Los Alamos National Laboratory and MIT led by Raymond Laflamme managed to spread a single bit of quantum information (qubit) across three nuclear spins in each molecule of a liquid solution of alanine or trichloroethylene molecules. They accomplished this using the techniques of nuclear magnetic resonance (NMR). This experiment is significant because spreading out the information actually made it harder to corrupt. Quantum mechanics tells us that directly measuring the state of a qubit invariably destroys the superposition of states in which it exists, forcing it to become either a 0 or 1. The technique of spreading out the information allows researchers to utilize the property of entanglement to study the interactions between states as an indirect method for analyzing the quantum information. Rather than a direct measurement, the group compared the spins to see if any new differences arose between them without learning the information itself. This technique gave them the ability to detect and fix errors in a qubit's phase coherence, and thus maintain a higher level of coherence in the quantum system. This milestone has provided argument against skeptics, and hope for believers. Currently, research in quantum error correction continues with groups at Caltech (Preskill, Kimble), Microsoft, Los Alamos, and elsewhere.

At this point, only a few of the benefits of quantum computation and quantum computers are readily obvious, but before more possibilities are uncovered theory must be put to the test. In order to do this, devices capable of quantum computation must be constructed. Quantum computing hardware is, however, still in its infancy. As a result of several significant experiments, nuclear magnetic resonance (NMR) has become the most popular component in quantum hardware architecture. Only within the past year, a group from Los Alamos National Laboratory and MIT constructed the first experimental demonstrations of a quantum computer using nuclear magnetic resonance (NMR) technology. Currently, research is underway to discover methods for battling the destructive effects of decoherence, to develop an optimal hardware architecture for designing and building a quantum computer, and to further uncover quantum algorithms to utilize the immense computing power available in these devices. Naturally this pursuit is intimately related to quantum error correction codes and quantum algorithms, so a number of groups are doing simultaneous research in a number of these fields. To date, designs have involved ion traps, cavity quantum electrodynamics (QED), and NMR. Though these devices have had mild success in performing interesting experiments, the technologies each have serious limitations. Ion trap computers are limited in speed by the vibration frequency of the modes in the trap. NMR devices have an exponential attenuation of signal to noise as the number of qubits in a system increases. Cavity QED is slightly more promising; however, it still has only been demonstrated with a few qubits. Seth Lloyd of MIT is currently a prominent researcher in quantum hardware. The future of quantum computer hardware architecture is likely to be very different from what we know today; however, the current research has helped to provide insight as to what obstacles the future will hold for these devices.

Future Outlook

At present, quantum computers and quantum information technology remains in its pioneering stage. At this very moment obstacles are being surmounted that will provide the knowledge needed to thrust quantum computers up to their rightful position as the fastest computational machines in existence. Error correction has made promising progress to date, nearing a point now where we may have the tools required to build a computer robust enough to adequately withstand the effects of decoherence. Quantum hardware, on the other hand, remains an emerging field, but the work done thus far suggests that it will only be a matter time before we have devices large enough to test Shor's and other quantum algorithms. Thereby, quantum computers will emerge as the superior computational devices at the very least, and perhaps one day make today's modern computer obsolete. Quantum computation has its origins in highly specialized fields of theoretical physics, but its future undoubtedly lies in the profound effect it will have on the lives of all mankind.

Quantum Information Science

Quantum information science concerns information science that depends on quantum effects in physics. It includes theoretical issues in computational models as well as more experimental topics in quantum physics including what can and cannot be done with quantum information. The term quantum information theory is sometimes used, but it fails to encompass experimental research in the area.

Subfields include:

- Quantum computing, which deals on the one hand with the question how and whether one can build a quantum computer and on the other hand, searching algorithms that harness its power

- Quantum computational complexity
- Quantum cryptography and its generalization, quantum communication
- Quantum error correction
- Quantum communication complexity
- Quantum entanglement, as seen from an information-theoretic point of view

Quantum teleportation is one well-known quantum information processing operation which reliably transfers an unknown quantum state from one point to another distant point, destroying the original state in the process.

Utility Computing

Utility computing is a business model whereby computer resources are provided on an on-demand and pay-per-use basis.

This is different with the conventional computing model in that customers do not have to invest in owning (peak need) resources anymore, but only are billed for the actual use of resources. As the utility computing provider can spread the customers' variance in resource needs, the utilization of the resources can be optimized. This is comparable to the use of electricity, gas, and most other utilities, hence the name utility computing.

As the Utility Computing service is based on usage, computing resources are metered and the user charged on that basis. Utility computing is sometimes also called On Demand Computing.

History

IBM conducted this kind of business offering computing power and database storage to big banks from its world wide data centers. As Intel increased the desktop power, the computer architecture has gone through terminal/mainframe, client/server, browser/middleware. Recently, it was re-initiated by Sun offering the Sun Grid service to consumers in 2000. HP introduced the Utility Data Center in 2001. Since 2000 many important computing companies have entered the market, but there have also been smaller organisations that have used utility computing. Some of these organisations use utility computing to help offset the cost of their own hardware, others use it to share the cost of resources within organisations. In December 2005, Alexa launched Alexa Web Search Platform, a Web search building tool for which the underlying power is utility computing. Alexa charges users for storage, utilization, etc. There is space in the market for specific industries and applications as well as other niche applications powered by utility computing. For example, PolyServe Inc. offers a clustered file system based on commodity server and storage hardare that creates highly available utility computing environments for mission-critical applications including Oracle and Microsoft SQL Server databases, as well as workload optimized solutions specifically tuned for bulk storage, high-performance computing, vertical industries such as financial services, seismic processing, and content serving. The Database Utility and File Serving Utility enable IT organisations to independently add servers or storage as needed, retask workloads to different hardware, and maintain the environment without disruption.

Enabling Utility Computing

HPC organisations have multiple options for enabling utility computing at their own organisations. Software solutions include:

- PolyServe's Database Utility and File Serving Utility
- Various Veritas solutions
- Platform's Enterprise Grid Orchestrator
- Egenera's BladeFrame
- Cassatt Collage
- Scali Manage

Similarly, Utility Computing is available in the form of pay-as-you-go hosting services for developers — these differ from most offerings in that there is no fixed monthly fee:

- Amazon S3 — Bulk storage and bandwidth for static content
- Amazon EC2 — Pay by the hour CPU
- NearlyFreeSpeech — Pay as you go web hosting for web pages, dynamic content, domains, DNS, etc
- Sun Microsystems Sun Grid — Pay by the CPU hour
- Strikeiron Web Services Marketplace — Pay per Web API call.
- USi, an AT&T company — USiPinnacle — Pay-as-you-go enterprise applications
- Zimki — Javascript based utility computing system. Pay by bandwidth, storage, and javascript operations.

DNA Computing

DNA computing is a form of computing which uses DNA and biochemistry and molecular biology, instead of the traditional silicon-based computer technologies. This field was initially developed by Leonard Adleman of the University of Southern California. In 1994, Adleman demonstrated a proof-of-concept use of DNA as a form of computation which was used to solve the seven-point Hamiltonian path problem. Since the initial Adleman experiments, advances have been made, and various Turing machines have been proven to be constructable. There are works over one dimensional lengths, bidimensional tiles, and even three dimensional DNA graphs processing. On April 28, 2004, Ehud Shapiro, Yaakov Benenson, Binyamin Gil, Uri Ben-Dor, and Rivka Adar at the Weizmann Institute announced in the journal Nature that they had constructed a DNA computer. This was coupled with an input and output module and is capable of diagnosing cancerous activity within a cell, and then releasing an anti-cancer drug upon diagnosis. DNA computing is fundamentally similar to parallel computing in that it takes advantage of the many different molecules of DNA to try many different possibilities at once. For certain specialized problems, DNA computers are faster and smaller than any other computer built so far. But DNA computing does not provide any new capabilities from the standpoint of computational complexity theory, the study of which computational problems are difficult to solve. For example, problems which grow exponentially with the size of the problem (EXPSPACE problems) on von Neumann machines still grow exponentially with the size of the problem on DNA machines. For very large EXPSPACE problems, the amount of DNA required is too large to be practical. (Quantum computing, on the other hand, *does* provide some interesting new capabilities). DNA computing overlaps with, but is distinct from, DNA Nanotechnology. The latter uses the specificity of Watson-Crick basepairing to make novel structures out of DNA. These structures can be used for DNA computing, but they do not have to be. Additionally, DNA computing can be done without using the types of molecules made possible by DNA Nanotechnology (as the above examples show).

Introduction to Quantum Computing

In quantum computing, we witness an exciting and very promising merge of two of the deepest and most successful scientific and technological developments of this century: quantum physics and computer science. In spite of the fact that its experimental developments are in their infancy, there has already been a variety of concepts, models, methods and results obtained at the theoretical level that clearly have lasting value.These concepts, methods and results are the main subject of the book. Knowledge from two areas is of importance for understanding the basic developments in quantum computing: namely, quantum physics and theoretical computer science. The book provides elements of both, and concentrates on the presentation of concepts, models, methods and results mainly from a computing point of view. No previous knowledge of quantum mechanics is required. By making no assumption of previous knowledge of quantum mechanics, the book explains the principles and also the mysteries of the basic physical phenomena behind quantum computing. It allows a computer scientist to understand the problems, models, methods and main results of quantum information processing.By making minimal assumptions of theoretical computer science results, the book allows a physicist to understand the problems, models, methods and results of quantum computing from a computer science point of view.The large number of examples, figures and, especially, exercises provide ample opportunity for students and readers to practice the material learned.An extensive Appendix provides a concentrated presentation of some of the basic frameworks within which quantum computing develops; quantum mechanics, Hilbert spaces and computational complexity theory.

The science of physics seeks to ask, and find precise answers to, basic questions about why nature is as it is. Historically, the fundamental principles of physics have been concerned with questions such as "what are things made of?" and "why do things move as they do?" In his *Principia*, Newton gave very wide-ranging answers to some of these questions. By showing that the same mathamatical equations could describe the motions of everyday objects and of planets, he showed that an everyday object such as a tea pot is made of essentially the *same sort of stuff* as a planet: the motions of both can be described in terms of their mass and the forces acting on them. Nowadays we would say that both move in such a way as to conserve energy and momentum. In this way, physics allows us to abstract from nature concepts such as energy or momentum which always obey fixed equations, although the same energy might be expressed in many different ways: for example, an electron in the large electron-positron collider at CERN, Geneva, can have the same kinetic energy as a slug on a lettuce leaf.

Another thing which can be expressed in many different ways is *information*. For example, the two statements "the quantum computer is very interesting" and "l'ordinateur quantique est tres interessant" have something in common, although they share no words. The thing they have in common is their *information* content. Essentially the same information could be expressed in many other ways, for example by substituting numbers for letters in a scheme such as a -> 97, b -> 98, c -> 99 and so on, in which case the english version of the above statement becomes 116 104 101 32 113 117 97 110 116 117 109.... It is very significant that information can be expressed in different ways without losing its essential nature, since this leads to the possibility of the automatic manipulation of information: a machine need only be able to manipulate quite simple things like integers in order to do surprisingly powerful information processing, from document preparation to differential calculus, even to translating between human languages. We are familiar with this now, because of the ubiquitous computer, but even fifty years ago such a widespread significance of automated information processing was not forseen.

However, there is one thing that all ways of expressing information must have in common: they all use real physical things to do the job. Spoken words are conveyed by air pressure fluctuations, written ones by arrangements of ink molecules on paper, even thoughts depend on neurons (Landauer 1991). The rallying cry of the information physicist is "no information without physical representation!" Conversely, the fact that information is insensitive to exactly how it is expressed, and can be freely translated from one form to another, makes it an obvious candidate for a fundamentally important role in physics, like energy and momentum and other such abstractions. However, until the second half of this century, the precise mathematical treatment of information, especially information processing, was undiscovered, so the significance of information in physics was only hinted at in concepts such as entropy in thermodynamics. It now appears that information may have a much deeper significance. Historically, much of fundamental physics has been concerned with discovering the fundamental particles of nature and the equations which describe their motions and interactions. It now appears that a different programme may be equally important: to discover the ways that nature allows, and prevents, *information* to be expressed and manipulated, rather than particles to move. For example, the best way to state exactly what can and cannot travel faster than light is to identify information as the speed-limited entity. In quantum mechanics, it is highly significant that the state vector must not contain, whether explicitly or implicitly, more information than can meaningfully be associated with a given system. Among other things this produces the wavefunction symmetry requirements which lead to Bose Einstein and Fermi Dirac statistics, the periodic structure of atoms, and so on.

The programme to re-investigate the fundamental principles of physics from the standpoint of information theory is still in its infancy. However, it already appears to be highly fruitful, and it is this ambitious programme that I aim to summarise.

Historically, the concept of information in physics does not have a clear-cut origin. An important thread can be traced if we consider the paradox of Maxwell's demon of 1871 (see also Brillouin 1956). Recall that Maxwell's demon is a creature that opens and closes a trap door between two compartments of a chamber containing gas, and pursues the subversive policy of only opening the door when fast molecules approach it from the right, or slow ones from the left. In this way the demon establishes a temperature difference between the two compartments without doing any work, in violation of the second law of thermodynamics, and consequently permitting a host of contradictions.

A number of attempts were made to exorcise Maxwell's demon (see Bennett 1987), such as arguments that the demon cannot gather information without doing work, or without disturbing (and thus heating) the gas, both of which are untrue. Some were tempted to propose that the 2nd law of thermodynamics could indeed be violated by the actions of an "intelligent being." It was not until 1929 that Leo Szilard made progress by reducing the problem to its essential components, in which the demon need merely identify whether a single molecule is to the right or left of a sliding partition, and its action allows a simple heat engine, called Szilard's engine, to be run. Szilard still had not solved the problem, since his analysis was unclear about whether or not the act of measurement, whereby the demon learns whether the molecule is to the left or the right, must involve an increase in entropy.

A definitive and clear answer was not forthcoming, surprisingly, until a further fifty years had passed. In the intermediate years digital computers were developed, and the physical implications of information gathering and processing were carefully considered. The thermodynamic costs of elementary information manipulations were analysed by Landauer and others during the 1960s (Landauer 1961, Keyes and Landauer 1970), and those of general computations by Bennett, Fredkin, Toffoli and others during the 1970s (Bennett 1973, Toffoli 1980, Fredkin and Toffoli 1982). It was found that almost anything can in principle be done in a reversible manner, i.e. with no entropy cost at all (Bennett and Landauer 1985). Bennett (1982) made explicit the relation between this work and Maxwell's paradox by proposing that the demon can indeed learn where the molecule is in Szilard's engine without doing any work or increasing any entropy in the environment, and so obtain useful work during one stroke of the engine. However, the information about the molecule's location must then be present in the demon's memory. As more and more strokes are performed, more and more information gathers in the demon's memory. To complete a thermodynamic cycle, the demon must *erase* its memory, and it is during this erasure operation that we identify an increase in entropy in the environment, as required by the 2nd law. This completes the essential physics of Maxwell's demon; further subtleties are discussed by Zurek (1989), Caves (1990), and Caves, Unruh and Zurek (1990).

The thread we just followed was instructive, but to provide a complete history of ideas relevent to quantum computing is a formidable task. Our subject brings together what are arguably two of the greatest revolutions in twentieth-century science, namely quantum mechanics and information science (including computer science). Classical information theory is founded on the definition of information. A warning is in order here. Whereas the theory tries to capture much of the normal meaning of the term 'information', it can no more do justice to the full richness of that term in everyday language than particle physics can encapsulate the everyday meaning of 'charm'. 'Information' for us will be an abstract term. Much of information theory dates back to seminal work of Shannon in the 1940's (Slepian 1974). The observation that information can be translated from one form to another is encapsulated and quantified in Shannon's noiseless coding theorem (1948), which quantifies the resources needed to store or transmit a given body of information. Shannon also considered the fundamentally important problem of communication in the presence of noise, and established Shannon's main theorem which is the central result of classical information theory. Error-free communication even in the presence of noise is achieved by means of 'error-correcting codes', and their study is a branch of mathematics in its own right. Indeed, the journal *IEEE Transactions on Information Theory* is almost totally taken up with the discovery and analysis of error-correction by coding. Pioneering work in this area was done by Golay (1949) and Hamming (1950).

The foundations of computer science were formulated at roughly the same time as Shannon's information theory, and this is no coincidence. The father of computer science is arguably Alan Turing (1912-1954), and its prophet is Charles Babbage (1791-1871). Babbage conceived of most of the essential elements of a modern computer, though in his day there was not the technology available to implement his ideas. A century passed before Babbage's Analytical Engine was improved upon when Turing described the Universal Turing Machine in the mid 1930s. Turing's genius (see Hodges 1983) was to clarify exactly what a calculating machine might be capable of, and to emphasise the role of programming, i.e. software, even more than Babbage had done. The giants on whose shoulders Turing stood in order to get a better view were chiefly the mathematicians David Hilbert and Kurt Godel. Hilbert had emphasised between the 1890s and 1930s the importance of asking fundamental questions about the nature of mathematics. Instead of asking "is this mathematical proposition true?" Hilbert wanted to ask "is it the case that every mathematical proposition can in principle be proved or disproved?" This was unknown, but Hilbert's feeling, and that of most mathematicians, was that mathematics was indeed complete, so that conjectures such as Goldbach's (that every even number can be written as the sum of two primes) could be proved or disproved somehow, although the logical steps might be as yet undiscovered.

Godel destroyed this hope by establishing the existence of mathematical propositions which were undecidable, meaning that they could be neither proved nor disproved. The next interesting question was whether it would be easy to identify such propositions. Progress in mathematics had always relied on the use of creative imagination, yet with hindsight mathematical proofs appear to be automatic, each step following inevitably from the one before. Hilbert asked whether this 'inevitable' quality could be captured by a 'mechanical' process. In other words, was there a universal mathematical method, which would establish the truth or otherwise of every mathematical assertion? After Godel, Hilbert's problem was re-phrased into that of establishing decidability rather than truth, and this is what Turing sought to address.

In the words of Newman, Turing's bold innovation was to introduce 'paper tape' into symbolic logic. In the search for an automatic process by which mathematical questions could be decided, Turing envisaged a thoroughly mechanical device, in fact a kind of glorified typewriter. The importance of the *Turing machine* (Turing 1936) arises from the fact that it is sufficiently complicated to address highly sophisticated mathematical questions, but sufficiently simple to be subject to detailed analysis. Turing used his machine as a theoretical construct to show that the assumed existence of a mechanical means to establish decidability leads to a contradiction. In other words, he was initially concerned with quite abstract mathematics rather than practical computation. However, by seriously establishing the idea of automating abstract mathematical proofs rather than merely arithmatic, Turing greatly stimulated the development of general purpose information processing. This was in the days when a "computer" was a person doing mathematics.

Modern computers are neither Turing machines nor Babbage engines, though they are based on broadly similar principles, and their computational power is equivalent (in a technical sense) to that of a Turing machine. I will not trace their development here, since although this is a wonderful story, it would take too long to do justice to the many people involved. Let us just remark that all of this development represents a great improvement in speed and size, but does not involve any change in the essential idea of what a computer is, or how it operates. Quantum mechanics raises the possibility of such a change, however.

Quantum mechanics is the mathematical structure which embraces, in principle, the whole of physics. We will not be directly concerned with gravity, high velocities, or exotic elementary particles, so the standard non-relativistic quantum mechanics will suffice. The significant feature of quantum theory for our purpose is not the precise details of the equations of motion, but the fact that they treat quantum amplitudes, or state vectors in a Hilbert space, rather than classical variables. It is this that allows new types of information and computing.

There is a parallel between Hilbert's questions about mathematics and the questions we seek to pose in quantum information theory. Before Hilbert, almost all mathematical work had been concerned with establishing or refuting particular hypotheses, but Hilbert wanted to ask what general type of hypothesis was even amenable to mathematical proof. Similarly, most research in quantum physics has been concerned with studying the evolution of specific physical systems, but we want to ask what general type of evolution is even conceivable under quantum mechanical rules.

The first deep insight into quantum information theory came with Bell's 1964 analysis of the paradoxical thought-experiment proposed by Einstein, Podolsky and Rosen (EPR) in 1935. Bell's inequality draws attention to the importance of *correlations* between separated quantum systems which have interacted (directly or indirectly) in the past, but which no longer influence one another. In essence his argument shows that the degree of correlation which can be present in such systems exceeds that which could be predicted on the basis of *any* law of physics which describes particles in terms of classical variables rather than quantum states. Bell's argument was clarified by Bohm (1951, also Bohm and Aharonov 1957) and by Clauser, Holt, Horne and Shimony (1969), and experimental tests were carried out in the 1970s (see Clauser and Shimony (1978) and references therein). Improvements in such experiments are largely concerned with preventing the possibility of any interaction between the separated quantum systems, and a significant step forward was made in the experiment of Aspect, Dalibard and Roger (1982), (see also Aspect 1991) since in their work any purported interaction would have either to travel faster than light, or possess other almost equally implausible qualities.

The next link between quantum mechanics and information theory came about when it was realised that simple properties of quantum systems, such as the unavoidable disturbance involved in measurement, could be put to practical use, in *quantum cryptography* (Wiesner 1983, Bennett *et. al.* 1982, Bennett and Brassard 1984; for a recent review see Brassard and Crepeau 1996). Quantum cryptography covers several ideas, of which the most firmly established is quantum key distribution. This is an ingenious method in which transmitted quantum states are used to perform a very particular communication task: to establish at two separated locations a pair of identical, but otherwise random, sequences of binary digits, without allowing any third party to learn the sequence. This is very useful because such a random sequence can be used as a cryptographic key to permit secure communication. The significant feature is that the principles of quantum mechanics guarantee a type of conservation of quantum information, so that if the necessary quantum information arrives at the parties wishing to establish a random key, they can be sure it has not gone elsewhere, such as to a spy. Thus the whole problem of compromised keys, which fills the annals of espionage, is avoided by taking advantage of the structure of the natural world.

While quantum cryptography was being analysed and demonstrated, the quantum computer was undergoing a quiet birth. Since quantum mechanics underlies the behaviour of all systems, including those we call classical ("even a screwdriver is quantum mechanical", Landauer (1995)), it was not obvious how to conceive of a distinctively quantum mechanical computer, i.e. one which did not merely reproduce the action of a classical Turing machine. Obviously it is not sufficient merely to identify a quantum mechanical system whose evolution could be interpreted as a computation; one must prove a much stronger result than this. Conversely, we know that classical computers can simulate, by their computations, the evolution of any quantum system... with one reservation: no classical process will allow one to prepare separated systems whose correlations break the Bell inequality. It appears from this that the EPR-Bell correlations are the quintessential quantum-mechanical property (Feynman 1982).

In order to think about computation from a quantum-mechanical point of view, the first ideas involved converting the action of a Turing machine into an equivalent reversible process, and then inventing a Hamiltonian which would cause a quantum system to evolve in a way which mimicked a reversible Turing machine. This depended on the work of Bennett (1973; see also Lecerf 1963) who had shown that a universal classical computing machine (such as Turing's) could be made reversible while retaining its simplicity. Benioff (1980, 1982) and others proposed such Turing-like Hamiltonians in the early 1980s. Although Benioff's ideas did not allow the full analysis of quantum computation, they showed that unitary quantum evolution is at least as powerful computationally as a classical computer.

A different approach was taken by Feynman (1982, 1986) who considered the possibility not of universal computation, but of universal *simulation*—i.e. a purpose-built quantum system which could simulate the *physical behaviour* of any other. Clearly, such a simulator would be a universal computer too, since any computer must be a physical system. Feynman gave arguments which suggested that quantum evolution could be used to compute certain problems more efficiently than any classical computer, but his device was not sufficiently specified to be called a computer, since he assumed that any interaction between adjacent two-state systems could be 'ordered', without saying how.

In 1985 an important step forward was taken by Deutsch. Deutsch's proposal is widely considered to represent the first blueprint for a quantum computer, in that it is sufficiently specific and simple to allow real machines to be contemplated, but sufficiently versatile to be a universal quantum simulator, though both points are debatable. Deutsch's system is essentially a line of two-state systems, and looks more like a register machine than a Turing machine (both are universal classical computing machines). Deutsch proved that if the two-state systems could be made to evolve by means of a specific small set of simple operations, then *any* unitary evolution could be produced, and therefore the evolution could be made to simulate that of any physical system. He also discussed how to produce Turing-like behaviour using the same ideas.

Deutsch's simple operations are now called quantum 'gates', since they play a role analogous to that of binary logic gates in classical computers. Various authors have investigated the minimal class of gates which are sufficient for quantum computation.

The two questionable aspects of Deutsch's proposal are its efficiency and realisability. The question of efficiency is absolutely fundamental in computer science, and on it the concept of 'universality' turns. A *universal* computer is one that not only can reproduce (i.e. simulate) the action of any other, but can do so without running too slowly. The 'too slowly' here is defined in terms of the number of computational steps required: this number must not increase exponentially with the size of the input. Deutsch's simulator is not universal in this strict sense, though it was shown to be efficient for simulating a wide class of quantum systems by Lloyd (1996). However, Deutsch's work has established the concepts of quantum networks (Deutsch 1989) and quantum logic gates, which are extremely important in that they allow us to think clearly about quantum computation.

In the early 1990's several authors (Deutsch and Jozsa 1992, Berthiaume and Brassard 1992, Bernstein and Vazirani 1993) sought computational tasks which could be solved by a quantum computer more efficiently than *any* classical computer. Such a quantum algorithm would play a conceptual role similar to that of Bell's inequality, in defining something of the essential nature of quantum mechanics. Initially only very small differences in performance were found, in which quantum mechanics permitted an answer to be found with certainty, as long as the quantum system was noise-free, where a probabilistic classical computer could achieve an answer 'only' with high probability. An important advance was made by Simon (1994), who described an efficient quantum algorithm for a (somewhat abstract) problem for which no efficient solution was possible classically, even by probabilistic methods. This inspired Shor (1994) who astonished the community by describing an algorithm which was not only efficient on a quantum computer, but also addressed a central problem in computer science: that of factorising large integers.

Shor discussed both factorisation and discrete logarithms, making use of a quantum Fourier transform method discovered by Coppersmith (1994) and Deutsch. Further important quantum algorithms were discovered by Grover (1997) and Kitaev (1995).

Just as with classical computation and information theory, once theoretical ideas about computation had got under way, an effort was made to establish the essential nature of quantum information—the task analogous to Shannon's work. The difficulty here can be seen by considering the simplest quantum system, a two-state system such as a spin half in a magnetic field. The quantum state of a spin is a continuous quantity defined by two real numbers, so in principle it can store an infinite amount of classical information. However, a measurement of a spin will only provide a single two-valued answer (spin up/spin down)—there is no way to gain access to the infinite information which appears to be there, therefore it is incorrect to consider the information content in those terms. This is reminiscent of the renormalisation problem in quantum electrodynamics. How much information can a two-state quantum system store, then? The answer, provided by Jozsa and Schumacher (1994) and Schumacher (1995), is *one two-state system's worth*! Of course Schumacher and Jozsa did more than propose this simple answer, rather they showed that the two-state system plays the role in quantum information theory analogous to that of the bit in classical information theory, in that the quantum information content of *any* quantum system can be meaningfully measured as the minimum number of two-state systems, now called quantum bits or qubits, which would be needed to store or transmit the system's state with high accuracy.

Let us return to the question of realisability of quantum computation. It is an elementary, but fundamentally important, observation that the quantum interference effects which permit algorithms such as Shor's are extremely fragile: the quantum computer is ultra-sensitive to experimental noise and impression. It is not true that early workers were unaware of this difficulty, rather their first aim was to establish whether a quantum computer had any fundamental significance at all. Armed with Shor's algorithm, it now appears that such a fundamental significance is established, by the following argument: either nature does allow a device to be run with sufficient precision to perform Shor's algorithm for large integers (greater than, say, a googol which is 1 followed by 100 zeroes) or there are fundamental natural limits to precision in real systems. Both eventualities represent an important insight into the laws of nature.

At this point, ideas of quantum information and quantum computing come together. For, a quantum computer can be made much less sensitive to noise by means of a new idea which comes directly from the marriage of quantum mechanics with classical information theory, namely *quantum error correction*. Although the phrase 'error correction' is a natural one and was used with reference to quantum computers prior to 1996, it was only in that year that two important papers, of Calderbank and Shor, and independently Steane, established a general framework whereby quantum information processing can be used to combat a very wide class of noise processes in a properly designed quantum system. Much progress has since been made in generalising these ideas (Knill and Laflamme 1997, Ekert and Macchiavello 1996, Bennett *et. al.* 1996b, Gottesman 1996, Calderbank *et. al.* 1997). An important development was the demonstration by Shor (1996) and Kitaev (1996) that correction can be achieved even when the corrective operations are themselves imperfect. Such methods lead to a general concept of 'fault tolerant' computing, of which a helpful review is provided by Preskill (1997).

If, as seems almost certain, quantum computation will only work in conjunction with quantum error correction, it appears that the relationship between quantum information theory and quantum computers is even more intimate than that between Shannon's information theory and classical computers. Error correction does not in itself guarantee accurate quantum computation, since it cannot combat all types of noise, but the fact that it is possible at all is a significant development.

A computer which only exists on paper will not actually perform any computations, and in the end the only way to resolve the issue of feasibility in quantum computer science is to build a quantum computer. To this end, a number of authors proposed computer designs based on Deutsch's idea, but with the physical details more fully worked out (Teich *et. al.* 1988, Lloyd 1993, Berman *et. al.* 1994, DiVincenco 1995b). The great challenge is to find a sufficiently complex system whose evolution is nevertheless both coherent (i.e. unitary) and controlable. It is not sufficient that only some aspects of a system should be quantum mechanical, as in solid-state 'quantum dots', or that there is an implicit assumption of unfeasible precision or cooling, which is often the case for proposals using solid-state devices. Cirac and Zoller (1995) proposed the use of a linear ion trap, which was a significant improvement in feasibility, since heroic efforts in the ion trapping community had already achieved the necessary precision and low temperature in experimental work, especially the group of Wineland who demonstrated cooling to the ground state of an ion trap in the same year (Diedrich *et. al.* 1989, Monroe *et. al.* 1995). More recently, Gershenfeld and Chuang (1997) and Cory *et. al.* (1996,1997) have shown that nuclear magnetic resonance (NMR) techniques can be adapted to fulfill the requirements of quantum computation, making this approach also very promising. Other recent proposals of Privman *et. al.* (1997) and Loss and DiVincenzo (1997) may also be feasible.

As things stand, no quantum computer has been built, nor looks likely to be built in the author's lifetime, if we measure it in terms of Shor's algorithm, and ask for factoring of large numbers. However, if we ask instead for a device in which quantum information ideas can be explored, then only a few quantum bits are required, and this will certainly be achieved in the near future. Simple two-bit operations have been carried out in many physics experiments, notably magnetic resonance, and work with three to ten qubits now seems feasible. Notable recent experiments in this regard are those of Brune *et. al.* (1994), Monroe *et. al.* (1995b), Turchette *et. al.* (1995) and Mattle *et. al.* (1996).

Fundamental of Quantum Compting

The power of quantum computing is based on several phenomena and laws of the quantum world that are fundamentally different from those one encounters in classical computing: complex probability amplitudes, quantum interference, quantum parallelism, quantum entanglement and the unitarity of quantum evolution. In order to understand these features, and to make a use of them for the design of quantum algorithms, networks and processors, one has to understand several basic principles which quantum mechanics is based on, as well as the basics of Hilbert space formalism that represents the mathematical framework used in quantum mechanics.

The chapter starts with an analysis of the current interest in quantum computing. It then discusses the main intellectual barriers that had to be overcome to make a vision of the quantum computer an important challenge to current science and technology. The basic and specific features of quantum computing are first introduced by a comparison of randomized computing and quantum computing. An introduction to quantum phenomena is done in three stages. First, several classical and similar quantum experiments are analysed. This is followed by Hilbert space basics and by a presentation of the elementary principles of quantum mechanics and the elements of classical reversible computing.

The aim of the chapter is to learn

- the main reasons why to be interested in quantum computing;
- the prehistory of quantum computing;
- the specific properties of quantum computing in comparison with randomized computing;
- the basic experiments and principles of quantum physics;
- the basics of Hilbert space theory;
- the elements of classical reversible computing.

Elements

The basic elements of quantum computing are easy to identify: quantum bits, quantum registers, quantum gates and quantum networks. However, at this point an analogy with classical computing ends. Quantum bits, registers, gates and networks are very different, have other properties and larger power than their classical counterparts.

A quantum bit can be in any state within an infinite set of states. A quantum register of n quantum bits can be, at the same time, in any of the infinitely many superpositions of basis states. The parallelism a quantum register can exhibit is striking. The key new feature is that a quantum register can be in an entangled state. On one side, entangled states with their non-locality features are a hallmark of quantum mechanics. On the other side, quantum entanglement is an important resource of quantum information processing.

There is a larger variety of quantum gates than of classical gates. There are already infinitely many one-input/output quantum gates. In addition, almost any two-input/output quantum gate is universal. A simple two input/output gate together with one-input rotation gates form a set of universal gates.

Learning Objectives

The aim of the chapter is to learn:

- the basic concepts concerning quantum bits and registers;
- the concept of quantum entanglement and the examples of its power;
- the basic examples of quantum gates and of quantum circuits;
- some examples of universal quantum gates and a method to show universality of quantum gates;
- the basic quantum arithmetical circuits;
- the concept of quantum superoperator circuits.

Algorithms

Quantum algorithms make use of several specific features of the quantum world, for example quantum superposition, to get from classical inputs, through entangled states, to classical outputs more efficiently than classical algorithms. A variety of quantum algorithms are presented in this chapter. They range from pioneering algorithms, simple but powerful, for several promise problems, through seminal Shor's algorithms and a variety of algorithms for various search problems and their modifications, due to Grover and others.

Design of faster-than-classical quantum algorithms for important algorithmic problems has been an interesting intellectual adventure and achievement. Their existence keeps being one of the key stimuli to those trying to overcome enormous technology problems to build (powerful) quantum computers. Methods to design quantum algorithms and to show limitations of quantum power have also been developed gradually and will be presented and illustrated in this chapter.

Learning Objectives

The aim of the chapter is to learn:

- the power of quantum superpositions, parallelism and entanglement;

- the efficient quantum algorithms for several basic promise problems;
- the quantum Fourier transform and its properties and implementation;
- Shor's quantum algorithms for integer factorization and discrete logarithm computation;
- the hidden subgroup problems and their role in quantum computing;
- a variety of search algorithms due to Grover and others;
- methods to design efficient quantum algorithms;
- methods to show lower bounds and limitations of quantum computing.

Automata

In addition to the study of problems of the design and analysis of algorithms and circuits, as well as of the computational complexity of algorithmic problems, another main method of theoretical computing to get an insight into the power of computational resources is to study models of quantum computing devices and the corresponding complexity classes. This will be done in this chapter for three most basic models of quantum automata: quantum versions of finite automata, Turing machines and cellular automata. Quantum finite automata are perhaps the most elementary model of quantum automata. They are in addition the only model so far for which it has been fully proved that they have larger power than their classical counterparts.

Quantum Turing machines are the main model to study the most fundamental questions concerning the power of quantum computing itself and the power of quantum versus classical computing. Quantum cellular automata are of a special interest.

They seem to be a model much closer to the physical reality than quantum Turing machines. In addition, it is still a major open problem whether quantum cellular automata are more powerful than quantum Turing machines.

Learning Objectives

The aim of the chapter is to learn:

- the basic models of one-way and two-way quantum finite automata as well as their computational power and space efficiency in comparison with classical finite automata;
- the basic models of quantum Turing machines and methods of implementing the main classical programming primitives in a reversible way;
- the types and precision of amplitudes needed to ensure sufficient accuracy of computation on quantum Turing machines;

- the basic models of quantum cellular automata and partitioned quantum cellular automata, as well as simulations between quantum cellular automata and quantum Turing machines.

Complexity

The study of complexity questions and of complexity classes, computational and communicational, has proved to be very enlightenin and important for classical computation. It has developed a firm theoretical basis for our understanding of the potentials and limitations of computational resources, models, and modes. There is reason to expect the same for the complexity investigations in quantum computation and communication.

It is of utmost importance to determine whether quantum classification of inherent computational complexity is indeed different from the classical one. Would this prove to be the case the very basic foundations of computing would be shaken.

Quantum computational complexity theory is characterized, as its classical counterpart, by a number of fundamental open problems concerning the proper inclusions of complexity classes. In order to get a better insight into these problems, and to test potential methods to solve them, the relativized quantum complexity theory is of interest and importance. It is also of importance to find out how much quantum features can speed up computations, shorten communications and achieve efficiency in size or space. Investigations of the potential impacts on the power of computing of the existence of slightly non-linear evolutions in quantum physics are also of interest.

Learning Objectives

The aim of the chapter is to learn:

- the way universal quantum Turing machines can be constructed;
- the basic quantum complexity classes and their properties;
- the basic relations between classical and quantum complexity classes;
- the basic results concerning relativized quantum complexity;
- the basic concepts of quantum communication complexity;
- a reduction of quantum communication protocols to quantum computation problems;
- the potential impacts of non-linearity on the power of quantum computing.

Crytopography

Secure communication is one of the areas of key importance for modern society in which quantum information transmission and processing seems to be able to bring significant contributions. For example, quantum cryptography may be the main defence against quantum code breaking in the future.

An important new feature of quantum cryptography is that security of quantum key generation and quantum cryptographic protocols is based on a more reliable fact, on the laws of nature as revealed by quantum mechanics, than in the case of classical cryptography, whose security is based on unproven assumptions concerning the computational hardness of some algorithmic problems.

It is difficult to overemphasize the importance of quantum cryptography for an understanding and utilization of quantum information processing. Quantum cryptography was the first area in which quantum laws were directly exploited to bring an essential advantage in information processing. Closely related are quantum teleportation and quantum superdense coding—special ways of the transmission of quantum or classical information usin one of the most puzzling phenomena of the quantum world—non-locality features of the quantum entanglement.

Learning Objectives

The aim of the chapter is to learn:

- several methods of secret key generation by two parties;
- a method of multiparty secret key generation;
- the unconditional security of quantum key generation;
- the basic quantum cryptographic protocols;
- the problems related to the security of quantum cryptographic protocols;
- the main principles, circuits and some applications of quantum teleportation;
- the quantum superdense coding procedure.

Processors

Theoretical investigations concerning quantum algorithms, automata, complexity, information theory and cryptography are of great interest and importance. However, progress in the experimental efforts to design quantum information-processing systems is crucial for seeing properly the overall perspectives of the future designs of real and powerful quantum computers, and for isolating and solving the problems that need to be dealt with if powerful quantum computers are ever to be built. It has been realised, from the very early days of research in quantum computing, at least by some, that powerful evolution of isolated quantum systems is hard to utilize in real quantum processors, because of their interaction with the environment that can destroy very large but fragile quantum superpositions; and because of the natural imperfections of (inherently analogue) quantum devices. In addition, quantum error correction was considered impossible. Fortunately, several developments brought the vision of quantum computers closer to reality. Quantum computation stabilization methods and quantum error correction codes have turned out to be possible and efficient. Techniques for fault-tolerant quantum computing have been developed. Finally, some promising technologies to design quantum gates, circuits, and processors have been identified and are being experimentally tested.

Learning Objectives

The aim of the chapter is to learn:

- the early proposals for quantum computers;
- the impacts of imprecision, dissipation and decoherence on quantum computing;
- the methods of designing and using quantum error-correcting codes;
- the basics of quantum fault-tolerant techniques;
- the basics of the main current technologies used, or considered, to develop experimental quantum processors.

Information

The development and the understanding of the basic concepts, methods and results of quantum information theory and of the faithful transmission of quantum information in time and space is the most fundamental problem of quantum information processing. In order to be able to understand and to utilize fully the information processing available in nature, the concepts of classical information theory need to be expanded to accumulate quantum information carriers. Three central problems concerning quantum information and its communication are dealt with, very briefly, in this chapter.

1. Quantum information theory. How to rebuild classical information theory on quantum foundations. How to define fundamental concepts of quantum information theory. How to identify and explore the inherently quantum elements of such a theory.
2. Quantum transmissions theory. How to use optimally quantum channels to send classical information and how to use optimally quantum and classical channels to transmit quantum information. How to define and determine the capacity of different quantum channels.
3. Quantum entanglement theory. How to quantify and manipulate entanglement and how to produce good entanglement.

Learning Objectives

The aim of the chapter is to learn:

- the basic concepts of quantum information theory;
- the basic concepts of quantum transmission;
- the basic techniques of quantum data compression;
- the basic techniques of communication through a noisy channel;
- the basic modes and measures of entanglement;
- the basic quantum entanglement concentration and purification techniques.

A CASE STUDY OF WORLD'S FIRST ELECTRONIC AUTOMATIC COMPUTER

When the United States entered World War II the Ordnance Department was faced with a task of gigantic proportions. (The Ordnance Department was renamed Ordnance Corps in 1950.) It was responsible for design, procurement, distribution, and maintenance of ordnance materiel for the Army Ground Forces, the Army Air Force, and, in some categories the Navy. This task immediately engendered an accelerated research and development programme. Of extreme importance in this programme was the preparation of firing and bombing tables. This work was conducted at the Ballistic Research Laboratory at Aberdeen Proving Ground, MD, where the experimental data necessary to the computation of such tables was also obtained. When it is realised that for each weapon- ammunition combination the preparation of a separate firing table is required, the magnitude of the computations involving an entirely new series of weapons is easily seen.

The preparation of firing and bombing tables was performed by the Ballistic Computing Section of the Ballistic Research Laboratory. This section was composed at that time of a few civilian employees who were trained and highly skilled in the conventional methods of computation. In addition to desk calculators the group had available the Bush Differential Analyzer, which was capable of handling many types of problems but also had certain limitations. Captain P. N. Gillon, who was in charge of ballistic computations at the laboratory, recognized the need for improved aids to computation to cope with the greatly expanding computational activities.

Early in 1942 additional personnel, including military, were acquired to work in the Ballistic Computing Section at Aberdeen Proving Ground. Despite this increase in personnel work began to pile up and in June 1942 a contract was made with the Moore School of Electrical Engineering of the University of Pennsylvania to operate its Bush Differential Analyzer exclusively for the Army. In September 1942 the

Chief of Ordnance granted permission to operate a computing branch at the Moore School as a substation of Aberdeen Proving Ground. In this way the Ordnance Department could meet its requirements in computing. The two analyzers were operated day and night during the war.

The group at the Moore School of Electrical Engineering was supervised by Lt. Herman Goldstine, a member of the Aberdeen staff, who was assigned there at captain Gillon's request to head the computational and training activities. Lt. Goldstine was especially well qualified for this assignment because of his outstanding mathematical ability and his understanding and appreciation of Ordnance problems in the field of ballistic computation

Early in 1943, Captain Goldstine (promoted in the interim) and Professor Brainerd brought to Lt. Colonel Gillon (promoted 1942) the outline of the technical concepts underlying the design of an electronic computer. The idea had been conceived by Dr. J. Mauchly in 1942 as a result of work he had done previously with problems in weather study and physics that required great masses of numerical information to be handled, and also as a result of his experience at the Moore School of Electrical Engineering in the calculation of trajectories. This outline was prepared at Captain Goldstine's request by Dr. Mauchly and Mr. J. P. Eckert, Jr. Lt. Colonel Gillon, who meanwhile had been assigned to the Office, Chief of Ordnance as Deputy Chief of the Service Branch of the Technical Division, realised fully that formidable opposition would be offered to the initiation and prosecution of a development of this sort, especially in view of the highly speculative character of its successful completion. However, he also fully realised that there existed an urgent need for some means to perform computing at high speeds, not only for ballistic computations but also for the research activities of the Ordnance Department. Therefore he undertook to obtain the necessary authorization for its initiation and assumed full responsibility for its support and supervision.

It was Colonel L. Simon, Lt. Colonel P. N. Gillon, Captain H. Goldstine, and Mr. S. Feltman who secured the support of the Ordnance Department and continually stimulated the Moore School of Electrical Engineering of the University of Pennsylvania to further their efforts with respect to aids to computation. Dr. J. Mauchly, Mr. J. P. Eckert, Jr., Professor G. Brainerd, Dr. H. Pender and other members of the University of Pennsylvania staff applied their abilities to the problem of designing an electronic automatic computer. The result was a proposal, which was submitted to the Chief of Ordnance on 8 April 1943.

The original agreement between the United States of America and the trustees of the University of Pennsylvania, dated 5 June 1943, called for six months of "research and development of an electronic numerical integrator and computer and delivery of a report thereon." (The initial letters of the words describing the device were used to form its name — ENIAC.) This initial contract, R.A.D. 1078-W-670-ORD-4926 committed $61,700 in Ordnance Department funds under appropriation number ORD 61166 P610-07-A1005-23. Nine supplements to this contract extended the work to 1946, increased the amount ultimately to a total of $486,804.22, assigned technical supervision to the Ballistic Research Laboratory at Aberdeen Proving Ground, and called for the delivery of a working "pilot model," first to be operable at the University of Pennsylvania and then to be delivered to the BRL at APG.

From this point forward, the research staff and faculty of the Moore School of Electrical Engineering under Dr. H. Pender undertook energetic prosecution of the development pursuant to the terms of the Ordnance contract. The project was placed under the supervision of Professor Brainerd, with Mr. J. P. Eckert, Jr., as chief engineer, and Dr. J. Mauchly who provided the original outline for this development, as principal consultant. The resident supervisor for the Ordnance Department, Captain H. Goldstine, not only exercised extraordinary detailed and highly competent supervision for the Army but also contributed greatly to the mathematical side of the undertaking. As in all important undertakings which achieve important results, this was a work of many individuals.

Many meetings and conferences were held during the early days of development of the electronic numerical integrator and computer (ENIAC). Naturally many technical decisions had to be made. Then, as now, universities had an insatiable appetite for research, but in this case it was essential that the Ordnance Department obtain an operating device within a reasonable period of time. For example, there was always the temptation to increase the capability of the ENIAC, hence, when mercury delay lines came up for consideration as internal memory, Lt. Colonel Gillon, as the responsible supervisor for the Ordnance Department, insisted on the tried and tested decade ring counters in spite of the inherently reduced storage capacity.

(However, in view of the great promise of the mercury delay lines he obtained authorization for a new and separate contract calling for a new machine, using these delay lines. This machine, when completed, was the EDVAC and will be discussed in the next chapter.)

In this way precious time for the development of the ENIAC was not lost. The ENIAC was constructed at the Moore School component by component, beginning with the cycling unit and an accumulator in June 1944. This was followed in rapid succession by the initiating unit and function tables in September 1945, and the divider and square-root unit in October 1945. Final assembly took place during the fall of 1945 and the ENIAC was formally dedicated at the Moore School of Electrical

Engineering of the University of Pennsylvania on 15 February 1946. Acceptance by the Ordnance Department took place in July 1946.

Four years had elapsed since the original suggestion by Dr. John W. Mauchly that an all-electronic computer be built which could rapidly perform the vast amount of calculations required for the solution of the many complex problems facing the Ordnance Department. All through 1946 the ENIAC remained at the Moore School, working out numerical solutions to problems in such fields as atomic energy and ballistic trajectories.

In the winter of 1946-1947 the ENIAC was dismantled at the Moore School of Electrical Engineering and the first units arrived at Aberdeen Proving Ground, MD, in January 1947. By August of 1947 the ENIAC became operational again. It was the world's first electronic automatic computer and it not only opened up greater possibilities for advances in science and engineering but also started a new multi-billion dollar industry.

War circumstances had made it imperative to construct the ENIAC out of conventional electronic circuits and elements with a minimum of redesign. This fact, together with the requirements for capacity, speed, and accuracy, led to an extremely large machine. Its 30 separate units, plus power supply and forced air cooling, weighed over thirty tons and occupied 1,800 square feet. Its 19,000 vacuum tubes (16 different types), 1,500 relays, and many thousands of resistors, capacitors, and inductors consumed about 174 kilowatts of electrical power.

The main part of ENIAC consisted of 42 panels arranged around three sides of a room. Each panel was about 9 feet high, 2 feet wide, and 1 foot thick. Air ducts at the top of all the panels were provided for drawing off the hot air around the tubes. There were also 5 portable panels which could be rolled from place to place.

ENIAC was the prototype from which most other modern computers evolved. It embodied almost all of the components and concepts of later high-speed, storage and control devices. The counters and accumulators of the machine, with more sophisticated innovations, were made up of combinations of these basic elements.

The various units were interconnected through two sets of coaxial lines carried in "trays" running around the length of the machine. One set was called digit trays and was used for carrying pulse groups representing numerical data from one unit to another. The other set was called programme trays and carried pulses controlling the sequence of operations of the different units and could be plugged into the trays in accordance with the set-up for any particular computation. The machine worked with numbers expressed in the decimal system and could handle numbers of ten digits. The decimal system was chosen, in spite of advantages of other systems, because of the familiarity of its use. The ENIAC could discriminate the sign of a number, compare quantities for equality, add, subtract, multiply, divide, and extract square roots. A maximum of twenty 10-digit decimal numbers could be stored. The accumulators combined the functions of an adding machine and storage unit. No central memory unit existed, storage being localized within the functioning units of the computer.

The primary aim of the designers was to achieve speed by making ENIAC as all-electronic as possible. The only mechanical elements in the final product were actually external to the calculator itself. These were an International Business Machines (IBM) Corporation card reader for input, and IBM card punch for output, and the 1,500 associated relays. Another design objective was to make the electronics simple and reliable. This goal was achieved by utilizing vacuum tubes in a minimum of basic circuit combinations. To ensure reliable operation, circuits were constructed of rigidly tested standard components, which were operated at current, voltage, and power levels below their normal ratings. Accuracy of computation was assured by designing the basic circuits to work independently of the variable tolerances of their components. Numbers were not represented by electrical quantities which could be affected by changes in tolerance, but only by the presence or absence of dynamic pulses. Pulse groups representing the digits of a single number were transmitted simultaneously on different lines, requiring eleven lines in each digit tray for the ten decimal digits and the sign.

The gate, a circuit which would produce an output dependent upon a specified input, performed the switching or logical AND function. (AND is a term peculiar to computer engineering. It is a mathematical operator used to denote a process of logic whereby a statement is true if and only if all input conditions are met or are true.) It consisted of a single pentode which had a control voltage applied to its suppressor grid. Its function was similar to that of a single pole switch in that it "opened" (i.e., passed a pulse pattern) when the suppressor grid was positive and "closed" when the suppressor grid was negative. The buffer, an isolating circuit used to avoid any reaction of a driven circuit upon the corresponding driving circuit, contained two or more tubes connected through a common load resistor to form a circuit with the logical properties of the word OR. (OR is a term peculiar to computer engineering. It is a mathematical operator used to denote a process of logic whereby a statement is true if at least one of the input conditions is met or is true.) The grids of the tubes were normally biased at the cut-off point so that a positive input to any tube in the combination produced a negative output. The flip-flop circuit contained two triodes so connected that only one would conduct at a given time. The bi-stable device had two inputs and two outputs. In the SET, or normal position, one side of the output was positive, the other negative. In the RESET or abnormal position, these polarities were reversed. Logically, the flip-flop performed the functions of memory and that of a double pole, double throw switch. The state of each flip-flop was indicated by a neon lamp on the front panel of the computer units. A group of ten flip-flops, (0-9), interconnected to count digit pulses, formed a decade ring counter which was capable of adding and storing numbers. The counter possessed the following characteristics:

1. At any one time only one flip-flop could be in the RESET state.
2. A pulse to the counter input reset the initial flip-flop in the chain.
3. The circuit could be cleared so that a specific flip-flop was in the RESET position while the others remained in the SET position.

Each flip-flop of a counter was termed a stage, and reception of a pulse at the input side advanced the counter by one stage. Information recirculated through the counter; i.e., the last stage was coupled to the first. A variation of the basic counter circuit, the PM (plus or minus) counter, controlled the sign of a number in the accumulator. Ten decade ring counters, one per decimal place, plus one PM counter, formed the basic arithmetic and storage unit of ENIAC, and was called the accumulator. The decade ring counters were equipped with ten transmission circuits so that when any ring passed the nine positions, a pulse was passed to the next ring in the series. Input pulses reaching the accumulator added to or subtracted from its contents. The accumulator was an essential element in all of ENIAC's arithmetic operations. Addition required two accumulators, one transferring its contents to the other. Subtraction, accomplished by a complement-and-add process, also used two accumulators. In normal multiplication four accumulators stored the multiplier and multiplicand and accumulated the partial products. In division they shifted the remainder and stored the numerator, denominator, and quotient. The function table utilized the accumulators for storage of the argument and accumulation of the function value. ENIAC was a synchronous system, operating under the control of pulses from a cycling unit. The pulses were emitted a 10-microsecond intervals. The over-all timing cycle or repetition rate was 200 microseconds, which was the time required for one addition. Pulses were transmitted to all units continuously and simultaneously, and each computer operation took an integral number of addition times. For checking and trouble-shooting purposes, the cycling unit circuitry included provisions for operation in a one-addition or one-pulse-at-a-time mode. The ENIAC was not originally designed as an internally-programmed computer. The programme was set up manually by varying switches and cable connections. However, means for altering the programme and repeating its iterative steps were built into the master programr. Digit trays, which were long racks of co-axial cables, carried the data from one functioning unit to another. Programme trays transferred instructions (i.e., programmes) in a similar manner. In purely repetitive calculations, the basic computing sequence was set by hand. The master programr automatically controlled repetition and changed the sequence as required. The master programr contained ten six-stage counters, each routing incoming programme pulses over a field of six output channels. The position of the counters was controlled by either the number of pulses which had been supplied to the output channels or by the number of pulses received at a special input terminal. In this fashion the number of sequences could be fixed in advance or made contingent on the results of a computation.

Each functioning unit of ENIAC was equipped with local programme control circuits. These circuits contained switches which were set for the function required. When the local programme circuit was stimulated by a programme pulse, the unit performed the desired operation. After this was completed a programme completion pulse was emitted, via the programme tray coaxial line, to the next unit in the operational sequence.

In addition to its cycling unit, twenty accumulators, and master programr, ENIAC included an initiating unit, a high-speed multiplier, a divider, a square-root unit, and three portable function tables.

The initiating unit turned ENIAC on and off, cleared it, and initiated computation.

The high-speed multiplier did its work in much the same fashion as a human would. It contained a built-in multiplication table capable of multiplying up to 9 times 9. Multiplication of the multiplicand by each digit of the multiplier took one addition time. The left and right hand figures of each product of a digit of the multiplicand and the multiplier were accumulated separately to form two partial products, which when combined, formed the final product. The multiplication process for two 10-digit numbers took 2.6 milliseconds.

The divider and square-root unit worked by repeated subtraction and addition, a time-consuming procedure which took an average of 25 milliseconds for a 10-digit number. The divisor was subtracted from the dividend, and the sign of the partial remainder was tested after each step. When the sign became negative, the remainder was shifted up-scale and the divisor was added until the sum became positive. An accumulator serving as a quotient register kept a count of the numbers of additions and subtractions for the successive decimal places. Extraction of square root was a similar process.

The principal purpose of the function tables, which actually were banks of switch-controlled resistor matrices, was the storage of the arbitrary functions called for by the problem. The switches selected one of 12 digits and two signs for each of the 104 values of an independent variable that were stored in each table. The functional similarity between later computers and the ENIAC is rather astounding when one considers the time difference in their development.

The ENIAC was built primarily for integration of the equations of external ballistics by a step-by-step process, but it was flexible enough to be applied to a wide range of large-scale computations other than numerical integration of differential equations.

There were three ways of supplying the machine with information (numbers or instructions). Numbers could be put into the machine by means of punch cards fed into the Card Reader, panel 46, or by means of switches on the Constant Transmitter, panels 37 to 39. Numbers or instructions could also be put into the ENIAC by means of the Function Tables, panels 43 to 45, where there were dial switches which were set by hand. Instructions could also go into the machine by setting the switches, and by plugging the inputs and outputs etc., of the wires or lines along which numbers and instructions traveled.

Information came out of the machine in two ways. Numbers came out punched on cards by the Summary Punch, panel 47. They were then printed in another room by means of a separate IBM tabulator. Numbers could also be read out of the machine by means of the lights in the neon bulbs mounted on each accumulator. These could be read when the panel was not computing.

In applying the ENIAC to a particular computation it was first necessary to break down the work into a number of basic computing sequences, the ordering of which was controlled by the master programr. Next, each sequence was broken down into the individual computing operations of which it was composed. These were then carried out through the interconnections of the arithmetical units of the machine.

In programming calculations other than for trajectories (for which the machine was primarily designed) the chief drawback was the small memory capacity into which numbers could be recorded and from which they could be read automatically. This memory capacity consisted of the twenty accumulators, but four of these were used for multiplication and four for division. Therefore no more than sixteen, and often fewer, would be available for storing intermediate results. This capacity was adequate for the original purpose of the machine but where other types of computations were involved their method of calculation was determined by this memory capacity.

The machine had an indefinitely large memory capacity in the form of punched cards, but recording into and reading from this memory was slow. Also, the attention of an operator was required in some cases to transfer cards from the punch to the reader. The increased range of the machine was thus obtained at the expense of speed and the fully automatic character of its operation.

The first few years of use of the ENIAC at Aberdeen Proving Ground were difficult ones for the operating and maintenance crews. The computer represented the largest collection of interconnected electronic circuitry then in existence, and its thousands of components had to remain operational simultaneously. The result was a huge preventive maintenance and testing programme, which finally led to some major modifications of the system.

Operating experience with the ENIAC indicated that 90% of the service interruptions were caused by vacuum tube failures. At the beginning of 1950 a tube surveillance programme was initiated whereby tubes were life-tested and statistical data on the failures were compiled. All this led to methods of tube testing which were unique at the time. The information gained, on the other hand, led to many improvements in vacuum tubes themselves. Procurement of large quantities of improved, reliable tubes, however, became a difficult problem because conventional tubes were not ideal for use in computers.

An additional problem involving vacuum tubes was that of dissipating the heat. This was a problem of major proportions and was never solved for the ENIAC. Special air conditioning had not been provided and the blower system was not adequate to dissipate the heat into the warm, humid atmosphere. The result was a shortening of tube life which caused long periods of inoperation. For example, the checking routine alone took about eight hours. Eventually modifications to the machine were made which eliminated about 3,000 tubes.

As previously mentioned ENIAC originally had not been designed as an internally stored fixed programme computer. Programming new problems meant weeks of checking and set up time, since the ENIAC was designed as a general- purpose computer with logical changes provided by plug-and-socket connections between accumulators, function tables, and input-output units. However, the ENIAC's primary area of application was ballistics, mainly the differential equations of motion. In view of this, the ENIAC was converted into an internally stored fixed-programme computer when Dr. John von Neumann of the Institute for Advanced Study at Princeton suggested that code selection be made by means of switches so that cable connections could remain fixed for most standard trajectory problems. After that improvement considerable time was saved when problems were changed.

The ENIAC performed arithmetic and transfer operations simultaneously. Concurrent operation caused programming difficulties. A converter code was devised to permit serial operation. Each function table, as a result of these changes, became available for the storage of 600 two-decimal digit instructions.

These revolutionary modifications, which were installed early in 1948 converted ENIAC into a serial instruction execution machine with internal parallel transfer of decimal information. The original plugable connections came to be regarded as permanent wiring by most BRL personnel.

By 1950 it was realised that the commercial source of electrical power utilized by ENIAC was too unstable for reliable operation. Fluctuations in voltage caused errors to occur in the machine and also loss of information. Since the ENIAC was operating on a 24-hour per day basis such interruptions were extremely undesirable.

The problem was finally solved by installing a motor generator as a source of power for the machine. The motor was supplied by the power line and in turn drove the generator which supplied the load to ENIAC. The inertia of the motor took care of fluctuations in power line voltage and kept the power to ENIAC constant.

In 1951 the converter code was revised by the addition of a faster- access function table which increased the stored programme capacity of the ENIAC. Previously all switches had to be set by hand. The new unit utilized plugboards which could be pre-wired and simply plugged in. This reduced set up time for each new problem, increased the memory, and speeded operations.

By July 1953 the final improvement had been made on the ENIAC. This was the Static Magnetic Memory installed by the Burroughs Corporation of Philadelphia, PA. By mid 1951 the engineers at BRL had realised the necessity of increasing the internal memory capacity of the ENIAC. Aside from the twenty high-speed storage registers in the machine, all other storage came from present switches or punched cards. The switches could not be modified during the programme and consumed considerable time for their initial setting. The punched cards were unduly slow for use as a high-speed internal memory medium.

The Burroughs Corporation had been investigating the techniques of using magnetic cores for circuits and storage elements and had demonstrated them. Because of the experience gained in these investigations the Burroughs Corporation was awarded the contract to design the Static Magnetic Memory for the ENIAC. It was to consist of 100 words of first access time storage.

An important consideration in the design of the Magnetic Memory system was the characteristics of the magnetic material used. The techniques for reproducing high-quality magnetic cores had not been fully perfected and so the Memory System was designed to operate reliably with the quality of cores available in quantity production.

The design of the Memory System itself had to take into consideration the characteristics already built into the ENIAC. They were not particularly adaptable to the new techniques that had been built up since the development and design of the ENIAC. The language problem was of paramount importance. The ENIAC used a pulse-count code so that, to represent a single decimal digit, ten signals were applied to a single wire. Therefore, to store 100 words of 10 decimal digits, plus its sign, 9,100 bits of storage would be required. Economy dictated that code converters should be used to translate the pulse-count code of the ENIAC to a four-bit binary expression to represent a single decimal digit. This code conversion reduced the number of storage bits from 9,100 to 4,100.

The address selection in the ENIAC was of a decimal code to select one of the 100 words of storage in the memory.

The problem was to develop a storage system, controlled by ENIAC, so that any one of the 100 words could be selected to store or to extract information on the command of ENIAC, and take less than one addition cycle. The memory was to contain its own power supply and necessary cooling ducts. Emphasis was to be placed on reliability and accessibility to all electronic and magnetic parts. The unit was designed and constructed by the Burroughs Corporation and installed for use. The interconnection between the Memory and ENIAC was through 48 lines. In addition to these signal lines, provisions were made for single-phase and three-phase power to the Memory.

During the period 1946 — 1955 the ENIAC was operated successfully for a total of 80,223 hours of operation. It performed about five thousand arithmetic operations for each second of its useful life. ENIAC led the computer field through 1952 when it served as the main computation machine for the solution of the scientific problems of the nation. It surpassed all other existing computers in solving problems involving a large number of arithmetic operations. It was the major instrument for the computation of all ballistic tables for the U.S. Army and Air Force. In addition to ballistics, the ENIAC's field of application included weather prediction, atomic energy calculations, cosmic ray studies, thermal ignition, random number studies, wind tunnel design, and other scientific uses. EDVAC and ORDVAC (subjects of following chapters) both faster than ENIAC, began to share the Computing Laboratory's workload with the ENIAC in 1953.

It became apparent almost immediately that the ENIAC would have to be modified if it were to remain competitive, economical, and efficient. Modifications were therefore made on the ENIAC. In addition to the modifications previously mentioned there was a high-speed electronic shifter, which reduced by 80% the time required for numerical shifting and eliminated numerous tubes and programme units. It was installed early in 1952.

In spite of modernization, however, and the fact that trouble-free operating time remained at about 100 hours per week, operating costs were far above those of the other machines. The workload was gradually shifted to these other machines and at 11:45 PM on 2 October 1955 the power to ENIAC was removed. The rapid progress of computer technology, spurred by the ENIAC itself, had made the device obsolete.

APPENDIX

QUANTUM COMPUTING TIMELINE

1970 — Stephen Wiesner invents conjugate coding.

1973 — Alexander Holevo publishes a paper showing that n qubits cannot carry more than n classical bits of information (a result known as "Holevo's theorem" or "Holevo's bound". Charles H. Bennett (computer scientist) shows that computation can be done reversibly.

1975 — R. P. Poplavskii publishes "Thermodynamical models of information processing" (in Russian), Uspekhi Fizicheskikh Nauk,115:3, 465–501 which showed the computational infeasibility of simulating quantum systems on classical computers, due to superposition principle.

1976 — Polish mathematical physicist Roman Ingarden, in one of the first attempts at creating a quantum information theory, shows that Shannon information theory cannot directly be generalized to the quantum case, but rather that it is possible to construct a quantum information theory which is a generalization of Shannon's theory.

1980s

1980 — Yuri I. Manin, publishes Computable and uncomputable (in Russian), Moscow, Sovetskoye Radio. This work exploits the exponential number of basis states needed to describe the evolution of a quantum system, and discusses the need for a theory of quantum computation that captures the fundamental principles of computation without committing to a physical realisation.

1981 — Richard Feynman in his talk at the *First Conference on the Physics of Computation*, held at MIT, observed that it appeared to be impossible in general to simulate an evolution of a quantum system on a classical computer in an efficient way. He proposed a basic model for a quantum computer that would be capable of such simulations.

Tommaso Toffoli introduced the reversible Toffoli gate, which, together with the NOT and XOR gates provides a universal set for quantum computation.

1984 — Charles Bennett and Gilles Brassard employ Wiesner's conjugate coding for distribution of cryptographic keys.

1985 — David Deutsch, at the University of Oxford, described the first universal quantum computer. Just as a universal Turing machine can simulate any other Turing machine efficiently, so the universal quantum computer is able to simulate any other quantum computer with at most a polynomial slowdown.

1991 — Artur Ekert invents entanglement based secure communication.

1993 — Dan Simon, at Université de Montréal, invented an oracle problem for which a quantum computer would be exponentially faster than conventional computer. This algorithm introduced the main ideas which were then developed in Peter Shor's factoring algorithm.

1994 — Peter Shor, at AT&T's Bell Labs in New Jersey, discovered a remarkable algorithm. It allowed a quantum computer to factor large integers quickly. It solved both the factoring problem and the discrete log problem. Shor's algorithm could theoretically break many of the cryptosystems in use today. Its invention sparked a tremendous interest in quantum computers, even outside the physics community.

In December, Ignacio Cirac, at University of Castilla-La Mancha at Ciudad Real, and Peter Zoller at the University of Innsbruck proposed an experimental realisation of the controlled-NOT gate with trapped ions.

1995 — Peter Shor and Andrew Steane simultaneously proposed the first schemes for quantum error correction. This is an approach to making quantum computers that can compute with large numbers of qubits for long periods of time. Errors are always introduced by the environment, but quantum error correction might be able to overcome them. This could be a key technology for building large-scale quantum computers that work. These early proposals had a number of limitations. They could correct for some errors, but not errors that occur during the correction process itself. A number of improvements have been suggested, and active research on this continues. An alternative to quantum error correction has been found. Instead of actively correcting the errors induced by the interaction with the environment, special states that are immune to the errors can be used. This approach, known as decoherence free subspaces, assumes that there is some symmetry in the computer-environment interaction. Christopher Monroe and David Wineland at NIST (Boulder, Colorado) experimentally realise the first quantum logic gate with trapped ions, according to Cirac and Zoller's proposal.

1996 — Lov Grover, at Bell Labs, invented the quantum database search algorithm. The quadratic speedup isn't as dramatic as the speedup for factoring, discrete logs, or physics simulations. However, the algorithm can be applied to a much wider variety of problems. Any problem that had to be solved by random, brute-force search, could now have a quadratic speedup.

1997 — David Cory, Amr Fahmy and Timothy Havel, and at the same time Neil Gershenfeld and Isaac L. Chuang at MIT published the first papers on quantum computers based on bulk spin resonance, or thermal ensembles. The computer is actually a single, small molecule, which stores qubits in the spin of its protons and neutrons. Trillions of trillions of these can float in a cup of water. That cup is placed in a nuclear magnetic resonance (NMR) machine, similar to the magnetic resonance imaging machines used in hospitals. This room-temperature (*thermal*) collection of molecules (*ensemble*) has massive amounts of redundancy, which allows it to maintain coherence for several seconds, much better than many other proposed systems.

1998 — First working 2-qubit NMR computers demonstrated by Jonathan A Jones and Michele Mosca at Oxford University and at the same time by Isaac L. Chuang at IBM's Almaden Research Center together with coworkers at Stanford University and MIT.

First working 3-qubit NMR computer.

First execution of Grover's algorithm.

2000 — First working 5-qubit NMR computer demonstrated at the Technical University of Munich.

First execution of order finding (part of Shor's algorithm) at IBM's Almaden Research Center and Stanford University.

First working 7-qubit NMR computer demonstrated at the Los Alamos National Laboratory.

2001 — First execution of Shor's algorithm at IBM's Almaden Research Center and Stanford University. The number 15 was factored using 10^{18} identical molecules, each containing seven active nuclear spins.

2002 — The Quantum Information Science and Technology Roadmapping Project, involving some of the main participants in the field, laid out the Quantum computation roadmap.

2002 — 11th UK conference on the Foundations of Physics, the Philosophy Centre, University of Oxford, September 9 — 13 sees the exposition of the theory of the *Quantum Time Bomb*.

2004 — First working pure state NMR quantum computer (based on parahydrogen) demonstrated at Oxford University and University of York.

2005 — Dr. Matthew Sellars of the Laser Physics Centre at the Australian National University in Canberra, Australia slowed down a light pulse to a few hundred meters per second. Slowing the light down allows information to be mapped on the light pulse, like memory in a conventional computer. To slow down the light, the researchers used a silicate crystal mixed with a rare earth metal called praseodymium.

In a paper published in the November issue of the journal *Nature Physics*, researchers at the Georgia Institute of Technology reported experimental evidence that coherence also extends to the internal spin degrees of freedom in Bose-Einstein condensate atoms.

University of Illinois at Urbana-Champaign scientists demonstrate quantum entanglement of multiple characteristics, potentially allowing multiple qubits per particle.

Two teams of physicists have measured the capacitance of a Josephson junction for the first time. The methods could be used to measure the state of quantum bits in a quantum computer without disturbing the state. PhysicsWeb

In December, the first quantum byte, or *qubyte*, is announced to have been created by scientists at The Institute of Quantum Optics and Quantum Information at the University of Innsbruck in Austria, with the formal paper published in the December 1st issue of Nature.

Harvard University and Georgia Institute of Technology researchers succeeded in transferring quantum information between "quantum memories" — from atoms to photons and back again.

Scientists at the National Institute of Standards and Technology (NIST) coaxed six atoms into spinning together in two opposite directions at the same time.

A scalable quantum computer chip for atomic qubits was built for the first time by researchers at the University of Michigan, offering hopes for making a practical quantum computer using conventional semiconductor manufacturing technology.

2006 — HP Labs' Quantum Information Processing Group begins finding ways to use photons, or light particles, for information processing, rather than the electrons used in digital electronic computers today. Their work holds promise for someday developing faster, more powerful and more secure computer networks.

Peter Zoller, from the University of Innsbruck in Austria, discovers method of using cryogenic polar molecules to make stable quantum memories.

Professor Winpenny at Manchester's School of Chemistry for the first time demonstrated how metal-containing rings that show properties necessary to act as qubits can be linked together using both organic and metal-organic fragments.

Researchers at Cambridge University and Toshiba announce a new quantum device that produces entangled photons.

Materials Science Department of Oxford, caged qubit in a buckyball (a Buckminster fullerene particle). This isolates a qubit to some extent, but not quite enough. The next step the researchers took was to apply the so-called 'bang-bang' method: the qubit is repeatedly hit with a strong pulse of microwaves which reverses the way in which it interacts with the environment. This allows the state of the qubit to be preserved. Bang-bang: a step closer to quantum supercomputers

Circuits built from high-critical-temperature superconductors might support quantum computing, according to experiments performed by physicists at Chalmers University of Technology (Goteborg, Sweden). Working with a group at Italy's University of L'Aquila, the physicists directly observed macroscopic quantum effects in high-critical-temperature Josephson junctions.

Physicists at The University of Texas at Austin use a laser trap to consistently capture and measure the same small number of atoms.

Researchers at the University of Pittsburgh develop a way to create semiconductor islands smaller than 10 nanometers in scale, known as quantum dots. The islands, made from germanium and placed on the surface of silicon with two-nanometer precision, are capable of confining single electrons.

Ohio University scientists discover how to make coherent light travel between quantum dots, facilitating communication in optical quantum computers.

Researchers from the University of Illinois at Urbana-Champaign use the Zeno Effect, repeatedly measuring the properties of a photon to gradually change it without actually allowing the photon to reach the programme, to search a database without actually "running" the quantum computer.

Vlatko Vedral of the University of Leeds and colleagues at the universities of Porto and Vienna found that the photons in ordinary laser light can be quantum mechanically entangled with the vibrations of a macroscopic mirror, no matter how hot the mirror is.

Professor Sam Braunstein at the University of York along with the University of Tokyo and the Japan Science and Technology Agency gave the first experimental demonstration of quantum telecloning.

Professors at the University of Sheffield develop a means to efficiently produce and manipulate individual photons at high efficiency at room temperature.

IBM scientists develop spin-excitation spectroscopy to manipulate the magnetism of individual atoms.

New error checking method discovered.

Method developed to count single electrons.

First 12 qubit quantum computer benchmarked.

Two dimensional ion trap developed for quantum computing.

Seven atoms placed in stable line, a step on the way to constructing a quantum gate, at the University of Bonn.

Scientists learn how to synchronize quantum properties of electrons at ends of a nanotube.

A team at Delft University of Technology in the Netherlands, using conventional microchip fabrication technology, has created a device that can manipulate the "up" or "down" spin-states of electrons on quantum dots.

University of Arkansas develops quantum dot molecules.

Spinning new theory on particle spin brings science closer to quantum computing.

University of Copenhagen developes quantum teleportation between photons and atoms.

University of Southern California developes new quantum error correction method.

University of Camerino scientists develope theory of macroscopic object entanglement, which could allow "repeaters" in quantum computers.

Scientists at Illinois at Urbana-Champaign find that quantum coherence is possible in incommensurate electronic systems.

University of Utah Scientist shows it's feasible to read data stored as nuclear 'Spins'

Electrons interacting with individual dopant atoms in silicon observed, a step to silicon based quantum computers.

2007 — Subwavelength waveguide developed for light.

REFERENCES

Aboba. Bernard 1993. *The Online User's Encyclopedia: Bulletin Boards and Beyond,* Reading. MA: Addison-Wesley.

ALA (American Library Association) 1995. *Access to Electronic Information, Services, and Networks: An Interpretation of the Library Bill of Rights,* Draft Guideline, (5 March) Washington. DC: American Library Association.

Anderson, B. 1991. *Imagined Communities: Reflections on the Origin and Spread of Nationalism,* revised edn. New York: Verso.

Benedikt, VI. 1992. 'Cyberspace: some proposals', in M. Benedikt (ed.), *Cyberspace, First Steps,* Cambridge, MA: MIT Press.

Biocca, F. 1992a. 'Vinual reality technology: a tutorial', *Journal of Communications,* 42(4).

Biocca, F. 1992b. 'Communication within virtual reality: creating a space for research', *Journal of Communications,* 42(4).

Bolter, J.D. 1984. *Turing's Man: Western Culture in the Computer Age.* Chapel Hill: University of North Carolina Press.

Bolter, J.D. 1991. *Writing Space: The Computer, Hypertext, and the History of Writing.* Hillsdale, NJ: Lawrence Erlbaum.

Brand, S. 1987. *The Media Lab: Inventing the Future at MIT,* New York: Viking Penguin.

Branscomb, Anne Wells 1993. 'Jurisdictional quandaries for global networks', in Linda M. Harasim (ed.), *Global Networks: Computers and International Communication,* Cambridge. MA: MIT Press, pp. 83-101.

Brenneman, W.L. Jr., Yarian, S. and Olson, A. 1982. *The Seeing Eye: Hermeneutical Phenomenology in the Study of Religion,* University Park: Pennsylvania State University Press.

Bukatman, S. 1993. *Terminal Identity: The Vinual Subject in Post-Modern Science Fiction,* Durham, NC: Duke University Press.

Burnside, Scott and Cairns, Alan 1993. 'Cops seize Teale story at border', *Ottawa Sun,* 29 November.

Bush, V. (1945). As We May Think. *Atlantic Monthly* 176, July 1945, pp.101-108.

Bush, V. 1946. *Endless Horizons,* Washington. DC: Public Affairs Press.

CAF (Computers and Academic Freedom) 1992. 'Banned Computer Material 1992; Policy - Examples of the Best Policies; Computers and Academic Freedom Statement - Draft'. Archives available at ftp eff.org. or through Gopher.

Callinicos, A. (1989). *Against Postmodernism.* Cambridge: Polity Press.

Canadian Library Association 1985. *Statement on Intellectual Freedom,* Ottawa: Canadian Library Association.

Carey, J. and Quirk, J.J. 1970. The mythos of the electronic revolution', *American Scholar,* Winter.

Chuang, I. L., Laflamme, R., Yamamoto, Y., "Decoherence and a Simple Quantum Computer," (1995).

Clinton, President William J. and Gore, Vice-President Albert. Jr. 1993. *Technology for America's Economic Growth: A New Direction to Build Economic Strength,* Washington, DC: White House (22 February).

D. Deutsch, A. Ekert, "Quantum Computation," Physics World, March (1998).

D. Deutsch, Proc. Roy. Soc. London, Ser. A 400, 97 (1985).

Darnton, Robert 1982. *The Literary Underground of the Old Regime,* Cambridge, MA: Harvard University Press.

Davey, Frank 1994. *Karla's Web: a Cultural Investigation of the Mahaffy-French Murders,* New York: Penguin.

De Grazia. Edward 1993. *Girls Lean Back Everywhere: the Law of Obscenity and the Assault on Genius.* New York: Vintage Books.

De Lacey, Justine 1987. The sexy computer', *Atlantic Monthly,* July: 18-26.

Delany, P., Landow, G. (1991). *Hypermedia and Literary Studies.* Cambridge, Mass.: The MIT Press.

Deleuze, G. and Guattari, F. 1987. *A Thousand Plateaus: Capitalism and Schizophrenia.* trans. B. Massumi. Minneapolis: University of Minnesota Press.

Depew. D.J. 1985. 'Narrativism, cosmopolitanism, and historical epistemology', *Clio,* 14(4).

Dery, M. 1993. *Culture Jamming: Hacking, Slashing, and Sniping in the Empire of Signs.* Westfield: Open Media.

Drake. William J. 1995. 'Part IV: Outlook & Conclusions', pp. 301-78 in William J. Drake (ed.). *The New Information Infrastructure: Strategies for US Policy,* New York: Twentieth Century Press.

Duncanson, John and Pron, Nick 1993. 'Computerised bulletin boards abuzz with Homolka trial details', *Toronto Star.* 31 July: A3.

Edgerton S. Y. Jr. 1975. *The Renaissance Rediscovery of Linear Perspective.* New York: Basic Books.

Evensen, L. (1988). Lokal og global koherens i elevers skriving. In *TRANS — Trondheim Papers in Applied Linguistics,* IV.

Fiske, J. 1993. *Power Plays, Power Works,* New York: Verso.

Fitting, P. 1991. 'The lessons of cyberpunk', in C. Penley and A. Ross (eds). *Technoculture:* Minneapolis: University of Minnesota Press.

Foucault, M. 1979. *Discipline and Punish,* New York: Vintage Books.

Freud, S. 1965. *Group Psychology and the Analysis of the Ego,* trans. J. Strachey, New York: Bantam.

Freud, S. 1989. *The Freud Reader,* ed. P. Gay, New York: Norton.

Fudpucker, Orville 1992. 'PC Magnet', *PC Magazine.* 14: 557.

Fumiss, Maureen 1993. 'Sex with a hard (disk) on: computer bulletin boards and pornography'. *Wide Angle.* 15(2): 19-37.

Gallop. Jane 1988. *Thinking Through the Body.* New York: Columbia University Press.

Game, Ann 1991. *Undoing the Social.* Toronto: University of Toronto Press.

Gane, M. 1988. *On Durkheim's Rules of Sociological Method,* London: Routledge.

Gibson, W. 1992. 'Academy leader', in M. Benedikt (ed.). *Cyberspace; Firm Steps.* Cambridge, MA: MIT Press.

Globe and Mail 1993. 'Public's right to know gains here, loses there'. *Globe and Mail,* 2 December: Al.

Gooderham. Mary 1994. 'College drives sex titles off info highway', *Globe and Mail,* 5 February: 1.

Grant, G. 1990. 'Transcendence through detournement in William Gibson's *Neuromancer,' Science-fiction Studies.* 17(5).

Greenberg. Alan and Hull. Ron 1992. 'What is Usenet?'. *McGill University Computing Centre Newsletter.* May/June: 2-7.

Hafner, Katie and Markoff, John 1991. *Cyberpunk: Outlaws and Hackers on the Computer Frontier.* London: Fourth Estate.

Haraway, D. 1991. A manifesto for cyborgs: science, technology and socialist feminism in the 1980s', in D. Haraway (ed.). *Simians, Cyborgs and Women,* New York: Routledge.

Harpold, T. (1991). Threnody: Psychoanalytic Digressions on the Subject of Hypertext In *Hypermedia and Literary Studies,* eds. Delaney, Landow, pp.171-181. Cambridge, Mass.: The MIT Press.

Harvey, D. (1989). *The Condition of Postmodernity.* Oxford: Basil Blackwell.

Hassan, I. (1987). *The postmodern turn.* Ohio: Ohio State University Press.

Hauben. Ronda 1993. 'The development of the international computer network: from ARPANET to Usenet News (on the nourishment or impediment of the Net.Commonwealth)'. Paper presented at the International Association for Mass Communication Research Conference, Europe in Turmoil: Communication and Democracy in Civil Society, 25-26 June, Dublin, Ireland. Copy available from the author.

Hayles, N. K. 1993. 'Virtual bodies and flickering signifiers', *October 66,* Fall.

Heidegger, M. 1977. *The Question concerning Technology and Other Essays,* trans. W. Lovitt. New York: Garland.

Heilig, M.L. 1992. 'El Cine del Futuro: the cinema of the future', trans. U. Feldman. *Presence.* 1(3).

Heim, M. 1993. *The Metaphysics of Virtual Reality.* New York: Oxford.

Hobsbawm, E.J. 1990. *Nations and Nationalism since 1780: Programme, Myth, Reality,* Cambridge: Cambridge University Press.

Hoffman. Taara Eden 1994. 'Cyberspace cannot be censored: *Wired* responds to Canadian ban of its April issue'. *Wired* press release, 23 March.

Horton. Mark and Spafford. Gene 1993. 'Rules of Usenet conduct'. Part of a series of documents compiled and distributed by Gene Spafford 1992/93 in news.announce.newusers.

Hunt. Lynn 1993. 'Introduction: obscenity and the origins of modernity, 1500-1800', in *The Invention of Pornography: Obscenity and the Origins of Modernity, 1500-1800,* New York: Zone Books, pp. 9-45.

Industry Canada 1994. 'The Canadian Information Highway: Building Canada's information and communications infrastructure', in *Spectrum. Information Technologies and Telecommunications Sector,* Ottawa: Industry Canada (April).

Industry Canada 1995. *I SC News,* electronically available: File name: 02-26-95. debra.dgbt. doc.ca File path: /pub/isc/Industry. Canada. News. Releases/1995. Date archived: Wed. 1 March 11:09:53 EST 1995.

Irigaray, Luce 1985. *This Sex Which Is Not One.* New York: Cornell University Press.

J. Preskill, "Battling Decoherence: The Fault-Tolerant Quantum Computer," Physics Today, June (1999).

J. Preskill, "Quantum Computing: Pro and Con," quant-ph/9705032 v3, 26 Aug 1997.

Jacqmotte, Benoit and Broadhurst, Michael 1993. 'Homolka newsgroup suspended', *McGill Tribune,* 16-22 November: 8.

Jameson, F. (1988). Cognitive Mapping. In *Marxism and the Interpretation of Culture,* eds. Nelson, G., Grossberg, L. Chicago: University of Illinois Press.

Jameson, F. (1991). *Postmodernism, or The Cultural Logic of Late Capitalism.* London: Verso.

Kelly, K. 1994. 'The electronic hive: embrace if. *Harper's.* 288: 1728.

Kendrick, Walter 1987. *The Secret Museum: Pornography in Modern Culture.* New York: Vintage Books.

Kristeva, J 1990. 'Psychoanalysis and the polis'. in Gayle L. Ormiston and Alan D. Schrift (eds). *Transforming the Hermenentic Context.* Albany. NY: SUNY Press.

Krueger, M. 1991. *Artificial Reality II,* Reading, MA: Addison-Wesley.

Kurland, M. 1984. 'Of God, humans and machines', in S. Ditlea (ed.), *Digitaldeli,* New York: Workman Publishing.

Lacan. J. 1977. *Ecrits,* New York: Norton.

Landow, G. (1991). The Rhetoric of Hypermedia: Some Rules for Authors. In *Hypermedia and Literary Studies,* eds. Delaney, Landow, pp.81-103. Cambridge, Mass.: The MIT Press.

Laurel, B. 1986. Towards the design of a computer based interactive fantasy system', PhD dissertation. Ohio State University.

Laurel, B. 1993. *Computers as Theatre.* Reading, MA: Addison-Wesley.

Lesser, Wendy 1994. *Pictures at an Execution: an Inquiry into the Subject of Murder.* Cambridge. MA: Harvard University Press.

Levy, Stephen 1994. *Hackers: Heroes of the Computer Revolution,* New York: Delta.

Lindberg, D.C. 1976. *Theories of Vision from Al-kindi to Kepler,* Chicago: University of Chicago Press.

Lukes, S. 1972. *Emile Durkheim: His Life and Work.* New York: Harper & Row.

Lynch, K. (1960). *The Image of the City.* Cambridge, Mass.: The MIT Press.

Marvin, Carolyn 1987. *When Old Technologies Were New: Thinking about Electric Communication in the Late Nineteenth Century.* New York: Oxford University Press.

Mazlish, B. 1967. 'The fourth discontinuity'. *Technology and Culture,* 8(1).

McCaffery, L. 1991. 'Introduction: the desert of the real', in L. McCaffery *(ed.). Storming the Reality Studio,* Durham, NC: Duke University Press.

McKenna, T. 1991. *The Archaic Revival,* New York: HarperCollins.

Mcknight, C, Dillon, A., Richardson, J. (1991). *Hypertext in Context.* Cambridge: Cambridge University Press.

McLaughlin, Margaret L. Osborne, Kerry K. and Smith, Christine B. 1995. 'Standards of conduct on Usenet', in Steven G. Jone (ed.), *Cybersociety: Computer-mediated Communication anil Community.* Thousand Oaks. CA: Sage. pp. 90-111.

McLuhan, M. 1964. *Understanding Media,* New York: McGraw Hill.

Mercille, Raynald (legal advisor) 1993. 'Memo to Ms. Frances Groen, Associate Director Public Service & Collections re: "Foreign press articles - Canadian Ban"', 3 December, Copy available from author.

Micelli, Pat 1994. 'Censorship: it's OK to read about Homolka on computer, lawyers say'. *McGill Daily.* 24 January: 3.

Miller. J.A. 1984. Montre a Premontre, *Analytica.* 37: 28-9.

Moon, Peter 1992. 'Network sex: is increasingly explicit material on some computer bulletin boards free speech, or obscenity?'. *Globe and Mail,* 20 July: 6.

Moulthorp, S. (1991). Reading from the Map: Metonymy and Metaphor in the Fiction of Working Paths. In *Hypermedia and Literary Studies,* eds. Delaney, Landow, pp.119-132. Cambridge, Mass.: The MIT Press.

Nelson, T.H. (1965). A File Structure for the Complex, The Changing and the Indeterminate. In *Association for Computing Macinery Proceedings of the 20th National Conference,* pp.84-100.

Nelson, T.H. 1972. 'As we will think', in *International Conference on Online interactive Computing, ONLINE 72 Conference Proceedings.* Uxbridge, UK: Brunel University.

Nelson, T.H. 1973. 'A conceptual framework for man-machine everything', *AFIPS Conference Proceedings, 42,* Washington, DC: Thompson Book Co.

Nielsen, M., "Quantum Computing," (unpublished notes) (1999).

Ong, W.J. 1977. *Interfaces of the Word,* Ithaca, NY: Cornell University Press.

Pagels, H.R. 1988. *The Dreams of Reason: The Computer and the Rise of the Sciences of Complexity.* New York: Bantam.

Palley, Marcia 1994. *Sex & Sensibility: Reflections on Forbidden Mirrors and the Will to Censor,* New York: Ecco Press.

Pearson, Ian 1991. 'Terminal sex', *Saturday Night.* February: 19-25.

Penley, C. 1989. *The Future of an Illusion: Film, Feminism and Psychoanalysis,* Minneapolis: University of Minnesota Press.

Petrek, Melissa and St Jude 1992. 'Putting It On The Line'. *Mondo 2000,* 6: 113-15.

QUIC on-line, "Decoherence and Error Correction," (1997).

R. v. *Bernardo between Her Majesty the Queen, and Karla Bernardo also known us Karla Teale* (1993). O.J. No. 2047. Action No. 125/93. Ontario Court of Justice - General Division. St Catharine's, Ontario. 5 July 1993.

R.P. Feynman, Int. J. Theor. Phys. 21, 467 (1982).

Raulet. G. 1991. 'The new Utopia: communication technologies', *Telos,* 24(1).

Raymond, Eric 1991. *The New Hacker's Dictionary.* Cambridge. MA: MIT Press.

Reese, W.L. 1980. *Dictionary of Philosophy and Religion,* Atlantic Highlands, NJ: Humanities Press.

Reid, Brian 1993. 'Usenet readership summary report'. Palo Alto. CA: Network Measurement Project at the DEC Western Research Laboratory (March).

Rice, Donald E. and Love. Gail 1987. 'Electronic Emotion', *Communication Research.* 14: 85-108.

Rosenthal. P. 1993. Jacked in: Fordism, Cyberpunk. Marxism', *Socialist Review.* 21(1):79-103.

Ross, A. 1989. 'Hacking away at the counter-culture', in C. Penley and A. Ross (eds). *Technoculture,* Minneapolis: University of Minnesota Press.

Ross, Andrew 1991. 'Hacking away at the counterculture", in *Strange Weather: Culture, Science and Technology in the Age of Limits.* New York: Verso, pp. 75-100.

Roszak, T. 1986. *The Cult of Information,* Glasgow: Paladin.

Rushkoff, D. 1994. *Cyberia: Life in the Trenches of Hyperspace,* San Francisco: Harper-Collins.

Sandfort, Sandy 1993. 'The intelligent island? *Wired.* September/October: 52-5. 116.

Sdorow, Lester 1990. *Psychology.* Iowa: Wm. C. Brown Publishers.

Shapiro, Bernard 1992. 'Memorandum to executive heads of all colleges and universities'. September. Available electronically at eff.org or Gopher: Message 1992Oct20.181236. 15507@ eff.org. Tuesday, 20 October.

Shelley, M. 1972. *Frankenstein,* New York: Penguin.

Sheppard, E. 1993. 'GIS and society: ideal and reality', position paper for NCGIA conference on Geographical Information Systems and Society, Friday Harbor WA. 11 November.

Shields, R. 1992. 'Truant proximity: presence and absence in the space of modernity', in *Environment and Planning D: Society and Space.* l0(2): 181-98.

Shor, P.W., *Algorithms for quantum computation: Discrete logarithms and factoring, in Proceedings of the 35th Annual Symposium on Foundations of Computer Science*, IEEE Computer Society Press (1994).

Smolla, Rodney A. 1993. *Free Speech in an Open Society.* New York: Vintage Books.

Spigel, Lynn 1992. *Make Room for TV: Television and the Family Ideal in Postwar America,* Chicago: University of Chicago Press.

Springer. C. 1991. 'The pleasure of the interface', *Screen,* 32(2): 303-23.

Stephenson, Neal 1993. 'Smiley's people'. *The New Republic.* 13 September: 26.

Stone, A. R. 1992. 'Will the real body please stand up', in M. Benedikt (ed.), *Cyberspace: First Steps.* Cambridge, MA: MIT Press.

Sutherland, I. 1963. 'Sketchpad: a man-machine graphical communication system', *AFIPS Conference Proceedings,* 28, Washington, DC: Thompson Book Co.

Sutherland, I. 1965. 'The ultimate display'. *Proceedings of the International Federation of Information Processing Congress. 2,* Amsterdam: North Holland.

Sutherland, I. 1968. 'A head-mounted three dimensional display', *AFIPS Conference Proceedings,* 33(1).

Tribe, Laurence 1991. 'The constitution in Cyberspace: law and liberty beyond the electronic frontier'. Keynote Address to the first US Conference on Computers, Freedom, & Privacy (April).

Tuan, Y.F. 1974. *Topophilia: A Study of Environmental Perception, Attitudes, and Values.* Englewood Cliffs, NJ: Prentice-Hall.

Tuan, Y.F. 1977. *Space and Place: The Perspective of Experience,* Minneapolis: University of Minnesota Press.

Turing, A. 1950. 'Computing machinery and intelligence,' *Mind,* 59: 236.

Venturi, R.. Brown, D. S., Izenour, S. (1972). *Learning from Las Vegas.* Cambridge, Mass.: The MIT Press.

Virilio, P. 1994. 'Cyberwar, God and television' (interviewer L. Wilson, trans. G. Illien), *CTHEORY* 21 October (c.theory@concordia.ca).

Weiner, N. 1948. *Cybernetics; or Control and Communication in the Animal and the Machine,* New York: John Wiley.

6

Research Methodology in Materials Science

INTRODUCTION

Materials science or materials engineering is an interdisciplinary field involving the properties of matter and its applications to various areas of science and engineering. This science investigates the relationship between the structure of materials at atomic or molecular scale and their macroscopic properties. It includes elements of applied physics and chemistry, as well as chemical, mechanical, civil and electrical engineering. With significant media attention to nanoscience and nanotechnology in recent years, materials science has been propelled to the forefront at many universities. It is also an important part of forensic engineering and forensic materials engineering, the study of failed products and components. Materials science is an interdisciplinary field involving the properties of matter and its applications to various areas of science and engineering. It includes elements of applied physics and chemistry, as well as chemical, mechanical, civil and electrical engineering. With significant media attention to nanoscience and nanotechnology in the recent years, materials science has been propelled to the forefront at many universities, sometimes controversially. The research activities in the Materials Science Division cover a broad spectrum from basic research (which dominates) to projects of an applied character, partly in direct cooperation with industry. There is a strong international cooperation within most research projects.

The present research programme can be divided into the following partly overlapping areas:

(i) Studies of properties of defects in semiconductors, including structural as well as electronic properties. The latter covers bulk, surface and interface defects, with several techniques including laser spectroscopy and magnetic resonance. A large variety of materials systems are covered.

(ii) studies of the electronic properties of semiconductor quantum structures, such as heterostructures, quantum wells, quantum wires and dots, and superlattices, with various spectroscopic techniques. The material systems involved are III-V and II-VI semiconductors and the Si-Ge system.

(iii) studies of bulk and surface bandstructure, geometrical surface structure and adsorption phenomena on clean surfaces from single crystals (semiconductors, metals, alloys) as well as from interfaces and polycrystalline materials, with photoemission (including synchrotron radiation), inverse photoemission, and other surface-sensitive techniques.

(iv) Preparation and characterization of epitaxial films and bulk material of semiconductors with chemical vapor deposition (CVD), liquid phase epitaxy (LPE) and sublimation techniques. Contact metallization is also a part of these studies. A strong emphasis on SiC and III-nitrides has developed during the last few years.

History

The choice material of a given era is often its defining point: the stone age, bronze age, and steel age are examples. Materials science is one of the oldest forms of engineering and applied science. Modern materials science evolved directly from metallurgy, which itself evolved from mining. A major breakthrough in the understanding of materials occurred in the late 19th century, when Willard Gibbs demonstrated that thermodynamic properties relating to atomic structure in various phases are related to the physical properties of the material. Important elements of modern materials science are a product of the space race: the understanding and engineering of the metallic alloys and other materials that went into the construction of space vehicles was one of the enablers of space exploration. Materials science has driven, and been driven by, the development of revolutionary technologies such as plastics, semiconductors, and biomaterials. Before the 1960s (and in some cases decades after), many *materials science* departments were named *metallurgy* departments, from a 19th and early 20th century emphasis on metals. The field has since broadened to include every class of materials, including: ceramics, polymers, semiconductors, magnetic materials, and biological materials such as medical implants.

Fundamentals

In materials science, rather than haphazardly looking for and discovering materials and exploiting their properties, one instead aims to understand materials fundamentally so that new materials with the desired properties can be created. The basis of all materials science involves relating the desired properties and relative performance of a material in a certain application to the structure of the atoms and phases in that material through characterization. The major determinants of the structure of a material and thus of its properties are its constituent chemical elements and the way in which it has been processed into its final form. These, taken together and related through the laws of thermodynamics, govern the material's microstructure, and thus its properties. An old adage in materials science says: "materials are like people; it is the defects that make them interesting". The manufacture of a perfect crystal of a material is physically impossible. Instead materials scientists manipulate the defects in crystalline materials such as precipitates, grain boundaries (Hall-Petch relationship), interstitial atoms, vacancies or substitutional atoms, creating a material with the desired properties. Not all materials have a regular crystal structure. Polymers display varying degrees of crystallinity. Glasses, some ceramics, and many natural materials are amorphous, not possessing any long-range order in their atomic arrangements. These materials are much harder to engineer than crystalline materials. Polymers are a mixed case, and their study commonly combines elements of chemical and statistical thermodynamics to give thermodynamical, rather than mechanical descriptions of physical properties. In addition to industrial interest, materials science has gradually developed into a field which provides tests for condensed matter or solid state theories. New physics emerges because of the diverse new material properties needed to be explained.

Classes of Materials

Materials science encompasses various classes of materials, each of which may constitute a separate field. Materials are sometimes classified by the type of bonding present between the atoms:

1. Ionic crystals
2. Covalent crystals
3. Metals
4. Intermetallics
5. Semiconductors
6. Polymers
7. Composite materials
8. Vitreous materials

Sub-fields of Materials Science

- Nanotechnology — rigorously, the study of materials where the effects of quantum confinement, the Gibbs-Thomson effect, or any other effect only present at the nanoscale is the defining property of the material; but more commonly, it is the creation and study of materials whose defining structural properties are anywhere from less than a nanometer to one hundred nanometers in scale, such as molecularly engineered materials.

- Crystallography — the study of how atoms in a solid fill space, the defects associated with crystal structures such as grain boundaries and dislocations, and the characterization of these structures and their relation to physical properties.
- Materials Characterization — such as diffraction with x-rays, electrons, or neutrons, and various forms of spectroscopy and chemical analysis such as Raman spectroscopy, energy-dispersive spectroscopy (EDS), chromatography, thermal analysis, electron microscope analysis, etc., in order to understand and define the properties of materials. See also List of surface analysis methods
- Metallurgy — the study of metals and their alloys, including their extraction, microstructure and processing.
- Biomaterials —- materials that are derived from and/or used with biological systems.
- Electronic and magnetic materials — materials such as semiconductors used to create integrated circuits, storage media, sensors, and other devices.
- Tribology -— the study of the wear of materials due to friction and other factors.
- Surface science/Catalysis — interactions and structures between solid-gas solid-liquid or solid-solid interfaces.
- Ceramics and refractories — high temperature materials including structural ceramics such as RCC, polycrystalline silicon carbide and transformation toughened ceramics

Some practitioners often consider rheology a sub-field of materials science, because it can cover any material that flows. However, modern rheology typically deals with non-Newtonian fluid dynamics, so it is often considered a sub-field of continuum mechanics. See also granular material.

- Glass Science — any non-crystalline material including inorganic glasses, vitreous metals and non-oxide glasses.

Topics that Form the Basis of Materials Science

- Thermodynamics, statistical mechanics, kinetics and physical chemistry, for phase stability, transformations (physical and chemical) and diagrams.
- Crystallography and chemical bonding, for understanding how atoms in a material are arranged.
- Mechanics, to understand the mechanical properties of materials and their structural applications.
- Solid-state physics and quantum mechanics, for the understanding of the electronic, thermal, magnetic, chemical, structural and optical properties of materials.
- Diffraction and wave mechanics, for the characterization of materials.
- Chemistry and polymer science, for the understanding of plastics, colloids, ceramics, liquid crystals, solid state chemistry, and polymers.
- Biology, for the integration of materials into biological systems.
- Continuum mechanics and statistics, for the study of fluid flows and ensemble systems.
- Mechanics of materials, for the study of the relation between the mechanical behavior of materials and their microstructures.

A Short List of Non-academic Materials Facilities

Government Labs

- Argonne National Laboratory
- Lawrence Berkeley National Laboratory
- Lawrence Livermore National Laboratory
- Los Alamos National Laboratory
- Max Planck Institute
- Oak Ridge National Laboratory

Important Journals

- Nature Materials
- Acta Materialia
- JOM
- Advanced Materials
- Computational materials science

- Advanced Functional Materials
- Journal of Materials Chemistry
- Journal of Materials Online — Open Access
- Metallurgical and Materials Transactions

Corporate Facilities

- DuPont
- GE Global Research
- IBM Thomas J. Watson Research Center

Materials in Industry

Radical materials advances can drive the creation of new products or even new industries, but stable industries also employ materials scientists to make incremental improvements and troubleshoot issues with currently used materials. Industrial applications of materials science include materials design, cost-benefit tradeoffs in industrial production of materials, processing techniques (casting, rolling, welding, ion implantation, crystal growth, thin-film deposition, sintering, glassblowing, etc.), and analytical techniques (characterization techniques such as electron microscopy, x-ray diffraction, calorimetry, nuclear microscopy (HEFIB), Rutherford backscattering, neutron diffraction, etc.). The overlap between physics and materials science has led to the offshoot field of *materials physics*, which is concerned with the physical properties of materials. The approach is generally more macroscopic and applied than in condensed matter physics. See the important publications in materials physics for more details on this field of study.

MSD Research Highlights

The Materials Science Division launches a new online research highlights database which contains an overview of the science that MSD performs. Learn about the many research endeavors that MSD scientists are currently investigating. Find it on this Web site by clicking on "Research Highlights" on the left navigation sidebar. The Materials Science Division (MSD) is the focal point for research in materials science at Argonne National Laboratory. Our mission is to develop new materials for society, and we do so with a team of materials scientists, physicists, and chemists who carry out collaborative research on a variety of problems. Typically, we can bring to bear fundamental research, involving synthesis, characterization and modeling, to improve performance of old materials, or design new materials.

Materials Science and Engineering

Understanding of how materials behave like they do, and why they differ in properties was only possible with the atomistic understanding allowed by quantum mechanics, that first explained atoms and then solids starting in the 1930s. The combination of physics, chemistry, and the focus on the relationship between the properties of a material and its microstructure is the domain of Materials Science. The development of this science allowed designing materials and provided a knowledge base for the engineering applications (Materials Engineering).

Structure

- At the atomic level: arrangement of atoms in different ways. (Gives different properties for graphite than diamond both forms of carbon.)
- At the microscopic level: arrangement of small grains of material that can be identified by microscopy. (Gives different optical properties to transparent vs. frosted glass.)

Properties are the way the material responds to the environment. For instance, the *mechanical, electrical and magnetic* properties are the responses to mechanical, electrical and magnetic forces, respectively. Other important properties are *thermal* (transmission of heat, heat capacity), *optical* (absorption, transmission and scattering of light), and the *chemical stability* in contact with the environment (like corrosion resistance). Processing of materials is the application of heat (heat treatment), mechanical forces, etc. to affect their microstructure and, therefore, their properties.

Historical Perspective

Materials are so important in the development of civilization that we associate Ages with them. In the origin of human life on Earth, the Stone Age, people used only natural materials, like stone, clay, skins, and wood. When people found copper and how to make it harder by alloying, the Bronze Age started about 3000 BC. The use of iron and steel, a stronger material that gave advantage in wars started at about 1200 BC. The next big step was the discovery of a cheap process to make steel around 1850, which enabled the railroads and the building of the modern infrastructure of the industrial world.

Why Study Materials Science and Engineering?

- To be able to select a material for a given use based on considerations of cost and performance.
- To understand the limits of materials and the change of their properties with use.
- To be able to create a new material that will have some desirable properties.

All engineering disciplines need to know about materials. Even the most "immaterial", like software or system engineering depend on the development of new materials, which in turn alter the economics, like software-hardware trade-offs. Increasing applications of system engineering are in materials manufacturing (industrial engineering) and complex environmental systems.

Advanced Materials

Materials used in "High-Tec" applications, usually designed for maximum performance, and normally expensive. Examples are titanium alloys for supersonic airplanes, magnetic alloys for computer disks, special ceramics for the heat shield of the space shuttle, etc.

Modern Material's Needs

- Engine efficiency increases at high temperatures: requires high temperature structural materials
- Use of nuclear energy requires solving problem with residues, or advances in nuclear waste processing.
- Hypersonic flight requires materials that are light, strong and resist high temperatures.
- Optical communications require optical fibers that absorb light negligibly.
- Civil construction – materials for unbreakable windows.
- Structures: materials that are strong like metals and resist corrosion like plastics.

Classification of Materials

Like many other things, materials are classified in groups, so that our brain can handle the complexity. One could classify them according to structure, or properties, or use. The one that we will use is according to the way the atoms are bound together:

Metals: valence electrons are detached from atoms, and spread in an 'electron sea' that "glues" the ions together. Metals are usually strong, conduct electricity and heat well and are opaque to light (shiny if polished). Examples: aluminum, steel, brass, gold.

Semiconductors: the bonding is covalent (electrons are shared between atoms). Their electrical properties depend extremely strongly on minute proportions of contaminants. They are opaque to visible light but transparent to the infrared. Examples: Si, Ge, GaAs.

Ceramics: atoms behave mostly like either positive or negative ions, and are bound by Coulomb forces between them. They are usually combinations of metals or semiconductors with oxygen, nitrogen or carbon (oxides, nitrides, and carbides). Examples: glass, porcelain, many minerals.

Polymers: are bound by covalent forces and also by weak van der Waals forces, and usually based on H, C and other non-metallic elements. They decompose at moderate temperatures (100 – 400 C), and are lightweight. Other properties vary greatly. Examples: plastics (nylon, Teflon, polyester) and rubber.

Other categories are not based on bonding. A particular microstructure identifies composites, made of different materials in intimate contact (example: fiberglass, concrete, wood) to achieve specific properties. Biomaterials can be any type of material that is biocompatible and used, for instance, to replace human body parts.

Information on Argonne's Materials Science Division

The Materials Science Division (MSD) is the focal point for research in materials science at Argonne National Laboratory. Our mission is to develop new materials for society, and we do so with a team of materials scientists, physicists and chemists who carry out collaborative research on a variety of problems. Typically, we can bring to bear fundamental research, involving synthesis, characterization and modeling, to improve performance of old materials, or design new materials. Current materials of interest include superconductors, magnetics, ferroelectrics, organic crystals and diamond coatings. We rely heavily on and support medium and large-scale facilities for materials science research, including BESSRC, a materials-oriented synchrotron-based research facility, and the IVEM-Tandem National Electron Microscope user facility. We are closely involved with other Argonne facilities such as the Advanced Photon Source and the Intense Pulsed Neutron Source. We also have a web of interactions with universities and industries. Our research is funded primarily by Basic Energy Sciences at the Department of Energy, and is mainly "fundamental" in character. That is, we are driven to understand the science underlying materials — questions like "what is the basis of superconductivity?" or "how is magnetism different in small structures?". From such research, we can learn to design and synthesize new materials, and control the physical properties of existing materials. Since materials are ultimately "useful" to society, materials science is intimately coupled with engineering and applications. So we have many partnerships with industries, and are always interested in performing mutually beneficial collaborative research. If you are an industrial scientist, browsing through our web pages, especially the highlights section, would be a good way to learn about what we do. If you are in the education field, we hope that our resources (internal access only) are useful to you. Please do not hesitate to contact me or any member of the division for further information. Other materials resources at Argonne, to which we are intimately linked, are found at www.techtransfer.anl.gov/techtour/materials.html. If you are interested in gee whiz — I recommend our highlights page and "telepresence." As an example of major new directions which we are pursuing, I direct your attention to nanosciences and aberration corrected electron microscopy. Here are a few links on these subjects:

- Future Plans for Nanoscience at Argonne
- Center for Nanoscale Materials
- Electron Microscopy Center
- Nanoscience at the University of Wisconsin
- National and International Professional Society Sites for Microscopy & Microanalysis
- Microscopy Links

School of Materials

The subject of biomaterials covers those materials that are used in the context of biology and medicine, generally to evaluate, treat, augment or replace any tissue, organ or function of the body. In surgery, a biomaterial may be a synthetic material used to replace part of a living system or to function in intimate contact with living tissue.

Other examples of biomaterials are small particles that are used for the delivery of drug molecules to target sites within the body. A number of biomaterials are produced using chemical, physical, mechanical processes that employ or mimic biological phenomena.

Research Interests

- Self assembled gels
- Nanofibrous materials
- Bioactive glasses
- Polymer hydrogels
- Glycobiology
- Enzyme Responsive Materials
- Ink Jet Printing
- Electrospinning
- Stem Cell Biology

Facilities

The Group has state of the art facilities, including fluorescence microscopy, fluorescence spectrophotometers and plate readers, HPLC, GPC, surface modification and analysis (including contact angle goniometer, atomic force microscopy, dip-pen nanolithography), cell culture facilities and mechanical testing (nano-indentor), Raman and IR Spectroscopy, electrospinning.

Biomimetic Materials Science

A research programme funded by the Swedish Foundation for Strategic Research (SSF). It involves well established research groups at three Swedish universities: Linköpings universitet, Lund University and Chalmers University of Technology. The focus of the programme is to mimic advantageous surface properties or processes of living organisms for materials science and technology by utilising and combining state of the art nano- and microfabrication, soft lithography, molecular imprinting, chemical modification, self assembly, and organic- and bioorganic synthesis. The research programme relies on a knowledge base that as been generated within the participating groups during the last 20 years, in particular within the Biomaterials Consortium (a joint CTH/LiU effort) funded by SSF.

Advances Due to New Materials

- 100-fold increase in the strength-to-density ratio of composite structural materials.
- reduction in the size of integrated circuit devices to less than one micron, and an increase in the size of flat screen displays to nearly one meter.
- 3-fold increase in the working temperature of structural ceramics, leading to significant improvements in the efficiency of turbine engines.
- 100-fold increase in the strength of permanent magnets.
- breakthrough in the superconductivity transition temperature, to a range suitable for engineering applications.
- 4-orders-of-magnitude increase in the transmission length of glass, leading to optical fiber communication systems.
- great increase in the hardness and chemical resistance of thin film coatings, leading to a 100-fold increase in the speed of cutting tools.

Current Research Includes

- integrated circuits containing 109 components per chip, further revolutionizing computer and information systems.

- optical computing, vastly increasing information processing and transmission speeds.
- efficient, large-area semiconductor coatings for photovoltaic power generation.
- "smart" materials for microscopic measurements of temperature, pressure and chemical environments.
- tougher ceramics and ceramic-based composites for use at high temperatures.
- extremely wear-resistant diamond coatings, deposited at low temperatures.
- more durable alloys, inter-metallic compounds, and metal matrix composites.
- high-strength polymeric materials.
- molecularly tailored films, membranes, and bio-materials for the replacement and regrowth of body parts.

Students in the Department of Materials Science and Engineering are conducting research that is laying the groundwork for future progress in these and other areas. The training and experience they receive prepares them to make new contributions as the materials field expands in scientific, technological, and economic importance. A major goal of the Department is to educate students for scientific and engineering leadership. They will develop the next generation of advanced materials and processes so essential for solving societal and environmental problems.

Description of the Field of Materials Science and Engineering

Everything we use is made of some material or a combination of materials. We use different types of materials — metals, ceramics, polymers, semiconductors, and composites — in our daily lives. Materials Science Engineering deals with all aspects of materials:

- extraction of materials from natural and recycled resources,
- selection of appropriate materials for a given application,
- manufacturing useful objects from raw materials,
- assurance of quality of manufactured products,
- study of the behavior of materials under various conditions,
- research and development of new materials and new ways to process them into useful objects,
- analysis of the performance of materials in service and investigate causes of failure

- fundamental investigation in the relationship between materials properties and their microstructure at different length scales, and
- fundamentals of the relationship between processing and microstructure at different length scale.

In short, Materials Science & Engineering is involved with all the processes that turn natural resources into useful products that impact all facets of our economy, such as aerospace, electronics, transportation, communication, construction, recreation, entertainment, environment and energy.

What is Being Done in this Field?

This is a very exciting time for the field. Ever increasing performance demands in aerospace, automotive, microelectronics, environmental and biotechnology are fueling the need for materials innovation. Significant advances in our ability to characterize and manipulate materials and materials systems at different length scales are providing novel and innovative materials solutions to meet these needs. A few examples will help illustrate this point. Materials science and engineering is playing a central role in nanotechnology. The central premise of nanotechnology is exploration of phenomena and properties that manifest themselves at the nanoscale. This premise is directly aligned with the core expertise and focus of the field (interrelationship between processing, structure and properties). Photonics and optoelectronics are poised to be the next revolutionary technology for computing and communications. Development of new materials and material systems to meet the needs of this technology are proceeding at a furious pace. In biotechnology, there is need for materials solutions for longer lasting implants, scaffolds for tissue engineering, biosensors, and novel diagnostic and therapeutic strategies. New energy and environmental technologies have significant needs for materials solutions in the areas of fuel cells, pollution reduction and energy efficiency. Higher strength and stiffness materials are needed for a variety of automotive and aerospace applications. Finally, significant advances in computational materials science are providing an entirely different approach to the development of new materials and understanding their performance.

What is the Demand for Materials Scientist and Engineers?

Materials scientists and engineers are employed in the manufacturing and service industries. Because of the wide ranging impact of materials on all technologies and industrial sectors, the materials science and engineering field offers a wide variety of employment opportunities. Excellent opportunities exist in all parts of the country. Materials engineers usually hold one of a variety of position titles such as metallurgist, metallurgical engineer, materials engineer/scientist, polymer engineer, ceramic engineer, manufacturing engineer, quality assurance engineer, process engineer, biomaterials scientist, corrosion engineer, and foundry engineer. The list is longer depending on the title that a particular employer attaches to the position. Employment opportunities and prospects have been very healthy. Materials scientists primarily work in research and development in academia, national labs and industrial labs. The focus of their work is on development of new materials, processes and fundamental research on the inter-relationship between processing, structure and properties.

What is the Scope of Materials Science and Engineering?

Materials science and engineering is an interdisciplinary field. Advances in materials enable technology progress in many fields. Historically, this connection between materials and technology has been so intimate that major periods in civilization have been named after the dominant material used in that era (e.g. Bronze Age, Iron Age). In the past few decades, at the core of the progress in such diverse fields as transportation, communication, electronics, energy and environment, are significant advances in materials. We address the scientific fundamentals of materials, their processing, and their engineering design for technological applications. The central theme of the field is shown in. We apply basic principles of chemistry, physics and biology in order to understand the structure of materials at all relevant length scales and how this structure determines its properties. We design scientific processes to fabricate materials to meet the needs of modern technology. Finally we focus on the performance of the material under specific use conditions. Perhaps, the most distinguishing feature of the discipline is the appreciation and focus on the interrelationships and interdependence between processing, structure, properties and performance.

What Does the MSE Department Have to Offer?

Materials scientists and engineers study the synthesis and processing of materials, their inner structure at different length scale, their properties, and their performance in machines and devices serving society. In the Materials Science & Engineering Department at University of Washington, the research and academic programmes unify all classes of materials: metals, ceramics, polymers, and electronic materials. The undergraduate MSE curriculum combines general core materials subjects, taken in the sophomore and junior year, followed by advanced elective subjects which treat specific topics. Because of flexibility in choice of elective subjects, students can tailor their academic programmes to suit their interests in a certain class of materials, for example, materials for the computer and electronics industry. Students receive instruction in the classroom and in the laboratory, where they learn to use research-grade equipment. At the graduate and research level, the Department has experienced rapid expansion into new areas including polymers, hybrids, biomaterials, biomimetics, nanomaterials, photonics and magnetic materials.

These new areas have applications in current and emerging industries and compliment our existing strengths in ceramics, metals, electronic materials and composites.

Brief History of the Department

The Early Years: Perhaps the first important name in the beginning of the MSE Department's history is that of the Reverend George F. Whitworth. Having lived in eastern mining regions and having firsthand knowledge of the mining business, the Reverend Whitworth came to Seattle in 1866 looking for coal. Upon his arrival, he was appointed the third president of the University of Washington. Within a year, he had also organised the Lake Washington Coal Company, which developed coal mines in Issaquah and Renton. Although Whitworth served as the University's president for only two years, his influence led to a state law that required the University to purchase local coal for its steam plant, a practice that continued until 1969. How much influence the Reverend Whitworth had on the event remains unknown, but on November 28, 1893, the Board of Regents established the School of Mining Engineering "to educate men for the industry." The proposed curriculum of the School was developed in 1894 and published in the University Catalog of that year, but the School itself did not materialize for several years. Instruction in mining and assaying began in 1895, taught by Professor Henry Landes, a geologist who also taught mineralogy. Initial instruction took place in the new, but not-quite-completed Administration Building, now Denny Hall, with classes held on the first floor and laboratory work conducted in "The Assay Shop," a temporary structure located 100 yards north of Denny Hall. After a transition period during which curriculum was developed, Dean Milnor Roberts was appointed to head the now-official School of Mining Engineering in 1901. This led to programme expansion, including broadened curricula, interactions with high schools, and increased student populations. This decade marked the full establishment of the School as a major part of the University's educational programme. After the Alaska-Yukon-Pacific Exposition of 1909 closed, the brick power house, located near the site of the current Suzzallo Library, was remodeled into offices, classrooms, and laboratory space for mining, metallurgy, ore dressing, and coal washing. This building, renamed Mines Hall served as the headquarters of the School until the 1920's.

A New Mines Laboratory: In 1911, the School of Mining Engineering was upgraded to the College of Mines. As enrollment in the College increased during the next decade, the space in Mines Hall became too small. Through the efforts of President Henry Suzzallo, Regent Winlock Miller, and mining professionals throughout the state, funds were appropriated for the first unit of a new Mines Laboratory. The College of Mines began moving into the first section of the Mines Laboratory in 1921, although most of the College remained in the old Mines Hall, awaiting completion of the second half of the new laboratory. However, in 1924, a fire that originated in the steam tunnels engulfed the old Mines Hall, destroying all but the walls. The College lost not only important contents of Mines Hall, including valuable maps and irreplaceable ores, but also its temporary home in Mines Hall. Consequently, the College was forced to crowd into the first unit of the Mines Laboratory. When the second unit of the Mines Laboratory was finally completed in 1927, it provided space not only for the mining, metallurgical, and ceramic engineering programmes, but also for the Bureau of Mines' Northwest Experiment Station and the Department of Civil Engineering. In addition, a few rooms were assigned to the Art Department for sculpture, metal, and pottery classes so that art students could take advantage of the equipment and materials in ceramic and metallurgy. In 1947, the building was renamed Roberts Hall in honor of Dean Milnor Roberts.

Period of Prosperity: For the College of Mines, the completion of Roberts Hall ushered in a period of prosperity. The modern structure, equipped with the latest apparatus and machinery, attracted wide interest. Enrollment increased, and industry came to view the Mines Laboratory as a headquarters for information. In 1946, a new Kiln Building was constructed to complement the larger Roberts Hall. The Kiln Building, since renamed after former Professor Hewitt Wilson, housed six kilns of different types for ceramic study. The year 1946 also marked the College's first name change, from the College of Mining to School of Mineral Engineering. In 1968, the name was changed again to the Department of Mining, Metallurgical and Ceramic Engineering. In 1983, the name was changed to the Department of Materials Science and Engineering

Modernized Equipment: In 1964, the 3-story Wilcox Hall was completed to provide additional space and facilities for the Department. The new, modern facilities included a JEM-6 electron microscope, a Philips microprobe analyzer, additional X-ray diffraction units, Instron testing machines, a helium leak detector, high frequency power generators with zone refiners and levitation melting apparatus, rolling and swaging mills, and a unique high temperature micro deformation facility. In addition, the labs were designed so that air could be filtered and conditioned to facilitate the use of precision instrumentation in research. Of particular importance in the long range was the development of electron microscopy. The JEM-7 high performance electron microscope was added in 1964 to the research facilities of the School of Mineral Engineering. It was one of the first of these models to be installed in the United States. Its resolution power was 4.5 Angstrom and made possible the direct observation of extended defects in crystalline materials. In later years, this facility would be upgraded with the addition of several new electron microscopes. Currently available resolution is 1.7 Angstroms, capable of resolving crystal lattice planes.

Emergence of Materials Science: In the 1980s, changes were taking place on the national scene with respect to metallurgy and ceramics. Research in these fields was coming together into a better defined field of materials research, especially as composite materials made their debut and as semiconductor device design made use of any and all materials. In the Department, external funding grew to an average of over $2 million annually toward the end of the decade, assisting the Department in developing high quality graduate research programmes. The first phase of a major facilities project began with the construction of a new building known then as Roberts Underground (now James I. Mueller Hall). Completed in November 1986, this building is located in front of Roberts Hall under the surface level of the former parking lot and is the home of ten laboratories, two classrooms, and an auditorium. Remodeling of Roberts Hall began in May of 1987. For this remodeling, Roberts Hall was completely gutted, and all interior walls removed. The building's steel columns were reinforced to bring the 1920s structure in line with current earthquake codes while preserving the original exterior appearance. Renovation was completed in 1989. Upgrading of equipment accompanied the building programme. The Department was able to purchase a new scanning electron microscope, a new mechanical testing system, and a new X-ray diffraction facility. Also added to the equipment inventory from research grants during this period were two high-resolution electron microscopes, one for high quality analysis and the other for atomic imaging, and a molecular beam epitaxy system for growth of compound semiconductor devices. These upgrades made the Department one of the better equipped programmes nationally for materials research and education. The overall facilities upgrade gave the Department one of the best physical facilities on campus, both in terms of external and internal appearance and in terms of functionality.

The Last Decade: In the 1990s, materials science and engineering continued to mature as a field. The distinguishing characteristic of this decade in the field was the increased focus on interdisciplinary research. Beginning in the late eighties, the Department started developing new interdisciplinary research programmes in computational materials science, biomimetics, electronic materials, surface science and composites. There was a noticeable and significant shift in the employers of the department. Increasingly, students were being recruited by users of advanced materials as opposed to materials processors and traditional materials industries (e.g. Intel as opposed to U.S. Steel). Finally, there was broad realisation of the importance of materials and increasingly, research in the field was being conducted by a large number of colleagues who are in other departments. A dramatic example of this is the University of Washington's Engineered Biomaterials Research Center (UWEB). This NSF funded ERC started in 1996 and is housed in the Department of Bioengineering. In the last five years, the Department has completed the transformation to an integrated materials science & engineering department. The undergraduate curriculum has been revised and now offers only one degree, a BS in Materials Science & Engineering. At the graduate and research level, new programmes have been initiated in polymers, biomaterials, nanomaterials, photonics and magnetic materials. The changes in the last five years are discussed in detail in this document.

Materials Science and Engineering?

Materials have been central to the growth, prosperity, security, and quality of life of humans since the beginning of history. Only in the last 25 years, and especially in the last decade, has the intellectual foundation of the field that we call materials science and engineering begun to take shape and to achieve recognition. This has occurred just as the field itself is expanding greatly and contributing significantly to society. Without new materials and their efficient production, our world of modern devices, machines, computers, automobiles, aircraft, communication equipment, and structural products could not exist. Materials scientists and engineers will continue to be at the forefront of these and other areas of science and engineering in the service of society as they achieve new levels of understanding and control of the basic building blocks of materials: atoms, molecules, crystals, and noncrystalline arrays.

Modern Materils

The fruits of the efforts of materials scientists and materials engineers over years and decades can be illustrated by literally hundreds of examples, and those few given below are but an inescapably arbitrary selection.

- The strength-to-density ratio of structural materials has increased dramatically throughout the industrial age. Modern advanced materials are approximately 50 times better than the cast iron of two centuries ago in this important engineering measure. To suspend a 25-ton weight vertically from the end of a cast iron rod would require a rod with a cross section of 1 in.×1 in. weighing about 4 lb/ft. To suspend the same weight from a modern high-strength polymer fiber would require a fiber with a cross section of 0.3 in.×0.3 in. weighing about 1 oz/ft. We experience the results of these advances every day, for example, in household appliances that are lighter and more efficient, in eyeglasses that are more comfortable, and in automobiles and airplanes that use less fuel and go faster.
- The efficiency with which heat energy is converted to mechanical or electrical energy in engines and power plants is another engineering measure important to society. This efficiency depends directly on the temperature at which the device can operate well; thus materials that are strong at high temperatures are desired. Superalloys can now operate at temperatures of over 2000°F, and advanced ceramics may push engine operating temperatures to 2500°F. The maximum theoretical efficiency of

such engines is about 80 percent, whereas the efficiency of conventional engines is limited to about 60 percent. The ultimate result is more efficient production of energy in the forms needed by society, with a concomitant reduction in cost, fuel requirements, and pollution.

- Before about the mid-1930s, the only permanent magnetic materials available were special steels. Modest improvements in the magnetic strength of these materials were made, but significant increases came only with the development of aluminum-nickel-cobalt alloys in the 1940s and 1950s. In the 1960s, the rare earth/cobalt alloys produced the next major jump, and the 1980s saw the development of the neodymium-iron-boron compounds. Today, permanent magnets have magnetic strengths more than 100 times greater than those available at the turn of the century. These and other magnetic materials are making possible smaller, more powerful motors and better and smaller sound systems, and they are carrying out many other hidden tasks in modern machines and devices.
- Superconductivity was first discovered in 1911. After some 60 years of effort, researchers developed materials suitable for practical use at temperatures up to 23° above absolute zero (23 K, i.e., 250° below 0°C). Then, beginning in 1986, working with entirely new classes of materials, researchers developed a material with a superconducting transition temperature of 39 K.Rapid progress in developing materials with even higher transition temperatures culminated in the present (1988) record of 125 K. This discovery not only is of great scientific interest, but it also promises to have a significant practical impact in a wide range of fields. The technical difficulties that prevent the general use of these materials today are precisely those connected with synthesis and processing that contribute the principal challenge to materials science and engineering as a whole.
- Scientists and technicians improved the transparency of silica glass slowly over the centuries from 3000 B.C. to 1966, when work on optical fibers was begun in earnest. Today, these fibers are some 100 orders of magnitude more transparent than they were in 1966. A single glass fiber 0.01 mm in diameter can transmit thousands of telephone conversations—many more by far than can be sent over a conventional cable.
- Even for abrasives and cutting tool materials, it is possible to find significant, often exponential increases in the performance of materials. Shows, for example, that cutting tool speeds have increased by a factor of 100 since the turn of the century, owing to the development of new materials. The

result is far more efficient manufacturing processes that lower the costs of goods we buy.

- In integrated electronic circuits, the number of components per chip has increased at exponential rates since about 1960, making possible the ubiquitous and economical use of the electronic chip we know today. This increase has been achieved partly through steady reductions in line widths through continuing improvements in photolithography. Integrated circuits, in turn, have led to computers and electronics that have revolutionized our lives. This achievement is a triumph for both materials scientists and materials engineers, who have mastered the complex interacting relationships between phenomena, materials, and processing.
- Innovations in materials processing have had enormous impacts on the factory floor. In the steel industry, for example, the average worker can now produce 6 times as much steel per hour as he could in the 1920s, and the finished steel is of higher quality.

Materials science and engineering influences our lives each time we buy or use a new device, machine, or structure. Some examples of developments now emerging from our laboratories include the following:

- integrated circuits that will contain as many as a billion components per chip and thus will further the revolution in information technologies that has reshaped modern societies;
- devices that can manipulate and store data optically and thus will contribute to a greatly increased use of optical technology in telecommunications and information storage;
- materials that can sense, in new ways, their environments of temperature, pressure, and chemistry for control of processes and machines;
- active polymeric materials whose properties, such as color or rigidity, depend on applied electrical or photonic fields, with applications ranging from electronic devices to building materials; and
- biomaterials that can serve as templates for the regrowth of human body parts, such as living tissue or organs.

Materials Science and Engineering as a Field

What is the nature of materials science and engineering, a field that so profoundly affects the quality of our lives in so many different ways? The intellectual core and definition of the field stem from a realisation concerning the application of all materials: whenever a material is being created, developed, or produced, the properties or phenomena the material exhibits are of central concern. Experience shows that the properties and phenomena associated with a material are intimately related to its composition and structure at all levels, including which atoms are present and how the atoms are arranged in the material, and that this structure is the result of synthesis and processing. The final material must perform a given task and must do so in an economical and societally acceptable manner. It is these elements—properties, structure and composition, synthesis and processing, and performance and the strong interrelationship among them—that define the field of materials science and engineering. These elements and their relationships are shown schematically the form of a tetrahedron.

In developing new materials, it is difficult to anticipate where seeking knowledge ends and applying it begins. Hence science and engineering are inextricably interwoven in the field of materials science and engineering. The field of materials science and engineering has evolved along many parallel and intertwined paths associated with academic disciplines, R&D laboratories, and the factory floor. It draws on areas as diverse as quantum mechanics on the one hand and societal needs, including manufacturing, on the other. A proper perspective from which to consider the field requires understanding of the roles of science and engineering and their synergies. At the science end of its spectrum, materials science and engineering is rooted in the classical disciplines of physics and chemistry. Condensed-matter physicists, solid-state chemists, and synthetic chemists form the bridge between fundamental science and a subset of that science on which modern materials science and engineering rests. These sciences aim to increase knowledge, and especially understanding, of structure, phenomena, behavior, or synthesis. Very often, the stimulation for this group to follow a particular direction of research may come from a technical problem. But the most important advances typically have been made when the research has been placed in a broad context and has been allowed to follow directions whose promise may not have been apparent at the outset.

Earlier in this century, the discovery and understanding of dislocations in crystals revolutionized our understanding of the strength of materials and led to the development of vastly improved structural materials. Understanding of the electronic structures of semiconductors, especially how they are influenced by impurities and in the vicinity of a surface, led to the development of the transistor and, subsequently, to the integrated circuit, which led to the microelectronic revolution. The deep understanding of the quantum mechanical energy levels of atoms and molecules and of the coupling of electronic motion to light and other forms of radiation made possible the invention of the laser. This discovery, in turn, led to a variety of solid-state lasers, which are used in communication and in information storage. In three consecutive years—1985, 1986, and 1987—three great advances in fundamental materials science were recognized by the awarding of Nobel Prizes:

1. In 1980, in the course of fundamental studies of electrons moving in semiconductor surfaces, an entirely new and unexpected effect, the quantum Hall effect (associated with almost total absences of electrical resistance), was discovered. It should be noted that this research was certainly stimulated in part by the enormous technical interest in electrons near semiconductor surfaces. The experiments were entirely dependent on recent progress in materials science and engineering, which had made possible the preparation of surfaces with extremely well-controlled properties. The full implications of the Hall effect for our understanding of the dynamics of surface electrons are still being developed.
2. In the early 1980s a radically new type of microscope, the scanning tunneling microscope, was developed. It depended on a subtle quantum mechanical effect, the tunneling of electrons *below* the tops of barriers (an event that could not happen under the laws of Newtonian mechanics). This technique led to incredibly accurate information about the positions of individual atoms on surfaces. Displacements of the order of 1 percent of the normal interatomic distance can be detected with the scanning tunneling microscope. Instruments of this kind can now be produced very cheaply (for about $25,000) and are responsible for exciting advances in such fields as surface physics, electrochemistry, and biology.
3. Superconductivity was discovered in 1911 in mercury, which lost all electrical resistance below 4.3 K above absolute zero. By the early 1970s, a painstaking materials science effort lasting more than 60 years had led to metallic compounds that remained superconducting at up to 23 K, an average increase of about 0.3 K/yr. No further progress occurred until 1986, when researchers studying entirely different classes of compounds discovered superconductivity at up to 39 K. Since then, based on accumulated knowledge of materials, compounds have been developed that remain superconducting at up to 125 K. Although major materials problems remain to be overcome (e.g., poor ductility and low critical currents), we may well be on the threshold of a technological revolution started by superconduction.

Breakthroughs such as these cannot be predicted or planned, but the environment conducive to their continued occurrence can be. It requires sustained support for and commitment to the basic science that undergirds materials science and engineering.

Collectively, practitioners of materials science and engineering generate and build on the field's scientific base. They understand and exploit the fundamentals of both basic science and engineering, and they translate scientific breakthroughs into forms beneficial to society. Semiconductor devices and integrated circuits would never have been developed if both science and engineering had not been understood; the development of a room-temperature laser required an understanding of semiconducting phenomena and structure (e.g., defects in solids) and of their relationship to processing. Similarly, building and processing of modern composite materials require an understanding of surface science and molecular bonding as well as a strong engineering foundation. Future development of superconducting materials is also essentially dependent on materials science and engineering because such advances require expertise in understanding materials phenomena and their relationship to structure and defects in the structure, to processing (which influences the structure), and to other properties such as brittleness and susceptibility to environmental degradation.

The general approach to solving materials problems for applications came from metallurgists. It was first used at the turn of the century and continued to develop as the relationship between structure, properties, and performance of metals was clearly established. Over time, the important role of processing in controlling structure was realised. The critical role of processing is a central theme of this report. Today, relationships between structure, properties, performance, and processing are understood to apply not only to metals, but also to all classes of materials. Thus modern materials engineering involves exploitation of relationships among the four basic elements of the field—structure and composition, properties, synthesis and processing, and performance basic science, and industrial and broader societal needs. Some important materials discoveries have been made by scientists, some by engineers, and still others by craftsmen. Many have been made by teams comprising all three types of individuals. Today, craftsmanship alone, in the absence of modern science and engineering, rarely suffices to bring about a new development in materials. Craftsmanship alone is also increasingly inadequate with respect to processing or production of materials. A crucial challenge for the future is to find ways of carrying out education, research, and engineering—including production—that encourage the maximum interaction among scientists and engineers, among mathematicians, physicists, chemists, and biologists, and among the four basic elements of materials science and engineering. Supporting such interactions is a difficult task requiring much wisdom, and, realistically, a willingness to make tradeoffs. But progress in accomplishing this task is both possible and essential.

Who are Materials Scientists and Engineers?

Materials scientists and engineers study the structure and composition of materials on scales ranging from the electronic and atomic through the microscopic to the macroscopic. They develop new materials, improve traditional materials, and produce materials reliably and economically through synthesis and processing. They seek to understand phenomena and to measure materials properties of all kinds, and they predict and evaluate the performance of real materials as structural or functional elements in engineering systems. This diversity of interests is mirrored in the fields of materials science and engineering practitioners, who come from a broad range of academic departments and disciplines. There is a growing realisation among scientists and engineers that, to develop materials for society, all four elements of materials science and engineering are needed. Even though an individual may identify with a physics, metallurgy, or other department in a university emphasizing a particular aspect of the field, it is implicitly and increasingly recognized that important contributions will come from various disciplines working together. The interdisciplinary nature of materials science and engineering and its growth as a field have also been recognized in the professional world outside academia. For example, the American Society for Metals, once the largest metallurgical society in the United States, has expanded to become a broad materials society with a new name, ASM International, with a membership numbering about 53,000. The Materials Research Society, established early in 1973, has been one of the fastest growing professional societies in the United States; its current membership includes approximately 8000 individuals. Many industrial and governmental research laboratories have been reorganised into groupings that cut across traditional disciplines and materials areas and have titles such as "materials synthesis," "materials chemistry," and "materials performance." As the science and engineering base of this new field of materials science and engineering develops, so must the process by which its practitioners are educated and the infrastructure and resources with which they approach their task.

Scope of this Report

This report discusses the vital role that materials science and engineering plays in the development of technology. Chapter 2 summarizes the committee's findings about the impact of materials science and engineering on private and public sector activities that are crucial to U.S. economic and strategic well-being. Opportunities for research are discussed from two perspectives: Chapter 3 describes needs for new materials and for novel methods of processing in terms of the functional roles of materials; Chapter 4 describes research opportunities in the context of the four basic elements of materials science and engineering, thus emphasizing the intellectual coherence of the field while also stressing the essential connection between basic research and progress in developing materials. Educational challenges posed by the national need to encourage such progress and to ensure an adequate supply of well-trained materials researchers are considered in Chapter 5, which briefly assesses resources available for educating materials scientists and engineers at various levels of the U.S. educational system and also emphasizes the significance of the field's multidisciplinary aspect. Chapter 6 presents the committee's findings about funding and facilities currently available—as well as those needed in the future—to support the research efforts of materials scientists and engineers who work at the perennially shifting boundary between gathering knowledge and applying it. Finally, to examine from a broader perspective its assessment that materials science and engineering is vital to the future development of U.S. technology, the committee also examined how a number of nations view materials science and engineering and its role in their development. The international perspective is presented in Chapter 7. The committee is convinced that its findings and recommendations, if implemented, will strengthen the field of materials science and engineering and, in so doing, will contribute immeasurably and in unanticipated ways to meeting U.S. needs for economic and strategic security as well as the future needs of mankind.

Welding

If we define welding in its broadest sense as the achievement of a metallic bond then we can find examples in the Bronze Age city, *Ur*, around 3,000 BC when swords were joined by hammering and jewellery was produced by hard soldering, but it took nearly 5,000 years for welding to become accepted as a suitable industrial process. During the Iron Age, forge welding came into its own. With the application of pressure and heat two metals could be fused together (blacksmith welding), although a fully fused joint could not be guaranteed, much depending on the operators skill and experience. During the 19th century the use of cast iron and steel for structural and mechanical engineering increased. Cast iron ships such as the *SS Great Britain* built by Brunel in 1845 showed the extent of construction until large scale steel production superseded cast iron. The problems with riveting such as weight and overlap demanded a more improved method of joining. The basic principles of modern welding processes were discovered in 1724 (pressure welding), 1820s (electric arc), and 1856 (resistance butt).

In the early 1900s the struggle began between riveting and welding, since the main advantages of welding were its improvement in structural design, weight saving and cost/time saving. During the 1930s welding was applied to the construction of German pocket battleships to keep the weight within the treaty limit of 10,000 tons. The Second World War forced many manufacturers to use the developing processes to increase productivity and reduce costs, this in turn accelerated welding technology to such an extent that welding is now regarded as a industry of its own

MSE: An Introduction

MSE is a field of Engineering — MSE stands for Materials Science and Engineering. The field encompasses the spectrum of materials: metals, ceramics, polymers (plastics), semiconductors, and combinations of materials called composites. Most fields of work or study have a bit of MSE in them! But let's start at the beginning..

What are Materials?

First, what are materials? That's easy. Look around. What do you see? Materials are everywhere! The clothes we wear are made from a variety of materials. Our home is made of materials — mostly manufactured. The glass in the windows, the vinyl siding, the ceramic dinnerware, the metal silverware, and everywhere we look we see products made from materials. Most products are made from many different kinds of materials to satisfy the needs of the product. One way to look at materials is to consider the various generic descriptions such as:

- Metals: Materials that are normally combinations of "metallic elements". These elements, when combined, usually have electrons that are non localized and as a consequence have generic types of properties. Metals usually are good conductors of heat and electricity. Also, they are quite strong but malleable and tend to have a lustrous look when polished.
- Ceramics: Ceramics are generally compounds between metallic and nonmetallic elements and include such compounds as oxides, nitrides, and carbides. Typically they are insulating and resistant to high temperatures and harsh environments.
- Plastics: Plastics (or polymers) are generally organic compounds based upon carbon and hydrogen. They are very large molecular structures. Usually they are low density and are not stable at high temperatures.
- Semiconductors: Semiconductors have electrical properties intermediate between metallic conductors and ceramic insulators. Also, the electrical properties are strongly dependent upon small amounts of impurities.
- Composites: Composites consist of more than one material type. Fiberglass, a combination of glass and a polymer, is an example. Concrete and plywood are other familiar composites. Many new combinations include ceramic fibers in metal or polymer matrix.

This type of description is too general to provide much insight into where and how materials are used and certainly not much about what a materials person does. For example, the dramatic role of iron throughout the ages is not really the result of it being "strong" as one might believe from it being a "metal". In reality, iron has been important because we can change its properties by heating and cooling it. The ability to change the properties and/or behavior of a material is what makes most materials useful and this is at the heart of what a materials person does! Lets look at materials from the vantage of a materials person and further lets couple that with how this view couples with the other engineering and science disciplines.

MSE and the Automobile

The automobile is perhaps the perfect everyday application for advances in materials science and engineering (MSE). A car is a complex device — there are nearly 15,000 parts in a passenger car — with dozens of very different systems present to make it function (make it drive, stop, have electricity, be safe, comfortable, and durable). These numerous systems give the car many opportunities to take advantage of improvements offered by MSE. New fabrication techniques can make parts lighter, stronger, easier to manufacture, more durable, and less expensive — all translating into benefits for the owner. Shown above are certain highlighted parts of the auto. Click on the label of the picture to learn how MSE is helping to better engineer today's auto parts — making your life safer and less expensive.

Rolling in Style — Bonded Polyurethane Wheels

Instead of conventional wheel covers, one manufacturing company has developed a durable and abuse resistant treatment which bonds directly to a steel or aluminum wheel. The advantages here are more than the stylish appearance — the bonded polyurethane provides corrosion and abrasion resistance and resistance to chemicals to the wheel. The weight is about the same as a typical plastic wheel cover, but the life of the steel or aluminum wheel is extended considerably with the protective coating applied.

Index of Learning Styles (ILS)

Students preferentially take in and process information in different ways: by seeing and hearing, reflecting and acting, reasoning logically and intuitively, analyzing and visualizing, steadily and in fits and starts. When mismatches exist between learning styles of most students in a class and the teaching style of the professor, the students may become bored and inattentive in class, do poorly on tests, get discouraged about the courses, the curriculum, and themselves, and in some cases change to other curricula or drop out of school. The *Index of Learning Styles* is an on-line instrument used to assess preferences on four dimensions (active/reflective, sensing/intuitive, visual/verbal, and sequential/global) of a learning style model formulated by Richard M. Felder and Linda K. Silverman. The instrument was developed by Richard M. Felder and Barbara A. Soloman of North Carolina State University. ILS Users should be aware of two important points:

1. The ILS results provide an indication of an individual's learning preferences and an even better indication of the preference profile of a group of students (e.g. a class), but they should not be over-interpreted. If someone

does not agree with the ILS assessment of his or her preferences, trust that individual's judgment over the instrument results.

2. A student's learning style profile provides an indication of possible strengths and possible tendencies or habits that might lead to difficulty in academic settings. The profile does not reflect a student's suitability or unsuitability for a particular subject, discipline, or profession. Labeling students in this way is at best misleading, and can be destructive if the student uses the label as justification for a major shift in curriculum or career goals. A learning style preference also does not serve as an excuse for a bad grade on the student's last physics test.

MSE and the Bicycle

Today's bikes are cool. Whether you have a racing bike, with slick tires on narrow wheels, or a fat-tire off-road maxed-out mountain bike, you know that better parts make better rides. The typical bike enthusiast enjoys keeping up with the latest technology advances — most of which are the result of advances in MSE. We've got some info on some interesting gear — stuff that contains ceramic, polymers, and metals. Take a look at the links to see what is hot.

Materials Engineering

We are constantly reminded that we live in a world that is both dependent on materials and limited by materials. Everything we see and use is made of materials derived from the earth — large buildings, supersonic aircraft, coffee cups, advanced computers, sports equipment, and biomedical devices such as artificial limbs, joints, and implants. All of these are made of materials having specific properties that are the result of carefully controlled processes to convert raw materials into useful engineering materials. Materials/metallurgical engineers deal with the science and technology of producing materials that are best suited for each application. New technologies developed through engineering science will continue to make startling changes in our lives in the 21st century, and metallurgical and materials engineers will continue to be key contributors to these changes and advances. Materials include metals, ceramics, polymers (plastics), and their combinations called composites. The activities of materials/metallurgical engineers range from materials production, including extraction from ores and recycling, to the design, development, and processing of these materials for use in aerospace, transportation, electronics, energy conversion, and biomedical systems. The importance of the field is evident when one considers that throughout history technological progress has been measured by how people have used the materials provided by nature: first the Stone Age, then the Bronze Age, the Iron Age, and now the Materials Age.

Your Career Path

Since materials are involved in virtually every aspect of our lives, there are generally more opportunities than graduates. Job placement and starting salaries are expected to be excellent. The future will bring increasing needs for new materials, ranging from a few pounds of superconductors or shape-memory devices to high-volume, economical materials for mass-production uses. It is clear that new and better processing methods will be needed to provide a continuing supply of minerals and raw materials from less rich, and more complex, natural ores. Also, means of reclaiming and recycling of solid wastes must be developed to conserve our natural resources and protect our environment. For these many reasons a survey by Graduating Engineer named the materials field as the top career choice.

Materials/metallurgical engineering graduates work in a variety of activities, including the extraction, production, processing, recycling, and selection and design of materials for aerospace, ground transportation, household appliances, energy conversion and utilization, biomedical applications, information and communication systems, electronic and magnetic devices, and optical and optoelectronic components. Job functions are varied and include manufacturing, research and development, design, sales and marketing, technical services, quality control and testing, performance and failure analysis, management and administration, and teaching.

Biomaterials

A biomaterial is any material, natural or man-made, that comprises whole or part of a living structure or biomedical device which performs, augments, or replaces a natural function. The Society For Biomaterials is a professional society which promotes advances in all phases of materials research and development by encouragement of cooperative educational programmes, clinical applications, and professional standards in the biomaterials field. Biomechanics is a related area of engineering. Biomechanics involves the structure and function of biological systems using the methods of mechanics. The human total hip system shown below offers a titanium, dual tapered stem design which provides a physiologic proximal load transfer, thus greatly reducing the chance of calcar resorption and distal hypertrophy. No fooling! The system provides an anatomic fit coupled with a straight stem design. The role of cartilage is played by polyethylene in this application. The reference source URL is *Biomet Corporation*. For more about hip replacement and conditions under which this is done, please link to the *Medline plus* website and learn more about hip joint replacement (many great illustrations). For an example of a B.S. undergraduate study of orthopedic implants, please link to the following *San Jose State University* senior project report What other parts of the human anatomy can be replaced? The image on the left, from *ASM-International*, demonstrates other replacement parts. In this way, biomaterials are contributing to longer, higher quality lives. Biomechanics deals with body movement and medicine. Biomechanical research is performed at many national and international universities. The *Centre of Biomechanics* at the Technical University of Hamburg, Germany, has high importance especially for local health care, and with speciality in the following areas: the quality of implants and medical equipment as well as the development of innovative methods to aid producers of surgical implants and equipment. Surgery methods and materials for implants are improved by the cooperation between biomechanics, materials science, mechanics, informatics, metrology and design. The image below demonstrates one example: hip joint replacement. Determination of the position of the shaft of a hip joint prosthesis in the femur at a planning station of the operating robot is shown. Corresponding to this planning, the milling of the cavitation for the shaft is done during the operation (so that one will have a *tailored* fit).

Both biomaterials and biomechanical expertise are needed to perform *in vitro testing* of spinal implants. The source of the image on the right is the *Institute of Orthopaedic Research and Biomechanics* at the University of Ulm in Germany. Materials Scientists continue to develop novel surface modifications to enhance textile performance. Wettability is one important characteristic of a surface. Wettability of textile fibers can be enhanced to assist the dyeing operation during processing; and the fibers can be made to be non-wettable for application in, for example, ski clothing. PhotoLink uses wettability technology, as illustrated below, to, for instance, improve the flow characteristics of a polymer membrane used in a medical, diagnostic test kit. The reference source URL is *SurModics, Inc.* Endo-vascular stents provide structural support vessels following angioplasty and other major medical procedures. After an angioplasty procedure, vessels can experience re-stenosis and eventually return to their original pre-operative diameter. In as many as 10% of the procedures, the vessels may even collapse immediately. To prevent the vessels from shrinking, endo-vascular prosthesis or stents are used. Stents are tubular structures consisting of a spring, wire mesh or slotted tubes that are deployed inside the vessel. Depending on the design and intended use (coronary/ peripheral), they can range in diameter from several millimeters to many times that size. Here, you are inside a vessel, seeing the stent in service. The actual stent in service image is a 1995 copyright of Vital Images, Inc. and the Stanford University *Department of Radiology*. The reference source URL for more information on vascular and orthopaedic, mechanical integrity and durability test devices is *EnduraTEC Systems*. EnduraTEC Systems is a manufacturer of mechanical fatigue testing equipment for the biomedical and general materials industries.

Semiconductor Materials

Whereas polymers are highly visible engineering materials with a major impact on contemporary society, semiconductors are relatively invisible but have a comparable social impact. Technology has clearly revolutionized society, but solid-state electronics is revolutionizing technology itself. A relatively small group of elements and compounds has an important electrical property, semi-conduction, in which they are neither good electrical conductors nor good electrical insulators. Instead, their ability to conduct electricity is intermediate. These materials are called semiconductors, and in general, they do not fit into any of the four structural materials categories based on atomic bonding. Metals are inherently good electrical conductors. Ceramics and polymers (non-metals) are generally poor conductors but good insulators. The three semiconducting elements (Si, Ge, and Sn) from column IVA of the periodic table serve as a kind of boundary between metallic and nonmetallic elements. Silicon (Si) and germanium (Ge), widely used elemental semiconductors, are excellent examples of this class of materials. [Another important semiconductor material is GaAs, a compound of the group IIIA element Ga; and the group V element, As.

One area of materials engineering is called "process engineering". It is perhaps best illustrated by the production of integrated circuit devices. An excellent montage representing IC processing is illustrated in the following IBM gif. Behind the Process Engineer, one see's a blow-up of the three-dimensional array of metallization lines that interconnect the various device regions on an integrated circuit. The gray substrate under the pink, white, yellow and green metallization pattern, is the silicon wafer, which is a semiconductor material. These interconnects are typically less than a micro-meter in thickness! The reference source URL is *IBM chip technology*

The metallization lines in the above figure connect regions of the semiconductor that have been specifically "doped" to change electrical performance. Doping involves substituting other elements (like phosphorous and boron, for example) for individual Si atoms in the Si-wafer. When differently doped regions of the semiconductor are properly positioned and electrically connected, transistors (for example) can be made.

The image to the left shows the first transistor, discovered by Bardeen, Brattain and Shockley at Bell Labs. The triangular hunk is a piece of Ge crystal. In 1947, when they switched to using tremendously pure materials, it dawned on Bardeen, Brattain and Shockley that they could build the circuit in the picture. It was an amplifier! For more about this important discovery, visit the source URL at *the PBS website*. For more about transistor regions in today's IC's, link to the following *web page*.

The complex, interconnected, metal lines on today's integrated circuits begin as a metallic thin-film layer, deposited on the top of a silicon wafer. Photolithography [use a search engine to find out what this is all about] is used to establish the architecture of the lines: subsequent etching steps define them. To learn more about the deposition of thin-film metals and to see some of the equipment used, go to *AltProcess.htm*. For cross-sectional view and operational description of six different IC (Integrated Circuits) devices, visit *these* International Rectifier web pages. To see detail of IC architecture, visit the *Materials Characterization* web pages of the WofMatE. The *pbs transistor* web pages offer further detail of typical IC device concepts and architecture.

The products of the process engineer in the microelectronics industry are represented in this montage (left), also from *IBM*. A typical IC (full die shot of the HP PA-8000 microprocessor using oblique illumination with blue and red gels) is shown on the right.

One step in the production of semiconductor devices involves the growth of a large (10 or more inches in diameter!) single crystal of silicon by the Czochralski process. In this process, a solid seed crystal is rotated and slowly extracted from a pool of molten Si. This is shown above. The various steps in the production of semiconductor devices are clearly illustrated on the web pages of *Fullman-Kinetics*, the source of the Czochralski image-sequence, above. [The Fullman-Kinetics web pages appear to no longer be available on the Internet, and this is a shame. They were excellent!] However, please visit the chip fabrication processing pages at this *German website*. You may also wish to visit this University of Delaware *link*.

In another IC processing step, after wafers of silicon are sliced from the single crystal and then polished, they are thermal-annealed in an oven. Below (left) we see Si wafers entering an oven for an annealing treatment. This is taken from the *Intel* web pages.

In a vacuum chamber, fine, intricate patterns are etched into silicon wafers with an ion discharge (above, right). This is another critical step in the production of integrated circuits. The violet glow is emitted by the ion plasma. The plasma etching process makes possible the small geometries need for very large scale integration in silicon chips. This image is taken from the *Lucent Technologies* web pages.

Now the above images illustrate methods applicable to the fabrication of integrated circuits (IC's) [also termed "chips"] used in the production of microelectronic devices. The *process engineer* plays a key role in the production of IC's. But the process engineer too is involved in the packaging of these microelectronic devices; and in the assembly of packaged device on to the printed circuit board (PCB). The whole sequence is quite elaborate and a comprehensive treatment is well outside the scope of these web pages. However, I would like to introduce you to one facet of IC packaging and that is the bonding of the IC chip to a suitable substrate. For this example, consider "flip chip" technology. The respective images presented below have been extracted from the flip chip, MEMS web pages of the MEMS Technology Application Center, now *CRONOS* Integrated Microsystems, Inc. MEMS stands for MicroElectroMechanical Systems.

'Flip chip' is a general term that describes a method of attaching an integrated circuit (ie, IC) to a substrate. The substrate can be another chip, a PC board, a special carrier or a multichip module. More specifically, flip chip is a technology in which one chip is placed face down (flip chipped) on to the substrate and attached through solder bumps that provide both mechanical and electrical connection. Flip chip provides a much higher interconnection density than traditional methods (i.e. wire bonding) because the interconnections are distributed across the entire chip surface rather than being restricted to the periphery of the chip.

This technology can be used to attach a MEMS chip to a die, as in the example introduced above. For information about MEMS and MEMS applications, visit the following *links* developed by Danny Banks in the UK.

The MEMS chip shown in the figure must be aligned so that the appropriate pads on the die and chip are in contact. Then the solder is heated to the reflow-temperature (a temperature where the solder "bumps" reflow and solidify upon subsequent cooling), thus providing both mechanical and electrical contact. Shown is a joined pair, chip to die, after solder reflow. A cross-section through a flip chip illustrating a typical solder bump appears on the left; and an actual array of re-flowed solder bumps (prior to assembly) is shown below.

If you are really into learning more about semiconductors from a materials perspective, visit the *following* web pages which offer a collection of really cool JAVA Applets!

Is it not easy to see that the materials scientist and materials engineer must necessarily play a key role in the design, production and quality assurance of semiconductor devices, microelectronics packages and MEM systems?

Opportunities for Materials Engineering Graduates

The percentage of materials engineers in the total of all engineers in the engineering profession is small: probably less than 5%. However, the need to apply basic materials principles to the solution of engineering problems is great. Certainly in today's high-tech society basic materials principles must be applied to almost all endeavors: thermal protection of the space shuttle, creation of the artificial hip, design of the titanium golf club; and production of advanced battery systems for the electric car, the artificial heart, and the lap-top computer. Industry and government have traditionally depended on a few individuals on a project to address, for example, materials selection and process issues (ie, a titanium, stainless steel or plastic artificial hip; which alloy; which fabrication sequence; a protective coating for corrosion and wear?). Without the benefit of a materials education, these individuals rely on handbook information, experience and vendor data to select materials and to determine the processing sequence. The B.S. degree in materials science and engineering teaches the inter-relationship between structure, properties and processing; factors which determine the in-service performance and durability of a component or product. Thus, the graduate of a materials science and engineering programme is uniquely prepared to contribute to any design team effort to fabricate a new device, product or component; or make an existing one work better. Academic programmes in the following areas offer such training: metallurgy, materials science, materials engineering, polymer chemistry, ceramics; plastics and composites engineering.

Graduates from materials programmes are readily hired by industry. Those who become involved in materials engineering but who do not have formal training in this area often return to academia to earn the M.S. or Ph.D. in one of the above fields so that they can better perform their job. There are a great deal more *materials jobs* than there are *materials engineers*. Any young person interested in science, math and chemistry, and considering engineering as a career option should consider the *materials science and engineering* career option.

As a first step in the process of considering the materials science and engineering career option, I suggest that you visit the *Career Resource Center for Materials Science and Engineering* web pages sponsored by the TMS-AIME, an organisation dedicated to the materials profession; or the *Materials Career Pages* maintained by The Institute of Materials in the United Kingdom. These pages provide an excellent, and continuously updated introduction to the field.

A couple of other web pages are worth a visit to learn more about materials engineering. Visit *the Nanozone*to learn about this new technology. *The University of Washington, The U.K. Science Museum*, and *Stange Matter* are all worth a visit!

You might want to read *Affirmations* by some of our students in the SJSU MatE programme to get the student's perspective.

Materials Characterization

Materials Characterization represents many different disciplines depending upon the background of the user. These concepts range from that of the scientist, who thinks of it in atomic terms, to that of the process engineer, who thinks of it in terms of properties, procedures, and quality assurance, to that of the mechanical engineer, who thinks of it in terms of stress distributions and heat transfer. The definition selected for the ASM-International Materials Characterization Handbook is as follows: "Characterization describes those features of composition and structure (including defects) of a material that are significant for a particular preparation, study of properties, or use, and suffice for reproduction of the material." This definition limits the characterization methods included in the Handbook [and this web page] to those that provide information about composition, structure, and defects and excludes those methods that yield information primarily related to materials properties, such as thermal, electrical, and mechanical properties. An important component of the materials engineering methodology involves knowledge of the structure of materials. Typical structure is necessarily viewed through a microscope.... an optical microscope, the electron microscope (imaging of electrons passed through a thin specimen in the transmission electron microscope TEM; or imaging by collecting electrons emitted from the surface of the material of interest in the scanning electron microscope SEM). Here are some structure related Internet images:Here is a typical optical microscope.

The principles are the same for the operation of a SEM or TEM; except the *light source* for an electron microscope is an electron gun, and the lenses are electromagnetic (they are not made from optical-grade glass). Electron microscopes require a vacuum column because electrons readily interact with air molecules and would become rapidly adsorbed. The reference source URL for the optical microscope image was the Lucent Technologies Microscapes site, which is no longer available. Do visit the *Bell Labs* web pages to see related images. On the upper right we see a photomicrograph of pyramid-shaped etch pits on the surface of a silicon wafer. What is the reason for formation of an 'etch-pit?' Well, there are defects in crystalline materials called *dislocations*. Where dislocations intersect a surface, a feature called an etch-pit can form. The pit will form if atomic impurities in the crystal are segregated to the dislocation (by thermal treatment) and if the specimen is subsequently etched (ie, the surface chemically attacked with an appropriate chemical etchant). The reference source URL is the *Bell Labs* web pages. This is a scanning electron micrograph (left) of a dendrite. When solid metal grows from the liquid state, a *tree-like* feature grows which is called a dendrite. The dendrite is, essentially, a single crystal feature. The growth of dendrites occurs when liquid metals solidify, and the phenomenon is analogous to the process of formation of ice crystals from supersaturated water vapor, for example. For a most interesting look at the dendrite growth process, visit this *Cal Tech* web site. Here is a scanning electron micrograph of a device region (right) on an integrated circuit. The white features are metallization lines. Here, we are looking normal to the surface of the silicon wafer and see the top-level of connective lines. In the next image, we will see a cross-section through metallization lines. The reference source URL is *Philips Research*, part of Philips Electronics.

Next, let us consider a cross-section through an integrated circuit (IC). View the series of images below. First, to get a good idea as to the various layers that make-up a modern IC, go to the following *LINK* where a schematic of a typical cross-section of a complementary metal oxide semiconductor (CMOS) device is presented (origin is Texas Instruments). For cross-sectional views and an operational description of six different IC devices, visit these *International Rectifier* web pages. The SEM image below, left, is an actual cross-section of a modern IC device showing the various metallization lines (yellow) embedded in passivation material (silicon nitride, for example). Being able to deposit a number of planar layers has made possible the scaling-down of the size of device regions and made possible more punch per chip! The reference source URL is *IBM Corporation*. On the right is an SEM section through 4 MB DRAM (Dynamic Random Access Memory) cells. The section was made by a new instrument called the Focused Ion Beam Microscope. It is capable of performing corrective micro-surgery on IC chips. The reference source for this cross-section is *FIB International* of Santa Clara, CA. This is a polycrystalline array of grains in an aluminum metallization line on an integrated circuit. It is a color photomicrograph. Each colored grain is a single crystal of aluminum, oriented differently with respect to its neighbors. The reference source URL is the *Bell Labs* web page. Photomicroscopy is an important tool in the characterization of engineering materials.

Another excellent Internet source of solid-state photomicrographs is the *Manchester Materials Science Center* (at the University of Manchester; UK) site. Link to *MATERIALS* to view various micrographs over a range of magnifications. Link to *FEATURES* to view special features which help the materials engineer to determine the type of alloy and its process history, and thus to help predict performance in service. The scanning electron micrograph (left) shows a typical TiC coating of 150 micrometers on Poco AXF-5Q graphite. These TiC coatings feature both an equiaxed structure adjacent to the coating-substrate interface, and columnar grains away from the interface. Additionally, these coatings adhere well to their graphite substrates even after fracture. Thicknesses for these coatings can be controlled from a few micrometers to 250 micrometers. The reference source URL is *Lanxide Coated Products* If you wish to know more about materials characterization, I invite you to turn to *PAGE II*. PAGE II will introduce you to other examples of materials characterization, including scanning probe microscopy, which offers the possibility to view, and manipulate, individual atoms and molecules on surfaces.

The Concept of Structure

The structure of a material may be divided into four levels: atomic structure, atomic arrangement, microstructure, and macrostructure. Although the main thrust of [the materials engineer] is to understand and control the microstructure and macro-structure of various materials, [she] must first understand the atomic and crystal structures. Atomic structure influences how the atoms are bonded together, which in turn helps one to categorize materials as metals, ceramics, and polymers and permits us to draw some general conclusions concerning the mechanical properties and physical behavior of these three classes of materials. This first image shows the coordination polyhedra for a superconductor material as shown on the web pages. It represents the basic repeat unit that, when aggregated with about 10^20 similar units, will create a monolith of the superconductor somewhat less in size than one cubic centimeter. The crystalline unit cell is one aspect of *structure* that the materials engineer must understand to produce functional superconductor devices. However, there are other aspects of a material's structure that too must be considered. The purpose of this web page is to introduce the reader to the concept of *structure*. Let us begin our discussion of *structure* by first considering the crystal structure of perovskites. Perovskites are a large family of crystalline ceramics that derive their name from a specific mineral known as perovskite. They are the most abundant minerals on earth and have been of continuing interest to geologists for the clues they hold to the planet's history.

The parent material, perovskite, was first described in the 1830's by the geoologist Gustav Rose, who named it after the famous Russian mineralogist Count Lev Aleksevich von Perovski. Currently, the most intensely studied perovskites are those that superconduct at liquid nitrogen temperatures. Superconducting perovskites were first discovered by IBM researchers Bednorz and Mueller who were examining the electrical properties of a family of materials in the Ba-La-Cu-O system. The *crystal model* above is a perovskite. The coordination polyhedra is only one way to represent a crystalline unit cell. Another way is to use a *ball and stick* model, with the balls representing atoms and the sticks, bonds between the atoms. Two representations of this are illustrated below. First, let us consider a basic unit cell, a cubic crystal system, as seen in three dimensions. Those of us who lack 3-dimensional depth perception can sometimes gain 3D information by moving our heads slightly from left to right while looking at an object. Similarly, all of us can project a 3-dimensional cube onto a 2-dimensional screen and then rotate it to provide information on its 3D nature. In other words, we can use a 2D perspective projection extrapolated to a 3D impression. To the left, you see a GIF animation of a unit cell of a three-dimensional (3D) crystal. The reference source URL is *University of Missouri at St. Louis* Other Internet sources showing the "ball and stick" unit cell structures of some of the more common materials are as follows: crystallography web pages from *Japan*, *The United Kingdom*, and *the USA (University of Buffalo in NY)*. You are encouraged to visit and explore these links: (i) FCC Cu; (ii) BCC Cr; (iii) Other FCC Structures and (iv) Laves Structures. If you link to the *following* pages, then you can download the software to do crystal projections and find other interesting things on your own. For example, there is a DOS programme which allows you to take ASCII files describing the three-dimensional position of atoms in a molecule (or for that matter, furniture in a room), and view it in interactive rotation, in perspective projection, in textured red-green stereo, or you can choose to just let it 'wobble' in place!

An example of such a crystal structure is illustrated on the left. For more useful freeware concerning crystal structure and such, check out this *University of Missouri at St. Louis link* ! For general information on crystal structure and crystal structure types, check out the following links: (a) *The U.S. Navy*, and (b) *Java educational applets from the University of Buffalo in New York*. So, the unit cell is the basic repeat-unit for describing a crystal. What is a crystal? Well most of us have seen mineral crystals. For example, consider amethyst. Amethyst is the purple variety of quartz and is a popular gemstone. If it were not for its widespread availability, amethyst would be very expensive.

The name "amethyst" comes from the Greek and means "not drunken." This was maybe due to a belief that amethyst would ward off the effects of alcohol, but most likely the Greeks were referring to the almost wine-like color of some stones that they may have encountered. Its color is unparalleled, and even other, more expensive purple gemstones are often compared to its color and beauty. The reference URL for this image is a *mineral supplier*. The image has Copyright ©1995,1996 by Amethyst Galleries, Inc.. The amethyst crystals, above-left, are large and well defined. Recall: there are billions and billions and billions of unit-cells that make up these individual crystals.

Let us now take a look at fluorite crystals which are smaller, more *regular* crystals, aggregated as a group. Fluorite is a mineral with a veritable bouquet of brilliant colors. Fluorite is well known and prized for its glassy luster and rich variety of colors. Again, this image has Copyright ©1995,1996 by Amethyst Galleries, Inc.. Now, let us move from aggregate fluorite crystals to aggregate galena crystals. Galena is PbS, or lead-sulfide. This fine specimen of the mineral Galena consists of hundreds of intergrown crystals. Most of these are tiny, not measuring more than 0.1" (3 mm) in diameter, but at least 20 of them exceed 0.3" (8 mm) in all dimensions. The crystals shown are of octahedral form with their tips often truncated by small cube-oriented faces. They have the standard dark-gray color, dull metallic luster, and opacity of Galena, and are dusted with a thin layer of superfine pyrite (Fe-S) or chalcopyrite (Fe/Cu-S), giving some of the crystals a dull golden appearance. With the introduction above, the reader may appreciate that there are must necessarily be *defects* associated with crystals. Defects too define *structure*. For example, consider the boundaries between individual crystals (or grains). Since these crystalline aggregates grow together with 'random' orientation, grain-boundaries necessarily exist: and they are defects as the atomic order along them is disrupted from that within individual grains.

These planar structures certainly must have something to do with, for example, how the aggregate will break apart if struck by a hammer blow. Note too the reference to *a dull golden appearance* of the galena specimen. The source of this discoloration is impurity particles. Iron sulfide and iron/copper sulfide grow on (and then into) the lead-sulfide crystals. These sulfides have different color properties than the lead-sulfide. It is indeed impurities and imperfections in the crystal structure of the amethyst and fluorite crystals, introduced above, that give those crystals *color*. Note in the case of the amethyst the non-uniformity of color, and thus the non-uniformity of chemical content! All of these concepts relate to the *structure and associated defects* of the materials being discussed. Now I share with you a few micro-structural images. The first will be a look "inside" a perovskite material: lanthanum aluminate. Let's not concern ourselves with the magnification. You can assume dimensions to be in the order of tens of microns.

What you will see is a non-perfect, but beautiful state of matter. In one of the superconducting perovskites, the degree of defect (such as that shown on the left) would determine how well the crystal would work as a superconductor. The structure determines properties. Enjoy the beauty and many natural wonders in the reference source, *The Molecular Expressions Photo Gallery at Florida State University*. For a second look at defect structure, consider the image on the right from *the NASA Science Academy web pages*. Here, we are looking at rather high magnification at a Group II-VI semiconductor compound, possibly ZnS. The color electron photomicrograph shows such common structural defects as a grain boundary (A), twin boundaries (B), and triangular-shaped dislocation etch pits (C). These defects were revealed by chemical etching of a wafer cut from a crystal of a II-VI semiconducting alloy, which was produced by directional solidification. Dislocations are another type of defect (line-defect) common to crystalline solids, and very, very important to their properties.

Reflect again on the poly-crystalline structure of the galena aggregate previously introduced. This is essentially a three dimensional view of how metals and alloys are structured. The sole difference is the scale of the grain-array. Commercial alloys are fine-grained, with grains (ie, crystals) typically 0.075 mmor so, in diameter.

Perhaps comparison of the galena aggregate to the image below will convince you that grain-boundaries play a role in the behavior of metals and alloys. Shown is the fracture surface of a high-strength alloy which failed by hydrogen embrittlement. This mode of failure is highly dependent on the size, orientation and chemical make-up of the grain boundaries. Please note the similarity of the galena specimen and this failure specimen, which was subject to inter-granular (ie, along-the-grain-boundary) fracture. The individual polyhedra facets define the grains. The source URL is the *'Analyze This'* web pages.

Metallography is a means to evaluate the grain-structure of materials. Shown on the right is a color photo-micrograph (a two-dimensional section through a polycrystalline array) of a common alloy or metal (brass or nickel, for example). To the trained metallurgist or materials engineer, the structure represents a face-centered-cubic material that has been worked and then "recrystallized" during an annealing treatment. The metal or alloy is in a soft, ductile state. I know you may not know what all of these terms mean. I am trying to illustrate the link between structure, properties and processing. I am trying to illustrate the perspective of the materials engineer and the importance of the *structure* concept. This image is the work of George Vander Voort of the International Metallographic Society. For more photomicrographs, visit the web pages of *Materials Evaluation and Engineering*. To reinforce the importance of grain structure to properties, please consider the photomicrograph below. Again, failure along grain boundaries of an engineering alloy is featured. The alloy is stainless steel (why is it called "stainless" steel.... do you know?). The failure mode is caustic stress corrosion cracking. Here, in a micrograph of the stainless steel, one can see how failure is proceding along the grain-boundaries from the free-surface of the component (top edge). Besides grain boundaries, what other *defects* do you see in this photomicrograph? The reference URL is *the Houston Failure Group*. Let's tie the concept of structure, and one's ability to "model" the atomic structure to a practical problem involving cracks. Consider, for example, a crack in a turbine blade in a jet engine..... or a flaw in the wall of a high-pressure gas cylinder. Can you see the value of determining the forces necessary to propagate an existing crack to catastrophic fracture in these instances? Computer modeling of atomic structures and determination of the resulting properties is a field called *computational materials science*. A view of the propagating crack tip in a molecular dynamic simulation of a fracture in an amorphous covalent solid is shown in the image. The solid is being pulled apart at the red atoms; the yellow arrows show the net force on each atom and the black lines show bonds. Such simulations promise atomic scale insight into the origins of cracks and the underlying mechanisms of fracture. The source URL for this image is the San Diego Supercomputer Center *Image of the Week* archives. *This* and other computational images were collected by the The San Diego Supercomputer Center (SDSC) at the University of California, San Diego.

REFERENCES

A.A. Hermas and I.M. Hassab-Allah: Microstructure, Corrosion and Mechanical Properties of 304 Stainless Steel Containing Copper, Silicon and Nitrogen, *Journal of Materials Science 36* (2001), pp. 3415-3422.

Armin Rahn (1993), *The Basics of Soldering, 1st ed.*, John Wiley and Sons (New York).

Bauccio, M. (ed.) (1994), *ASM Engineering Materials Reference Book, 2nd ed.*, ASM International (Materials Park, OH).

Beer, F.P., Johnston, Jr., E.R. (1981), *Mechanics of Materials*, McGraw-Hill, Inc. (New York).

Dieter, G.E. (1993), *Mechanical Metallurgy*, McGraw-Hill (New York).

Domininghaus, H. (1993), *Plastics for Engineers: Materials, Properties, Applications*, Hanser Publishers (Munich).

Gere J.M., Timoshenko, S.P. (1984), *Mechanics of Materials, 2nd ed.*, Brooks/Cole (Monterey, CA).

H. Hänninen, J. Romu, R. Ilola, J. Tervo and A. Laitinen: Effects of Processing and Manufacturing of High Nitrogen-Containing Stainless Steels on their Mechanical, Corrosion and Wear Properties, *Journal of Materials Processing Technology 117 (2001)*, pp. 424-430.

Norton, P.B., Esposito, J.J. (officers) (1994), *Encyclopaedia Britannica, 15th ed.*, Encyclopaedia Britannica, Inc. (Chicago).

Oberg, E., Jones, F.D., Horton, H.L., Ryffel, H.H. (1996), *Machinery's Handbook, 25th ed.*, Industrial Press (New York).

Parker, S.P. (1994), *Dictionary of Science and Technical Terms, 5th ed.*, McGraw-Hill (New York).

Rahn, Armin (1993), *The Basics of Soldering, 1st ed.*, John Wiley and Sons (New York).

Tres, P.A. (1998), *Designing Plastic Parts for Assembly, 3rd ed.*, Hanser Publishers (Munich).